The London Bus Handbook

British Bus Publishing

3rd Edition

Body codes used in the Bus Handbook series:

Type:
A	Articulated vehicle
B	Bus, either single-deck or double-deck
BC	Interurban - high-back seated bus
C	Coach
M	Minibus with design capacity of 16 seats or less
N	Low-floor bus (*Niederflur*), either single-deck or double-deck
O	Open-top bus (CO = convertible; PO = partial open-top)

Seating capacity is then shown. For double-decks the upper deck quantity is followed by the lower deck.

Door position:
C	Centre entrance/exit
D	Dual doorway.
F	Front entrance/exit
R	Rear entrance/exit (no distinction between doored and open)
T	Three or more access points

Equipment:
L	Lift for wheelchair	TV	Training vehicle.
M	Mail compartment	RV	Used as tow bus or engineer's vehicle.
T	Toilet	w	Vehicle is withdrawn and awaiting disposal.

e.g. - B32/28F is a double-deck bus with thirty-two seats upstairs, twenty-eight down and a front entrance/exit.
N43D is a low-floor bus with two or more doorways.

Re-registrations:
Where a vehicle has gained new index marks, the details are listed at the end of each fleet showing the current mark, followed in sequence by those previously carried starting with the original mark.

Regional books in the series:
The Scottish Bus Handbook
The Ireland & Islands Bus Handbook
The North East Bus Handbook
The Yorkshire Bus Handbook
The North West Bus Handbook
The East Midlands Bus Handbook
The West Midlands Bus Handbook
The Welsh Bus Handbook
The Eastern Bus Handbook
The London Bus Handbook
The South East Bus Handbook
The South West Bus Handbook

Annual books are produced for the major groups:
The Stagecoach Bus Handbook
The Go-Ahead Bus Handbook
The First Bus Handbook
The Arriva Bus Handbook
The National Express Handbook (bi-annual)
Most editions for earlier years are available direct from the publisher.

Associated series:
The Hong Kong Bus Handbook
The Malta Bus Handbook
The Leyland Lynx Handbook
The Model Bus Handbook
The Postbus Handbook
The Mailvan Handbook
The Overall Advertisement Bus Handbook - Volume 1
The Toy & Model Bus Handbook - Volume 1 - Early Diecasts
The Fire Brigade Handbook (fleet list of each local authority fire brigade)
The Police Range Rover Handbook

Some earlier editions of these books are still available. Please contact the publisher on 01952 255669.

The London Bus Handbook

This edition of the London Bus Handbook is the third from British Bus Publishing. The operators included in this edition are those who provide tendered and commercial services within the London region, primarily Transport for London (TfL). Also included is a number of operators who provide significant coaching activities, along with Croydon Tramlink.

Quality photographs for inclusion in the series are welcome, for which a fee is payable. Original digital pictures are preferred and these should be supplied at the highest resolution available, on either CD or DVD. Unfortunately, the publishers cannot accept responsibility for any loss and they request that you show your name on each disc supplied.

To keep the fleet information up to date we recommend the Ian Allan publication, *Buses*, published monthly, or for more detailed information, the PSV Circle or LOTS monthly news sheets.

The writer and publishers would be glad to hear from readers should any information be available which corrects or enhances that given in this publication.

Principal Editors - Colin Lloyd, Keith Grimes and Jef Johnson
Series Editor - Bill Potter

Acknowledgements:
We are grateful to David Donati, Tom Johnson, Stuart Martin, Frank Messenger, LOTS, the PSV Circle, London's Transport Museum staff, the operators and the management and officials of Transport for London for their kind assistance and co-operation during the compilation of this book.

The cover photographs are by Richard Godfrey and Mark Lyons.

Page1: During 2005, the last of the Routemasters were withdrawn from London's streets. However, in a bid to retain a token number, TfL introduced two special Heritage routes using RMs. Operated by First London (route 9) and East London Bus Group (route 15) the vehicles run over a truncated version of the existing routes. Displaying heritage number RM1933, East London/Stagecoach 12133, ALD933B, illustrates the initial advert that has since been replaced by special, individual adverts. *Mark Lyons*

Earlier editions of the area covered by the London Bus Handbook:

1st Edition 6/03 -   ISBN 1-897990-35-9
2nd Edition 9/04 -   ISBN 1-904875-44-0

ISBN 1 904875 45 9
Published by *British Bus Publishing Ltd*
16 St Margaret's Drive, Telford, TF1 3PH

Telephone: 01952 255669 - Facsimile 01952 222397 - www.britishbuspublishing.co.uk
© British Bus Publishing Ltd, October 2006

Contents

ALLIED

Allied - Aron

Allied Coachlines Ltd; Aron Coachlines Ltd, 47 Wallingford Road, Uxbridge, UB8 2RW

AR	T54PDA	Mercedes-Benz 208D	Mercedes-Benz	M8L	1999	private owner, 2002
AL	BU04EYW	Mercedes-Benz 1836RL	Mercedes-Benz Touro	C48FT	2004	
AL	BU04EYY	Mercedes-Benz 1836RL	Mercedes-Benz Touro	C48FT	2004	
AR	BU04EYZ	Mercedes-Benz 1836RL	Mercedes-Benz Touro	C48FT	2004	
AR	BX05UWA	Mercedes-Benz 1836RL	Mercedes-Benz Touro	C49FT	2005	
AR	BX05UWB	Mercedes-Benz 1836RL	Mercedes-Benz Touro	C49FT	2005	
AL	BX05UWD	Mercedes-Benz 1836RL	Mercedes-Benz Touro	C49FT	2005	
AL	BX55FVE	Mercedes-Benz 1836RL	Mercedes-Benz Touro	C49FT	2005	
AR	BU06CVC	Mercedes-Benz 0510	Mercedes-Benz Tourino	C30FT	2006	
AR	BX06UNE	Mercedes-Benz Sprinter 413cdi	Mercedes-Benz	M16	2006	

AL - Allied Coachlines; AR - Aron Coachlines
Web: www.alliedcoaches.co.uk; www.aroncoachlines.co.uk

During 2004-05 Allied of west London received seven integral Mercedes-Benz 1836RL fitted with the Touro body. Three similar examples carry the livery of parent company Aron. New in 2002, BF52SYV was seen in March 2006 shortly before being replaced. *Colin Lloyd*

ANDERSON

Anderson - London Mini Coaches

Anderson Travel Ltd, 178a Tower Bridge Road, Bermondsey, SE1 3LS

London Mini Coaches Ltd, 23 Airlinks Industrial Estate, Spitfire Way, Hounslow, TW5 9NR

LM	W236PBR	Mercedes-Benz Sprinter 412	Onyx	M16	2000	
AN	FJ51JYG	Toyota Coaster BB50R	Caetano Optimo V	C26F	2001	
AN	YD02PXA	Bova Futura FHD12.340	Bova Futura	C53F	2002	
AN	YD02PXB	Bova Futura FHD12.340	Bova Futura	C53F	2002	
AN	YD02PXC	Bova Futura FHD12.340	Bova Futura	C53F	2002	
AN	YJ03GXM	Bova Futura FHD12.340XE	Bova Futura	C49FT	2003	
AN	YJ03GXN	Bova Futura FHD12.340XE	Bova Futura	C49FT	2003	
AN	YJ03GXP	Bova Futura FHD12.340XE	Bova Futura	C49FT	2003	
AN	YJ03GXR	Bova Futura FHD12.340XE	Bova Futura	C49FT	2003	
AN	YJ04BNL	VDL Bus SB4000XF	Van Hool T9 Alizée	C53F	2004	MacPhail, Newarthill, 2006
AN	YJ04BNN	VDL Bus SB4000XF	Van Hool T9 Alizée	C53F	2004	MacPhail, Newarthill, 2006
AN	FJ05APO	Volvo B12B	Plaxton Panther	C49FT	2005	
AN	FJ05APV	Volvo B12B	Plaxton Panther	C49FT	2005	
AN	FJ05APX	Volvo B12B	Plaxton Panther	C53F	2005	
AN	FJ05APY	Volvo B12B	Plaxton Panther	C53F	2005	
AN	YJ05FXC	VDL Bova Futura FHD12.340XE	VDL Bova	C49FT	2005	
AN	YJ05FXD	VDL Bova Futura FHD12.340XE	VDL Bova	C49FT	2005	
AN	YJ05FXE	VDL Bova Futura FHD12.340XE	VDL Bova	C49FT	2005	
AN	YJ05FXF	VDL Bova Futura FHD21.340XE	VDL Bova	C49FT	2005	
AN	YJ05FXG	VDL Bova Futura FHD12.340XE	VDL Bova	C53F	2005	
LM	WA05JWJ	Mercedes-Benz Vario 0815	Sitcar Beluga 2	C25F	2005	
LM	WA05JWK	Mercedes-Benz Vario 0815	Sitcar Beluga 2	C25F	2005	
LM	WA05JWL	Mercedes-Benz Vario 0815	Sitcar Beluga 2	C25F	2005	
LM	YX05DHY	Mercedes-Benz Sprinter 413cdi	Ferqui/Optare Soroco	C16F	2005	
LM	YX05DHZ	Mercedes-Benz Sprinter 616cdi	Ferqui/Optare Soroco Plus	C16F	2005	
LM	YN55KWH	Mercedes-Benz Sprinter 616cdi	Unvi/Esker Riada 616	C18F	2005	
LM	WA06GRU	Mercedes-Benz Vario 0815	Sitcar Beluga 2	C25F	2006	
LM	WA06GRX	Mercedes-Benz Vario 0815	Sitcar Beluga 2	C25F	2006	
LM	WA06GRZ	Mercedes-Benz Vario 0815	Sitcar Beluga 2	C25F	2006	
AN	YJ06GKY	VDL Bova Magiq HD122.340	VDL Bova	C32FT	2006	
AN	YJ06GKZ	VDL Bova Futura FHD12.340XE	VDL Bova	C49FT	2006	

AN - Anderson Travel; LM London Mini Coaches
Web: www.andersontravel.co.uk; www.lmcoaches.co.uk
Named vehicles: FJ51JYG Lauren Savannah; YD02PXA Jill Wendy; YD02PXB Rebecca Sophie; YD02PXC Kit Amanda; YJ03GXM Hannah Jo-Ann; YJ03GXN Francesca Kate; YN03GXP Daisy Laura; YN03GXR Chloe Anna; FJ05APO Emma Jane; FJ05APV Marie Yvonne; FJ05APX Leah Grace; FJ05APY Evie May; YJ05FXC Charlotte May; YJ05FXD Jenny Ann; YJ05FXE Elizabeth Cerys; YJ05FXF Tracey Lorraine; YJ05FXG Georgia Kate; YJ06GKY Kerry Leticia; YJ06GKZ Julie Ann.

Anderson of Bermondsey allocates names to all its coaches. Shown here on Dutch-built VDL Bova Futura integral YJ05FXF is Tracey Lorraine. The coach is seen passing through Trafalgar Square in May 2006.
Colin Lloyd

ARRIVA LONDON

Arriva London North Ltd, 16 Watsons Road, Wood Green, London, N22 4TZ
Arriva London South Ltd, Croydon Bus Garage, Brighton Road, South Croydon, CR2 6EL

| ADL1 | EC | V701LWT | Dennis Dart SLF 10.2m | | Alexander ALX200 | | N27D | 1999 | |

ADL2-8			Dennis Dart SLF 10.2m		Alexander ALX200		N30D	2000	
2	EC	W602VGJ	4	EC	W604VGJ	6	EC	W606VGJ	8	EC	W608VGJ
3	EC	W603VGJ	5	EC	W605VGJ	7	EC	W607VGJ			

ADL9-23			Dennis Dart SLF 10.8m		Alexander ALX200		N33D	1999
9	TC	V609LGC	13	TC	V613LGC	17	TC	V617LGC	21	TC	V621LGC
10	TC	V610LGC	14	TC	V614LGC	18	TC	V618LGC	22	TC	V622LGC
11	TC	V611LGC	15	TC	V615LGC	19	TC	V619LGC	23	TC	V623LGC
12	TC	V612LGC	16	TC	V616LGC	20	TC	V620LGC			

ADL61-81			Dennis Dart SLF 9.4m		Alexander ALX200		N26D	2000	Arriva The Shires, 2005
61	EC	W461XKX	66	EC	W466XKX	72	EC	W472XKX	77	EC	W477XKX
62	EC	W462XKX	67	EC	W467XKX	73	EC	W473XKX	78	EC	W478XKX
63	EC	W463XKX	68	EC	W468XKX	74	EC	W474XKX	79	EC	W479XKX
64	EC	W464XKX	69	EC	W469XKX	75	EC	W475XKX	81	EC	W481XKX
65	EC	W465XKX	71	EC	W471XKX	76	EC	W476XKX			

ADL969-983			Dennis Dart SLF 10.2m		Alexander ALX200		N27D	1998
969	DX	S169JUA	973	DX	S173JUA	977	DX	S177JUA	981	DX	S181JUA
970	DX	S170JUA	974	DX	S174JUA	978	DX	S178JUA	982	DX	S182JUA
971	DX	S171JUA	975	DX	S175JUA	979	DX	S179JUA	983	DX	S183JUA
972	DX	S172JUA	976	DX	S176JUA	980	DX	S180JUA			

| CW1 | WN | W218CDN | DAF SB120 10.2m | | Wright Cadet | | N31D | 2000 | |

Illustrating the ALX200 body styling is Arriva London's ADL2, W602VGJ. It is seen leaving Turnpike Lane station in November 2005, and is one of a batch of seven, 10.2m examples delivered new to Edmonton depot in June 2000 for route 444. *Colin Lloyd*

DDL1-18
Dennis Dart SLF 10.1m   Plaxton Pointer 2   N26D   1998

#			#			#			#		
1	TH	S301JUA	6	TH	S306JUA	11	TH	S311JUA	15	EC	S315JUA
2	TH	S302JUA	7	TH	S307JUA	12	TH	S312JUA	16	DX	S316JUA
3	TH	S303JUA	8	TH	S308JUA	13	TH	S313JUA	17	DX	S317JUA
4	TH	S304JUA	9	TH	S309JUA	14	TH	S314JUA	18	DX	S318JUA
5	TH	S305JUA	10	TH	S310JUA						

DLA1-64
DAF DB250 10.6m   Alexander ALX400   N45/21D   1998-99

#			#			#			#		
1	WN	R101GNW	17	WN	S217JUA	33	WN	S233JUA	49	TH	S249JUA
2	TH	S202JUA	18	WN	S218JUA	34	WN	S234JUA	50	TH	S250JUA
3	TH	S203JUA	19	WN	S219JUA	35	WN	S235JUA	51	TH	S251JUA
4	TH	S204JUA	20	WN	S220JUA	36	WN	S236JUA	52	TH	S252JUA
5	TH	S205JUA	21	WN	S221JUA	37	WN	S237JUA	53	TH	S253JUA
6	TH	S206JUA	22	WN	S322JUA	38	TH	S238JUA	54	TH	S254JUA
7	TH	S207JUA	23	WN	S223JUA	39	TH	S239JUA	55	TH	S255JUA
8	TH	S208JUA	24	WN	S224JUA	40	TH	S240JUA	56	TH	S256JUA
9	TH	S209JUA	25	WN	S225JUA	41	TH	S241JUA	57	TH	S257JUA
10	TH	S210JUA	26	WN	S226JUA	42	TH	S242JUA	58	TH	S258JUA
11	WN	S211JUA	27	WN	S227JUA	43	TH	S243JUA	59	TH	S259JUA
12	WN	S212JUA	28	WN	S228JUA	44	TH	S244JUA	60	TH	S260JUA
13	WN	S213JUA	29	WN	S229JUA	45	WN	S245JUA	61	TH	S261JUA
14	WN	S214JUA	30	WN	S230JUA	46	WN	S246JUA	62	TH	S262JUA
15	WN	S215JUA	31	WN	S231JUA	47	WN	S247JUA	63	TH	S263JUA
16	WN	S216JUA	32	WN	S232JUA	48	TH	S248JUA	64	TH	S264JUA

DLA72-92
DAF DB250 10.6m   Alexander ALX400   N45/19D*   1999

#			#			#			#		
72	E	S272JUA	78	E	S278JUA	83	E	S283JUA	88	DX	S288JUA
73	E	S273JUA	79	E	S279JUA	84	E	S284JUA	89	DX	S289JUA
74	E	S274JUA	80	E	S280JUA	85	E	S285JUA	90	DX	S290JUA
75	E	S275JUA	81	E	S281JUA	86	DX	S286JUA	91	E	S291JUA
76	E	S276JUA	82	E	S282JUA	87	DX	S287JUA	92	E	S292JUA
77	E	S277JUA									

DLA93-125
DAF DB250 10.6m   Alexander ALX400   N45/19D*   1999   *DLA124/5 are N45/17D

#			#			#			#		
93	E	T293FGN	102	SF	T302FGN	110	SF	T310FGN	118	E	T318FGN
94	E	T294FGN	103	SF	T303FGN	111	SF	T311FGN	119	E	T319FGN
95	E	T295FGN	104	SF	T304FGN	112	N	T312FGN	120	E	T320FGN
96	SF	T296FGN	105	SF	T305FGN	113	SF	T313FGN	121	E	T421GGO
97	SF	T297FGN	106	SF	T306FGN	114	SF	T314FGN	122	E	T322FGN
98	SF	T298FGN	107	SF	T307FGN	115	SF	T315FGN	123	E	T323FGN
99	SF	T299FGN	108	SF	T308FGN	116	E	T316FGN	124	E	T324FGN
100	SF	T110GGO	109	SF	T309FGN	117	E	T317FGN	125	EC	T325FGN
101	SF	T301FGN									

DLA126-189
DAF DB250 10.2m   Alexander ALX400   N43/21D*   1999-2000   *several are now N43/18D

#			#			#			#		
126	TH	V326DGT	142	BN	V342DGT	158	N	V358DGT	174	N	W374VGJ
127	TH	V327DGT	143	BN	V343DGT	159	N	V359DGT	175	TC	W432WGJ
128	TH	V628LGC	144	BN	V344DGT	160	BN	V660LGC	176	TC	W376VGJ
129	TH	V329DGT	145	BN	V345DGT	161	BN	V361DGT	177	TC	W377VGJ
130	TH	V330DGT	146	BN	V346DGT	162	BN	V362DGT	178	TC	W378VGJ
131	TH	V331DGT	147	BN	V347DGT	163	BN	V363DGT	179	TC	W379VGJ
132	TH	V332DGT	148	BN	V348DGT	164	BN	V364DGT	180	TC	W433WGJ
133	TC	V633LGC	149	BN	V349DGT	165	BN	V365DGT	181	TC	W381VGJ
134	TC	V334DGT	150	BN	V650LGC	166	N	V366VGJ	182	TC	W382VGJ
135	TC	V335DGT	151	BN	V351DGT	167	N	W367VGJ	183	TC	W383VGJ
136	TC	V336DGT	152	BN	V352DGT	168	N	W368VGJ	184	TC	W384VGJ
137	DX	V337DGT	153	BN	V353DGT	169	N	W369VGJ	185	TC	W385VGJ
138	DX	V338DGT	154	N	V354DGT	170	N	W431WGJ	186	TC	W386VGJ
139	DX	V339DGT	155	N	V355DGT	171	N	W371VGJ	187	TC	W387VGJ
140	N	V640LGC	156	TC	V356DGT	172	N	W372VGJ	188	TC	W388VGJ
141	N	V341DGT	157	TC	V357DGT	173	N	W373VGJ	189	TC	W389VGJ

Arriva London's first low-floor double-deck vehicles were a batch of DAF DB250s with Alexander ALX400 bodies. Pictured in Lower Clapton Road on route 253 is DLA13, S213JUA. The total number of this combination of chassis and bodywork was three hundred and eighty-nine, but some mid-life examples are now being transferred to other Arriva companies. However, the DLA class remains the largest single type with the Arriva London group. *Richard Godfrey*

DLA190-223

	DAF DB250 10.2m			Alexander ALX400			N43/21D	2000			
190	E	W434WGJ	199	E	W399VGJ	208	TC	W408VGJ	216	TC	X416FGP
191	E	W391VGJ	200	E	W435WGJ	209	BN	W409VGJ	217	TC	X417FGP
192	E	W392VGJ	201	E	W401VGJ	210	E	W438WGJ	218	TC	X418FGP
193	E	W393VGJ	202	E	W402VGJ	211	E	W411VGJ	219	TC	X419FGP
194	E	W394VGJ	203	E	W403VGJ	212	E	W412VGJ	220	TC	X501GGO
195	F	W395VGJ	204	N	W404VGJ	213	BN	W413VGJ	221	TC	X421FGP
196	E	W396VGJ	205	BN	W436WGJ	214	WN	W414VGJ	222	TC	X422FGP
197	E	W397VGJ	206	BN	W437WGJ	215	TC	X415FGP	223	TC	X423FGP
198	E	W398VGJ	207	TC	W407VGJ						

DLA224-256

	DAF DB250 10.2m			Alexander ALX400			N43/20D*	2000-01	*seating varies		
224	TC	X424FGP	233	WN	X433FGP	241	AR	X441FGP	249	E	X449FGP
225	E	X425FGP	234	AR	X434FGP	242	AR	X442FGP	250	TC	X506GGO
226	E	X426FGP	235	AR	X435FGP	243	AR	X443FGP	251	TC	X451FGP
227	WN	X427FGP	236	N	X436FGP	244	AR	X504GGO	252	TC	X452FGP
228	WN	X428FGP	237	E	X437FGP	245	AR	X445FGP	253	TC	X453FGP
229	WN	X429FGP	238	E	X438FGP	246	AR	X446FGP	254	TC	X454FGP
230	AR	X502GGO	239	AR	X439FGP	247	AR	X447FGP	255	TC	X507GGO
231	AR	X431FGP	240	AR	X503GGO	248	E	X448FGP	256	TC	X508GGO
232	AR	X432FGP									

DLA270-320

	DAF DB250 10.2m			Alexander ALX400			N43/20D*	2000-01	*seating varies		
270	E	Y452UGC	283	AR	Y483UGC	296	SF	Y496UGC	309	SF	Y509UGC
271	BN	Y471UGC	284	AR	Y484UGC	297	SF	Y497UGC	310	SF	Y527UGC
272	TH	Y472UGC	285	AR	Y485UGC	298	SF	Y498UGC	311	N	Y511UGC
273	WN	Y473UGC	286	AR	Y486UGC	299	SF	Y499UGC	312	BN	Y512UGC
274	WN	Y474UGC	287	AR	Y487UGC	300	SF	Y524UGC	313	BN	Y513UGC
275	WN	Y475UGC	288	AR	Y488UGC	301	SF	Y501UGC	314	BN	Y514UGC
276	N	Y476UGC	289	AR	Y489UGC	302	SF	Y502UGC	315	BN	Y529UGC
277	AR	Y477UGC	290	BN	Y523UGC	303	SF	Y503UGC	316	SF	Y516UGC
278	AR	Y478UGC	291	SF	Y491UGC	304	SF	Y504UGC	317	BN	Y517UGC
279	AR	Y479UGC	292	SF	Y492UGC	305	SF	Y526UGC	318	N	Y518UGC
280	AR	Y522UGC	293	SF	Y493UGC	306	SF	Y506UGC	319	BN	Y519UGC
281	AR	Y481UGC	294	SF	Y494UGC	307	SF	Y507UGC	320	BN	Y531UGC
282	AR	Y482UGC	295	SF	Y495UGC	308	u	Y508UGC			

Walthamstow bus station, situated adjacent to both the tube and overground stations, and Edmonton's DLA366, LJ03MWF, is en route to Barnet Church. This is one of the batch purchased in 2003 to convert route 34 from single to double-deck operation following an increase in passenger numbers. *Colin Lloyd*

DLA322-336

			DAF DB250 10.2m			TransBus ALX400			N45/20D	2003
322	TH	LG52DAO	326	TH	LG52DBV	330	TH	LG52DCF	334	TH	LG52DCX
323	TH	LG52DAU	327	TH	LG52DBY	331	TH	LG52DCO	335	TH	LG52DCY
324	TH	LG52DBO	328	TH	LG52DBZ	332	TH	LG52DCU	336	TH	LG52DCZ
325	TH	LG52DBU	329	TH	LG52DCE	333	TH	LG52DCV			

DLA337-389

			DAF DB250 10.2m			TransBus ALX400			N45/20D	2003
337	TH	LJ03MFX	351	EC	LJ03MKZ	364	EC	LJ03MKL	377	SF	LJ03MTK
338	TH	LJ03MFY	352	EC	LJ03MLE	365	EC	LJ03MWE	378	SF	LJ03MTU
339	TH	LJ03MFZ	353	EC	LJ03MLF	366	EC	LJ03MWF	379	SF	LJ03MTV
340	TH	LJ03MGE	354	EC	LJ03MLK	367	EC	LJ03MWG	380	SF	LJ03MTY
341	TH	LJ03MGU	355	EC	LJ03MJX	368	EC	LJ03MWK	381	SF	LJ03MTZ
342	TH	LJ03MGV	356	EC	LJ03MJY	369	EC	LJ03MWL	382	SF	LJ03MUA
343	TH	LJ03MDV	357	EC	LJ03MKA	370	SF	LJ03MUY	383	SF	LJ03MUB
344	TH	LJ03MDX	358	EC	LJ03MKC	371	SF	LJ03MVC	384	SF	LJ03MYU
345	TH	LJ03MDY	359	EC	LJ03MKD	372	SF	LJ03MVD	385	SF	LJ03MYV
346	SF	LJ03MDZ	360	EC	LJ03MKE	373	SF	LJ03MVE	386	SF	LJ03MYX
347	TH	LJ03MEU	361	EC	LJ03MKF	374	SF	LJ03MSY	387	SF	LJ03MYY
348	EC	LJ03MKU	362	EC	LJ03MKG	375	SF	LJ03MTE	388	SF	LJ03MYZ
349	EC	LJ03MKV	363	EC	LJ03MKK	376	SF	LJ03MTF	389	TH	LJ03MZD
350	EC	LJ03MKX									

DLP15-20

			DAF DB250 10.6m			Plaxton President			N45/19D	1999
15	E	T215XBV	17	E	T217XBV	19	E	T219XBV	20	E	T220XBV
16	E	T216XBV	18	E	T218XBV						

The London Bus Handbook

Having just departed the northern extremity of route 279, Arriva's DLP78, LJ51OSZ, from Edmonton depot, leaves Waltham Cross in March 2006. Enfield and Wood Green depots operate both DLA and DLP types of DAF DB250 chassis with respectively Alexander ALX400 or Plaxton President bodies. *Richard Godfrey*

DLP40-75

DAF DB250 10.6m | Plaxton President | N45/24D | 2001

40	WN	Y532UGC	49	WN	Y549UGC	58	WN	LJ51DKF	67	WN	LJ51DLD
41	WN	Y541UGC	50	WN	LJ51DJU	59	WN	LJ51DKK	68	WN	LJ51DLF
42	WN	Y542UGC	51	WN	LJ51DJV	60	WN	LJ51DKL	69	WN	LJ51DLK
43	WN	Y543UGC	52	WN	LJ51DJX	61	WN	LJ51DKN	70	WN	LJ51DLN
44	WN	Y544UGC	53	WN	LJ51DJY	62	WN	LJ51DKO	71	WN	LJ51DLU
45	WN	Y533UGC	54	WN	LJ51DJZ	63	WN	LJ51DKU	72	WN	LJ51DLV
46	WN	Y546UGC	55	WN	LJ51DKA	64	WN	LJ51DKV	73	WN	LJ51DLX
47	WN	Y547UGC	56	WN	LJ51DKD	65	WN	LJ51DKX	74	WN	LJ51DLY
48	WN	Y548UGC	57	WN	LJ51DKE	66	WN	LJ51DKY	75	WN	LJ51DLZ

DLP76-90

DAF DB250 10.2m | Plaxton President | N43/20D | 2002

76	E	LJ51OSX	80	E	LJ51ORC	84	E	LJ51ORK	88	E	LF02PKD
77	E	LJ51OSY	81	E	LJ51ORF	85	E	LJ51ORL	89	E	LF02PKE
78	E	LJ51OSZ	82	E	LJ51ORG	86	E	LF02PKA	90	E	LF02PKJ
79	E	LJ51ORA	83	E	LJ51ORH	87	E	LF02PKC			

DLP91-110

DAF DB250 10.6m | Plaxton President | N45/20D | 2002

91	E	LF52URS	96	E	LF52URX	101	E	LF52URG	106	E	LF52URM
92	E	LF52URT	97	E	LF52URB	102	E	LF52URH	107	E	LF52UPP
93	E	LF52URU	98	E	LF52URC	103	E	LF52URJ	108	E	LF52UPR
94	E	LF52URV	99	E	LF52URD	104	E	LF52URK	109	E	LF52UPS
95	E	LF52URW	100	E	LF52URE	105	E	LF52URL	110	E	LF52UPT

DPP421-431

Dennis Dart SLF 10m | Plaxton Pointer | N34F | 1997 | Arriva East Herts & Essex, 1998

421	TC	R421COO	424	TC	R424COO	427	TC	R427COO	430	EC	R430COO
422	TC	R422COO	425	TC	R425COO	428	EC	R428COO	431	EC	R431COO
423	TC	R423COO	426	TC	R426COO	429	EC	R429COO			

Consisting of one hundred and thirty four buses, Arriva London's DW class is divided between four depots, all using the South operating licence, one of two licences held by Arriva London. Seen departing West Croydon bus station on route 403 is DW44, one of Beddington Farm's allocation that has gained a cherished registration, VLT244, originally supplied to Routemaster RM244. *Keith Grimes*

DW1-50

DAF DB250 10.3m   Wrightbus Pulsar Gemini   N43/22D   2003

1	TC	801DYE	14	TC	LJ03MWC	27	TC	LJ53BGK	39	CN	LJ53NHF
2	TC	LJ03MWN	15	TC	LJ03MWD	28	TC	LJ53BGO	40	CN	LJ53NHG
3	TC	LJ03MWP	16	CN	LJ03MVF	29	TC	LJ53BGU	41	CN	LJ53NHH
4	TC	LJ03MWU	17	TC	LJ03MVG	30	TC	LJ53NHV	42	CN	LJ53NHK
5	TC	LJ03MWV	18	TC	LJ53NHT	31	TC	WLT531	43	CN	LJ53NHL
6	TC	LJ03MVT	19	TC	WLT719	32	TC	LJ53NHY	44	CN	VLT244
7	TC	WLT807	20	TC	LJ53BFP	33	TC	LJ53NHZ	45	CN	LJ53NHN
8	TC	LJ03MVV	21	TC	LJ53BFU	34	TC	734DYE	46	CN	LJ53NHO
9	TC	LJ03MVW	22	TC	822DYE	35	CN	LJ53NJF	47	CN	LJ53NHP
10	TC	LJ03MVX	23	TC	LJ53BFX	36	CN	LJ53NJK	48	CN	WLT348
11	TC	LJ03MVY	24	TC	LJ53BFY	37	CN	LJ53NJN	49	CN	LJ53NGU
12	TC	LJ03MVZ	25	TC	725DYE	38	CN	LJ53NHE	50	CN	LJ53NGV
13	TC	LJ03MWA	26	TC	LJ53BGF						

DW51-93

VDL Bus DB250 10.3m   Wrightbus Pulsar Gemini   N43/22D   2004

51	CN	LJ04LDX	62	BN	LJ04LDC	73	BN	LJ04LGK	84	BN	LJ04LFX
52	CN	LJ04LDY	63	BN	LJ04LDD	74	BN	LJ04LGL	85	BN	WLT385
53	CN	LJ04LDZ	64	BN	WLT664	75	BN	LJ04LGN	86	BN	LJ04LFZ
54	CN	LJ04LEF	65	BN	LJ04LDF	76	BN	WLT676	87	BN	LJ04LGA
55	BN	LJ04LEU	66	BN	LJ04LDK	77	BN	LJ04LGV	88	BN	LJ04LGC
56	BN	656DYE	67	BN	LJ04LDL	78	BN	LJ04LGW	89	BN	LJ04LGD
57	BN	LJ04LFB	68	BN	LJ04LDN	79	BN	LJ04LGX	90	BN	LJ04LGE
58	BN	LJ04LFD	69	BN	LJ04LDU	80	BN	LJ04LGY	91	BN	LJ04LFG
59	BN	LJ04LFE	70	BN	WLT970	81	BN	LJ04LFU	92	BN	LJ04LFH
60	BN	LJ04LFF	71	BN	LJ04LGF	82	BN	LJ04LFV	93	BN	LJ04LFK
61	BN	LJ04LDA	72	BN	LJ04LGG	83	BN	LJ04LFW			

DW94-102

VDL Bus DB250 10.3m   Wrightbus Pulsar Gemini   N43/22D   2004

94	CN	LJ54BFP	97	CN	WLT997	99	CN	LJ54BFZ	101	CN	LJ54BGF
95	CN	VLT295	98	CN	LJ54BFY	100	CN	LJ54BGE	102	CN	LJ54BGK
96	CN	LJ54BFV									

DW103-134 — VDL Bus DB250 10.3m — Wrightbus Pulsar Gemini — N43/22D — 2005

103	BA	LJ05BJV	111	BA	LJ05BHP	119	BA	LJ05BMY	127	BA	LJ05BNL
104	BA	LJ05BJX	112	BA	LJ05BHU	120	BA	LJ05BMZ	128	BA	LJ05GKX
105	BA	LJ05BJY	113	BA	LJ05BHV	121	BA	LJ05BNA	129	BA	LJ05GKY
106	BA	LJ05BJZ	114	BA	LJ05BHW	122	BA	LJ05BNB	130	BA	LJ05GKZ
107	BA	LJ05BKA	115	BA	LJ05BHX	123	BA	LJ05BND	131	BA	LJ05GLF
108	BA	LJ05BHL	116	BA	LJ05BHY	124	BA	LJ05BNE	132	BA	LJ05GLK
109	BA	LJ05BHN	117	BA	LJ05BHZ	125	BA	LJ05BNF	133	BA	LJ05GLV
110	BN	LJ05BHO	118	BA	LJ05BMV	126	BA	LJ05BNK	134	BA	LJ05GLY

DWL1-22 — DAF SB120 10.2m — Wrightbus Cadet — N31D — 2001

1	BN	Y801DGT	7	BN	LJ51DDK	13	BN	LJ51DDX	18	BN	LJ51DFC
2	BN	Y802DGT	8	BN	LJ51DDL	14	BN	LJ51DDY	19	BN	LJ51DFD
3	BN	Y803DGT	9	BN	LJ51DDN	15	BN	LJ51DDZ	20	BN	LJ51DFE
4	BN	Y804DGT	10	BN	LJ51DDO	16	BN	LJ51DEU	21	BN	LJ51DFF
5	BN	Y805DGT	11	BN	LJ51DDU	17	BN	LJ51DFA	22	BN	LJ51DFG
6	BN	Y806DGT	12	BN	LJ51DDV						

DWL23-29 — DAF SB120 10.8m — Wrightbus Cadet 2 — N34D — 2002

23	E	LF02PLU	25	E	LF02PLX	27	E	LF02PMO	29	E	LF02PMV
24	E	LF02PLV	26	E	LF02PLZ						

DWL30-55 — DAF SB120 10.2m — Wrightbus Cadet 2 — N30D — 2002

30	WN	LF02PMX	37	WN	LF02PNO	44	WN	LF52UTB	50	WN	LF52UOB
31	WN	LF02PMY	38	WN	LF02PNU	45	WN	LF52UNW	51	WN	LF52UOC
32	WN	LF02PNE	39	WN	LF02PNV	46	WN	LF52UNX	52	WN	LF52UOD
33	WN	LF02PNJ	40	WN	LF02PNX	47	WN	LF52UNY	53	WN	LF52UOE
34	WN	LF02PNK	41	WN	LF02PNY	48	WN	LF52UNZ	54	WN	LF52USZ
35	WN	LF02PNL	42	WN	LF02POA	49	WN	LF52UOA	55	WN	LF52UTA
36	WN	LF02PNN	43	WN	LF02POH						

DWL56-67 — DAF SB120 10.2m — Wrightbus Cadet 2 — N30D — 2003

56	E	LJ03MUW	59	CN	LJ03MZG	62	CN	LJ03MYH	65	CN	LJ03MYM
57	CN	LJ03MZE	60	CN	LJ03MZL	63	CN	LJ03MYK	66	CN	LJ53NGX
58	CN	LJ03MZF	61	CN	LJ03MYG	64	CN	LJ03MYL	67	CN	LJ53NGY

DWS1-18 — VDL Bus SB120 9.4m — Wrightbus Cadet2 — N26D — 2003

1	CN	LJ53NGZ	6	CN	LJ53NFT	11	CN	LJ53NFZ	15	CN	LJ53NGN
2	CN	LJ53NHA	7	CN	LJ53NFU	12	CN	LJ53NGE	16	CN	LJ53NFE
3	CN	LJ53NHB	8	CN	LJ53NFV	13	CN	LJ53NGF	17	CN	LJ53NFF
4	CN	LJ53NHC	9	CN	LJ53NFX	14	CN	LJ53NGG	18	CN	LJ53NFG
5	CN	LJ53NHD	10	CN	LJ53NFY						

MA1-76 — Mercedes-Benz O530G 18m — Mercedes-Benz Citaro — AB49T — 2004

1	LV	BX04MWW	20	LV	BX04MXU	39	LV	BX04NEJ	58	LV	BX04MZL
2	LV	BX04MWY	21	LV	BX04MXV	40	LV	BX04MYG	59	LV	BX04MZN
3	LV	BX04MWZ	22	LV	BX04MXW	41	LV	BX04MYH	60	LV	BX04NBK
4	LV	BX04MXA	23	LV	BX04MXY	42	LV	BX04MYJ	61	LV	361CLT
5	LV	205CLT	24	LV	324CLT	43	LV	BX04MYK	62	LV	BX04NCF
6	LV	BX04MXC	25	LV	BX04MYA	44	LV	BX04MYL	63	LV	BX04NCJ
7	LV	BX04MXD	26	LV	BX04MYB	45	LV	BX04MYM	64	LV	BX04NCN
8	LV	BX04MXE	27	LV	BX04MYC	46	LV	BX04MYN	65	LV	BX04NCU
9	LV	BX04MXG	28	LV	BX04MYD	47	LV	BX04MYR	66	LV	BX04NCV
10	LV	BX04MXH	29	LV	BX04MYF	48	LV	BX04MYS	67	LV	BX04NCY
11	LV	BX04MXJ	30	LV	330CLT	49	LV	BX04MYT	68	LV	BX04NCZ
12	LV	BX04MXK	31	LV	BX04MYZ	50	LV	BX04MYU	69	LV	BX04NDC
13	LV	BX04MXL	32	LV	BX04NDD	51	LV	BX04MYV	70	LV	70CLT
14	LV	BX04MXM	33	LV	BX04NDG	52	LV	BX04MYW	71	LV	BX04NDF
15	LV	BX04MXN	34	LV	BX04NDU	53	LV	BX04MYZ	72	LV	BX04NDJ
16	LV	BX04MXP	35	LV	BX04NDV	54	LV	BX04MZD	73	LV	BX04NDK
17	LV	217CLT	36	LV	BX04NDY	55	LV	BX04MZE	74	LV	BX04NDL
18	LV	BX04MXS	37	LV	BX04NDZ	56	LV	BX04MZG	75	LV	BX04NDN
19	LV	519CLT	38	LV	BX04NEF	57	LV	BX04MZJ	76	LV	BX04NEN

The operator with most articulated buses in use in London is Arriva with one hundred and fifty seven now in service on routes 29, 38, 73, 149 and night routes N29 and N149. Based at the newly rebuilt depot in Edmonton, Mercedes-Benz Citaro MA153, BX55FXT, is pictured operating route 29, as it is about to pass Turnpike Lane station on its way to Trafalgar Square. *Colin Lloyd*

MA77-157

Mercedes-Benz O530G 18m   Mercedes-Benz Citaro   AB49T   2005

77	AE	BX05UWV	98	AE	398CLT	118	AE	BX55FVU	138	EC	BX55FWZ
78	AE	BX05UWW	99	AE	BX55FUW	119	AE	319CLT	139	EC	BX55FXB
79	AE	BX05UWY	100	AE	BX55FUY	120	AE	BX55FVW	140	EC	BX55FXC
80	AE	480CLT	101	AE	BX55FVA	121	AE	BX55FVY	141	EC	BX55FXE
81	AE	BU05VFE	102	AE	BX55FVB	122	AE	BX55FVZ	142	EC	BX55FXF
82	AE	BU05VFF	103	AE	BX55FVC	123	AE	BX55FWG	143	EC	BX55FXG
83	AE	BX05UXC	104	AE	BX55FVD	124	AE	BX55FWH	144	EC	BX55FXH
84	AE	BU05VFG	105	AE	BX55FVF	125	EC	BX55FWJ	145	EC	BX55FXJ
85	AE	185CLT	106	AE	BX55FVG	126	EC	BX55FWK	146	EC	BX55FXK
86	AE	BU05VFH	107	AE	BX55FVH	127	EC	BX55FWL	147	EC	BX55FXL
87	AE	BU05VFJ	108	AE	BX55FVJ	128	EC	BX55FWM	148	EC	BX55FXM
88	AE	BX05UXD	109	AE	BX55FVK	129	EC	BX55FWN	149	EC	BX55FXO
89	AE	BX55FWA	110	AE	BX55FVL	130	EC	BX55FWP	150	EC	BX55FXP
90	AE	BX55FWB	111	AE	BX55FVM	131	EC	BX55FWR	151	EC	BX55FXR
91	AE	BX55FUH	112	AE	BX55FVN	132	EC	BX55FWS	152	EC	BX55FXS
92	AE	BX55FUJ	113	AE	BX55FVQ	133	EC	BX55FWT	153	EC	BX55FXT
93	AE	593CLT	114	AE	BX55FVP	134	EC	BX55FWU	154	EC	BX55FXU
94	AE	BX55FUO	115	AE	BX55FVR	135	EC	BX55FWV	155	EC	BX55FXV
95	AE	BX55FUP	116	AE	BX55FVS	136	EC	BX55FWW	156	EC	BX55FXW
96	AE	BX55FUT	117	AE	BX55FVT	137	EC	BX55FWY	157	EC	BX55FXY
97	AE	BX55FUU									

PDL1-18

Dennis Dart SLF 8.8m   Plaxton Pointer MPD   N29F*   2000   *16-18 are N25F

1	EC	V421DGT	6	EC	V426DGT	11	EC	V431DGT	15	AR	V435DGT
2	EC	V422DGT	7	EC	V427DGT	12	EC	V432DGT	16	AR	W136VGJ
3	EC	V423DGT	8	EC	V428DGT	13	EC	V433DGT	17	AR	W137VGJ
4	EC	V424DGT	9	EC	V429DGT	14	AR	V434DGT	18	AR	W138VGJ
5	EC	V425DGT	10	EC	V430DGT						

East Croydon on a sunny morning finds PDL117, LJ05GOP, on route 312. This is one of seven ADL-class 10.1m Dennis Darts delivered during 2005. These buses arrived in London in the now standard all-red livery rather than the former 'cow-horns' style applied to Arriva London's buses for several years. *Colin Lloyd*

PDL19-38

			Dennis Dart SLF 10.7m			Plaxton Pointer 2			N31D		2000	
19	CN	X519GGO	24	CN	X524GGO	29	DX	X529GGO	34	DX	X534GGO
20	CN	X471GGO	25	CN	X475GGO	30	DX	X481GGO	35	DX	X485GGO
21	CN	X521GGO	26	CN	X526GGO	31	DX	X531GGO	36	DX	X536GGO
22	CN	X522GGO	27	CN	X527GGO	32	DX	X532GGO	37	DX	X537GGO
23	CN	X523GGO	28	DX	X478GGO	33	DX	X533GGO	38	DX	X538GGO

PDL39-49

			Dennis Dart SLF 8.8m			Plaxton Pointer MPD			N29F		2001	*converting to N23F
39	AR	X239PGT	42	AR	X242PGT	45	AR	X546GGO	48	AR	X248PGT
40	AR	X541GGO	43	AR	X243PGT	46	AR	X246PGT	49	AR	X249PGT
41	AR	X241PGT	44	AR	X244PGT	47	AR	X247PGT			

PDL50-69

			Dennis Dart SLF 8.8m			Plaxton Pointer MPD			N29F		2001-02	
50	TH	LJ51DAA	55	TH	LJ51DBV	60	TH	LJ51DCF	65	E	LJ51DCY
51	TH	LJ51DAO	56	TH	LJ51DBX	61	E	LJ51DCO	66	E	LJ51DCZ
52	TH	LJ51DAU	57	TH	LJ51DBY	62	TH	LJ51DCU	67	E	LJ51DDA
53	TH	LJ51DBO	58	TH	LJ51DBZ	63	CN	LJ51DCV	68	E	LJ51DDE
54	TH	LJ51DBU	59	TH	LJ51DCE	64	E	LJ51DCX	69	E	LJ51DDF

PDL70-94

			TransBus Dart 8.8m			TransBus Mini Pointer			N29F		2002	
70	E	LF02PTZ	77	EC	LF52UON	83	E	LF52URZ	89	E	LF52USJ
71	E	LF52UOG	78	EC	LF52UOO	84	E	LF52USB	90	u	LF52USL
72	EC	LF52UOH	79	EC	LF52UOP	85	E	LF52USC	91	E	LF52URN
73	EC	LF52UOJ	80	EC	LF52UOR	86	E	LF52USD	92	E	LF52URO
74	EC	LF52UOK	81	EC	LF52UNV	87	E	LF52USG	93	E	LF52URP
75	EC	LF52UOL	82	E	LF52URY	88	E	LF52USH	94	E	LF52URR
76	EC	LF52UOM									

PDL95-116

			ADL Dart 9.3m			ADL Pointer			N27D		2004	
95	EC	LJ54BCX	101	EC	LJ54BBF	107	EC	LJ54LHG	112	EC	LJ54LHN
96	EC	LJ54BAA	102	EC	LJ54BBK	108	EC	LJ54LHH	113	EC	LJ54LHO
97	EC	LJ54BAO	103	EC	LJ54BBN	109	EC	LJ54LHK	114	EC	LJ54LHP
98	EC	LJ54BAU	104	EC	LJ54BBO	110	EC	LJ54LHL	115	EC	LJ54LHR
99	EC	LJ54BAV	105	EC	LJ54BBU	111	EC	LJ54LHM	116	EC	LJ54LGV
100	EC	LJ54BBE	106	EC	LJ54LHF						

PDL117-123

			ADL Dart 10.1m			ADL Pointer			N29D		2005	
117	TC	LJ05GOP	119	TC	LJ05GOX	121	TC	LJ05GPK	123	TC	LJ05GPU
118	TC	LJ05GOU	120	TC	LJ05GPF	122	TC	LJ05GPO			

PDL124-136 ADL Dart 9.3m ADL Pointer N24D 2006

124	TH	LJ56APZ	128	TH	LJ56ARX	131	TH	LJ56ASU	134	TH	LJ56AOW
125	TH	LJ56ARF	129	TH	LJ56ARZ	132	TH	LJ56ASV	135	TH	LJ56AOX
126	TH	LJ56ARO	130	TH	LJ56ASO	133	TH	LJ56ASX	136	TH	LJ56AOY
127	TH	LJ56ARU								

VLA1-55 Volvo B7TL 10.6m TransBus ALX400 4.4m N49/22D 2003

1	N	LJ03MYP	15	N	LJ03MXH	29	N	LJ53BDO	43	N	LJ53BCV
2	N	LJ03MYR	16	N	LJ03MXK	30	N	LJ53BDU	44	N	LJ53BCX
3	N	LJ03MYS	17	N	LJ03MXL	31	N	LJ53BDV	45	N	LJ53BCY
4	N	LJ03MYT	18	N	LJ03MXM	32	N	LJ53BDX	46	N	LJ53BAA
5	N	LJ03MXV	19	N	LJ03MXN	33	N	LJ53BDY	47	N	LJ53BAO
6	N	LJ03MXW	20	N	LJ03MXP	34	N	LJ53BDZ	48	N	LJ53BAU
7	N	LJ03MXX	21	N	LJ53BFK	35	N	LJ53BEO	49	N	LJ53BAV
8	N	LJ03MXY	22	N	LJ53BFL	36	N	LJ53BBV	50	N	LJ53BBE
9	N	LJ03MXZ	23	N	LJ53BFM	37	N	LJ53BBX	51	N	LJ53BBF
10	N	LJ03MYA	24	N	LJ53BFN	38	N	LJ53BBZ	52	N	LJ53BBK
11	N	LJ03MYB	25	N	LJ53BFO	39	N	LJ53BCF	53	N	LJ53BBN
12	N	LJ03MYC	26	N	LJ53BCZ	40	N	LJ53BCK	54	N	LJ53BBO
13	N	LJ03MYD	27	N	LJ53BDE	41	N	LJ53BCO	55	N	LJ53BBU
14	N	LJ03MYF	28	N	LJ53BDF	42	N	LJ53BCU			

VLA56-73 Volvo B7TL 10.6m TransBus ALX400 4.4m N49/22D 2004

56	WD	LJ04LFL	61	WD	LJ04LFS	66	WD	LJ04YWV	70	N	LJ04YWZ
57	WD	LJ04LFM	62	WD	LJ04LFT	67	WD	LJ04YWW	71	N	LJ04YXA
58	WD	LJ04LFN	63	WD	LJ04YWS	68	WD	LJ04YWX	72	N	LJ04YXB
59	WD	LJ04LFP	64	WD	LJ04YWT	69	WD	LJ04YWY	73	N	LJ04YWE
60	WD	LJ04LFR	65	WD	LJ04YWU						

VLA74-128 Volvo B7TL 10.6m ADL ALX400 N49/22D* 2004-05 *104-28 are N45/20D

74	AR	LJ54BGO	88	AR	LJ54BDF	102	AR	LJ54BCU	116	N	LJ54BKG
75	AR	LJ54BEO	89	AR	LJ54BDO	103	AR	LJ54BCV	117	N	LJ54BKK
76	AR	LJ54BEU	90	AR	LJ54BDU	104	N	LJ05BKY	118	N	LJ54BKL
77	AR	LJ54BFA	91	AR	LJ54BDV	105	N	LJ05BKZ	119	N	LJ54BKN
78	AR	LJ54BFE	92	AR	LJ54BDX	106	N	LJ05BLF	120	N	LJ54BKO
79	AR	LJ54BFF	93	AR	LJ54BDY	107	N	LJ05BLK	121	N	LJ54BKU
80	AR	LJ54BFK	94	AR	LJ54BDZ	108	N	LJ05BLN	122	N	LJ54BKV
81	AR	LJ54BFL	95	AR	LJ54BBV	109	N	LJ05BLV	123	N	LJ54BKX
82	AR	LJ54BFM	96	AR	LJ54BBX	110	N	LJ05BLX	124	N	LJ54BJE
83	AR	LJ54BFN	97	AR	LJ54BBZ	111	N	LJ05BLY	125	N	LJ54BJF
84	AR	LJ54BFO	98	AR	LJ54BCE	112	N	LJ05BMO	126	N	LJ54BJK
85	AR	LJ54BCY	99	AR	LJ54BCF	113	N	LJ05BMU	127	N	LJ54BJO
86	AR	LJ54BCZ	100	AR	LJ54BCK	114	N	LJ05BKD	128	N	LJ54BJU
87	AR	LJ54BDE	101	AR	LJ54BCO	115	N	LJ05BKF			

VLA129-143 Volvo B7TL 10.1m ADL ALX400 N45/19D 2005

129	DX	LJ05GLZ	133	DX	LJ05GPY	137	DX	LJ05GRU	141	DX	LJ05GSU
130	DX	LJ05GME	134	DX	LJ05GPZ	138	DX	LJ05GRX	142	DX	LJ55BTE
131	DX	LJ05GMF	135	DX	LJ05GRF	139	DX	LJ05GRZ	143	DX	LJ55BTF
132	DX	LJ05GPX	136	DX	LJ05GRK	140	DX	LJ05GSO			

VLA144-179 Volvo B7TL 10.1m ADL ALX400 N45/19D 2005

144	BN	LJ55BTO	153	BN	LJ55BRV	162	BN	LJ55BUP	171	BN	LJ55BUZ
145	BN	LJ55BTU	154	BN	LJ55BRX	163	BN	LJ55BUR	172	BN	LJ55BVD
146	BN	LJ55BTV	155	BN	LJ55BRZ	164	BN	LJ55BUS	173	BN	LJ55BVE
147	BN	LJ55BTX	156	BN	LJ55BSO	165	BN	LJ55BUT	174	BN	LJ55BVF
148	BN	LJ55BTY	157	BN	LJ55BSU	166	BN	LJ55BUU	175	BN	LJ55BVG
149	BN	LJ55BTZ	158	BN	LJ55BSV	167	BN	LJ55BUV	176	BN	LJ55BVH
150	BN	LJ55BUA	159	BN	LJ55BSX	168	BN	LJ55BUW	177	BN	LJ55BVK
151	BN	LJ55BUE	160	BN	LJ55BSY	169	BN	LJ55BUX	178	BN	LJ55BVL
152	BN	LJ55BPZ	161	BN	LJ55BSZ	170	BN	LJ55BUY	179	BN	LJ55BVM

The first production double-deck buses from Northern Ireland builder Wrightbus were delivered to Arriva London's Wood Green depot in 2001. Given prefix VLW (Volvo Low-floor Wrightbus), they entered service on all routes operated by Wood Green and Palmers Green depots. Allocated to the latter is VLW4, LJ51DJK, on route 102 at Brent Cross shopping centre in January 2006. A refurbishment programme for these buses has now commenced with repaints that omit the cream relief. *Richard Godfrey*

VLW1-41   Volvo B7TL 10.1m   Wrightbus Eclipse Gemini   N41/22D   2001-02

1	WN	Y581UGC	12	WN	VLT12	22	WN	LJ51DGY	32	WN	VLT32
2	WN	Y102TGH	13	WN	LJ51DFX	23	WN	LJ51DGZ	33	WN	LJ51DHO
3	WN	LJ51DJF	14	WN	LJ51DFY	24	WN	LJ51DHA	34	WN	LJ51DHP
4	WN	LJ51DJK	15	WN	LJ51DFZ	25	WN	LJ51DHC	35	WN	LJ51DHV
5	WN	LJ51DJO	16	WN	LJ51DGE	26	WN	LJ51DHD	36	WN	LJ51DHX
6	WN	LJ51DFK	17	WN	LJ51DGF	27	WN	VLT27	37	WN	LJ51DHY
7	WN	LJ51DFL	18	WN	LJ51DGO	28	WN	LJ51DHF	38	WN	LJ51DHZ
8	WN	LJ51DFN	19	WN	LJ51DGU	29	WN	LJ51DHG	39	WN	LJ51DJD
9	WN	LJ51DFO	20	WN	LJ51DGV	30	WN	LJ51DHK	40	WN	LJ51DJE
10	WN	LJ51DFP	21	WN	LJ51DGX	31	WN	LJ51DHL	41	WN	LJ51OSK
11	WN	LJ51DFU									

VLW42-104   Volvo B7TL 10.1m   Wrightbus Eclipse Gemini   N41/22D   2002-03

42	WN	LF02PKO	58	WN	LF02PTU	74	WN	LF52UTM	90	DX	LF52URA
43	WN	LF02PKU	59	WN	LF02PTX	75	WN	LF52USM	91	DX	LF52UPD
44	WN	LF02PKV	60	WN	LF02PTY	76	WN	LF52USN	92	DX	WLT892
45	WN	LF02PKX	61	WN	LF02PVE	77	WN	LF52USO	93	DX	LF52UPG
46	WN	LF02PKY	62	WN	LF02PVJ	78	WN	LF52USS	94	DX	LF52UPH
47	WN	VLT47	63	WN	LF02PVK	79	WN	LF52UST	95	DX	WLT895
48	WN	LF02PLJ	64	WN	LF02PVL	80	WN	LF52USU	96	DX	LF52UPK
49	WN	LF02PLN	65	WN	LF02PVN	81	WN	LF52USV	97	AR	WLT897
50	WN	LF02PLO	66	WN	LF02PVO	82	WN	LF52USW	98	AR	LF52UPM
51	WN	WLT751	67	WN	LF52UTC	83	WN	LF52USX	99	AR	LG52DDA
52	WN	LF02PSO	68	WN	LF52UTE	84	WN	LF52USY	100	AR	LG52DDE
53	WN	LF02PSU	69	WN	LF52USE	85	WN	LF52UPV	101	AR	LG52DDF
54	WN	WLT554	70	WN	LF52UTG	86	DX	LF52UPW	102	AR	LG52DDJ
55	WN	LF02PSY	71	WN	LF52UTH	87	DX	LF52UPX	103	AR	LG52DDK
56	WN	LF02PSZ	72	WN	WLT372	88	DX	WLT888	104	AR	LG52DDL
57	WN	LF02PTO	73	WN	LF52UTL	89	DX	LF52UPZ			

Of the five double-deck routes operated from Arriva London's Tottenham depot, the 168 runs the furthest south crossing many of Arriva's other services. For several years, a favourite spot for bus enthusiasts and photographers is the famous Elephant and Castle in south London and this provides the backdrop for this view of VLW196, LJ53BEY. *Richard Godfrey*

VLW105-179   Volvo B7TL 10.1m   Wrightbus Eclipse Gemini   N41/22D   2002-03

105	DX	LJ03MHU	124	AR	LF52UOX	143	SF	LG03MFA	162	SF	LG03MRX
106	DX	LJ03MHV	125	AR	LF52UOY	144	SF	LG03MFE	163	SF	LG03MRY
107	DX	LJ03MHX	126	AR	LF52UPA	145	SF	LG03MFF	164	SF	LG03MSU
108	DX	LJ03MHY	127	AR	LF52UPB	146	SF	LG03MFK	165	SF	LG03MSV
109	DX	LJ03MHZ	128	AR	LF52UPC	147	SF	LG03MBF	166	SF	LG03MSX
110	DX	LJ03MJE	129	AR	LG52DAA	148	SF	LG03MBU	167	SF	LG03MMU
111	DX	LJ03MJF	130	AR	LJ03MGZ	149	SF	LG03MBV	168	SF	LG03MMV
112	DX	LJ03MJK	131	AR	LJ03MHA	150	SF	LG03MBX	169	AR	LG03MMX
113	DX	LJ03MJU	132	AR	LJ03MHE	151	SF	LG03MBY	170	AR	LG03MOA
114	DX	LJ03MJV	133	AR	LJ03MHF	152	SF	LG03MDE	171	AR	LG03MOF
115	DX	LJ03MGX	134	AR	LJ03MHK	153	SF	LG03MDF	172	AR	LG03MOV
116	DX	LJ03MGY	135	AR	LJ03MHL	154	SF	LG03MDK	173	AR	VLT173
117	AR	LF52UPN	136	AR	LJ03MHM	155	SF	LG03MDN	174	AR	LG03MPF
118	AR	LF52UPO	137	AR	LJ03MHN	156	SF	LG03MDU	175	AR	LG03MPU
119	AR	LF52UOS	138	AR	LJ03MFN	157	SF	LG03MPX	176	AR	LG03MPV
120	AR	LF52UOT	139	AR	LJ03MFP	158	SF	LG03MPY	177	AR	LG03MLL
121	AR	LF52UOU	140	SF	LJ03MFU	159	SF	LG03MPZ	178	AR	LG03MLN
122	AR	LF52UOV	141	SF	LJ03MFV	160	SF	LG03MRU	179	AR	LG03MLV
123	AR	LF52UOW	142	SF	LG03MEV	161	SF	LG03MRV			

VLW180-199   Volvo B7TL 10.6m   Wrightbus Eclipse Gemini   N45/24D   2003

180	AR	LJ03MLX	185	AR	LJ03MMF	190	AR	LJ03MXR	195	AR	LJ53BEU
181	AR	LJ03MLY	186	AR	LJ03MMK	191	AR	LJ03MXS	196	AR	LJ53BEY
182	AR	LJ03MLZ	187	AR	LJ03MKM	192	AR	LJ03MXT	197	AR	LJ53BFA
183	AR	LJ03MMA	188	AR	LJ03MKN	193	AR	LJ03MXU	198	AR	LJ53BFE
184	AR	LJ03MME	189	AR	LJ03MYN	194	AR	LJ03MWX	199	AR	LJ53BFF

Special event vehicles:

RM5 AR	VLT5	AEC Routemaster R2RH	Park Royal	B36/28R	1959	
RM6 N	VLT6	AEC Routemaster R2RH	Park Royal	B36/28R	1959	
RML901 EC	WLT901	AEC Routemaster R2RH/1	Park Royal	B40/32R	1959	
RM1124 E	124CLT	AEC Routemaster R2RH	Park Royal	B36/28R	1959	
RMC1453 u	453CLT	AEC Routemaster R2RH	Park Royal	B36/28R	1962	Arriva East Herts & Essex, 1998
RMC1464 u	464CLT	AEC Routemaster R2RH	Park Royal	O36/28R	1962	Arriva East Herts & Essex, 1998
RM2217 N	CUV217C	AEC Routemaster R2RH	Park Royal	B36/28R	1965	
RML2355 N	CUV355C	AEC Routemaster R2RH/1	Park Royal	B40/32R	1965	
RML2360 N	CUV360C	AEC Routemaster R2RH/1	Park Royal	B40/32R	1965	On loan from LT Museum
RML2403 u	JJD403D	AEC Routemaster R2RH/1	Park Royal	B40/32R	1966	On loan from LT Museum

Ancillary vehicles:

L515-554

	Leyland Olympian ON2R50C13Z4 Northern Counties			B47/27D	1990

515	TCt	G515VBB	**520**	TCt	G520VBB	**538**	TCt	G538VBB	**554**	TCt	G554VBB
517	TCt	G517VBB	**521**	TCt	G521VBB	**551**	TCt	G551VBB			

M573 CNt	GYE573W	MCW Metrobus DR101/14	MCW	TV	1981	London Buses, 1994
M1075 ARt	B75WUL	MCW Metrobus DR134/1	MCW	TV	1984	London Buses, 1994
M1084 CNt	B84WUL	MCW Metrobus DR134/1	MCW	TV	1984	London Buses, 1994

M1124-1405

	MCW Metrobus DR101/17	MCW	TV	1984-85	London Buses, 1994

1124	ARt	B124WUL	**1170**	CNt	B170WUL	**1312**	ARt	C312BUV	**1327**	ARt	C327BVU
1126	ARt	B126WUL	**1231**	ARt	B231WUL	**1313**	ARt	C313BUV	**1332**	CNt	C332BVU
1130	ARt	B130WUL	**1248**	ARt	B248WUL	**1320**	CNt	C320BUV	**1367**	ARt	C367BVU
1136	ARt	B136WUL	**1253**	ARt	B253WUL	**1326**	ARt	C326BVU	**1405**	ARt	C405BUV
1140	ARt	B140WUL	**1300**	ARt	B300WUL						

Previous registrations:

70CLT	BX04NDE	VLT12	LJ51DFV
124CLT	124CLT, VYJ806	VLT27	LJ51DHE
185CLT	BU05VFD	VLT32	LJ51DHN
205CLT	BX04MXB	VLT47	LF02PKZ
217CLT	BX04MXR	VLT173	LJ03MPE
319CLT	BX55FVV	VLT244	LJ53NHM
324CLT	BX04MXZ	VLT295	LJ54BFU
330CLT	BX04MYY		
361CLT	BX04NBL	WLT348	LJ53NGO
398CLT	BX55FUV	WLT372	LF52UTJ
480CLT	BX05UWZ	WLT385	LJ04LFY
519CLT	BX04MXT	WLT531	LJ53NHX
593CLT	BX55FUM	WLT554	LF02PSX
656DYE	LJ04LFA	WLT664	LJ04LDE
725DYE	LJ53BGE	WLT676	LJ04LGU
734DYE	LJ53NJE	WLT719	LJ53NHU
801DYE	LJ03MWM	WLT751	LF02PRZ
822DYE	LJ53BFV	WLT807	LJ03MVU
BX55FWH	BX55FWH, 124CLT	WLT888	LF52UPY
LF52USE	LF52USE, VLT25	WLT892	LF52UPE
T324FGN	T324FGN, 99D53451	WLT895	LF52UPJ
T325FGN	T325FGN, 99D53440	WLT987	LF52UPL
V423DGT	V435DGT	WLT970	LJ04LDV
V435DGT	V423DGT	WLT997	LJ54BFX

Depots and allocations

Ash Grove (Ash Grove, E8) - AE

Citaro Artic	MA77	MA78	MA79	MA80	MA81	MA82	MA83	MA84
	MA85	MA86	MA87	MA88	MA89	MA90	MA91	MA92
	MA93	MA94	MA95	MA96	MA97	MA98	MA99	MA100
	MA101	MA102	MA103	MA104	MA105	MA106	MA107	MA108
	MA109	MA110	MA111	MA112	MA113	MA114	MA115	MA116
	MA117	MA118	MA119	MA120	MA121	MA122	MA123	MA124

Barking (Ripple Road) - DX

Dart	DDL16	DDL17	DDL18	PDL28	PDL29	PDL30	PDL31	PDL32
	PDL33	PDL34	PDL35	PDL36	PDL37	PDL38	DLA86	DLA87
	DLA88	DLA89	DLA90	DLA137	DLA138	DLA139	ADL969	ADL970
	ADL971	ADL972	ADL973	ADL974	ADL975	ADL976	ADL977	ADL978
	ADL979	ADL980	ADL981	ADL982	ADL983			
Volvo B7TL	VLA129	VLA130	VLA131	VLA132	VLA133	VLA134	VLA135	VLA136
	VLA137	VLA138	VLA139	VLA140	VLA141	VLA142	VLA143	VLW86
	VLW87	VLW88	VLW89	VLW90	VLW91	VLW92	VLW93	
	VLW94	VLW95	VLW96	VLW105	VLW106	VLW107	VLW108	VLW109
	VLW110	VLW111	VLW112	VLW113	VLW114	VLW115	VLW116	

Battersea (Hester Road) - BA

DB250	DW103	DW104	DW105	DW106	DW107	DW108	DW109	DW110
	DW111	DW112	DW113	DW114	DW115	DW116	DW117	DW118
	DW119	DW120	DW121	DW122	DW123	DW124	DW125	DW126
	DW127	DW128	DW129	DW130	DW131	DW132	DW133	DW134

Brixton (Streatham Hill) - BN *outstation: Old Tram Depot, Brixton Hill*

SB120	DWL1	DWL2	DWL3	DWL4	DWL5	DWL6	DWL7	DWL8
	DWL9	DWL10	DWL11	DWL12	DWL13	DWL14	DWL15	DWL16
	DWL17	DWL18	DWL19	DWL20	DWL21	DWL22		
DB250	DLA142	DLA143	DLA144	DLA145	DLA146	DLA147	DLA148	DLA149
	DLA150	DLA151	DLA152	DLA153	DLA159	DLA160	DLA161	DLA162
	DLA163	DLA164	DLA165	DLA205	DLA206	DLA209	DLA213	DLA271
	DLA290	DLA312	DLA313	DLA314	DLA315	DLA317	DLA319	DLA320
	DW55	DW56	DW57	DW58	DW59	DW60	DW61	DW62
	DW63	DW64	DW65	DW66	DW67	DW68	DW69	DW70
	DW71	DW72	DW73	DW74	DW75	DW76	DW77	DW78
	DW79	DW80	DW81	DW82	DW83	DW84	DW85	DW86
	DW87	DW88	DW89	DW90	DW91	DW92	DW93	
Volvo B7TL	VLA144	VLA145	VLA146	VLA147	VLA148	VLA149	VLA150	VLA151
	VLA152	VLA153	VLA154	VLA155	VLA156	VLA157	VLA158	VLA159
	VLA160	VLA161	VLA162	VLA163	VLA164	VLA165	VLA166	VLA167
	VLA168	VLA169	VLA170	VLA171	VLA172	VLA173	VLA174	VLA175
	VLA176	VLA177	VLA178	VLA179				

The London Bus Handbook

Croydon (Beddington Farm Road) - CN

Dart	PDL19	PDL20	PDL21	PDL22	PDL23	PDL24	PDL25	PDL26
	PDL27	PDL63						
SB120	DWL57	DWL58	DWL59	DWL60	DWL61	DWL62	DWL63	DWL64
	DWL65	DWL66	DWL67	DWS1	DWS2	DWS3	DWS4	DWS5
	DWS6	DWS7	DWS8	DWS9	DWS10	DWS11	DWS12	DWS13
	DWS14	DWS15	DWS16	DWS17	DWS18			
DB250	DW16	DW35	DW36	DW37	DW38	DW39	DW40	DW41
	DW42	DW43	DW44	DW45	DW46	DW47	DW48	DW49
	DW50	DW51	DW52	DW53	DW54	DW94	DW95	DW96
	DW97	DW98	DW99	DW100	DW101	DW102		
Training Buses	M573	M1084	M1170	M1320	M1332			

Croydon (Brighton Road, South Croydon) - TC

Dart	ADL9	ADL10	ADL11	ADL12	ADL13	ADL14	ADL15	ADL16
	ADL17	ADL18	ADL19	ADL20	ADL21	ADL22	ADL23	DPP421
	DPP422	DPP423	DPP424	DPP425	DPP426	DPP427	PDL117	PDL118
	PDL119	PDL120	PDL121	PDL122	PDL123			
DB250	DLA133	DLA134	DLA135	DLA136	DLA156	DLA157	DLA175	DLA176
	DLA177	DLA178	DLA179	DLA180	DLA181	DLA182	DLA183	DLA184
	DLA185	DLA186	DLA187	DLA188	DLA189	DLA207	DLA208	DLA215
	DLA216	DLA217	DLA218	DLA219	DLA220	DLA221	DLA222	DLA223
	DLA224	DLA250	DLA251	DLA252	DLA253	DLA254	DLA255	DLA256
	DW1	DW2	DW3	DW4	DW5	DW6	DW7	DW8
	DW9	DW10	DW11	DW12	DW13	DW14	DW15	DW17
	DW18	DW19	DW20	DW21	DW22	DW23	DW24	DW25
	DW26	DW27	DW28	DW29	DW30	DW31	DW32	DW33
	DW34							
Training Buses	L515	L517	L520	L521	L538	L551	L554	

Edmonton (Towpath Road, Stonehill Business Park) - EC

Dart	ADL1	ADL2	ADL3	ADL4	ADL5	ADL6	ADL7	ADL8
	ADL61	ADL62	ADL63	ADL64	ADL65	ADL66	ADL67	ADL68
	ADL69	ADL71	ADL72	ADL73	ADL74	ADL75	ADL76	ADL77
	ADL78	ADL79	ADL81	DDL15	DPP428	DPP429	DPP430	DPP431
	PDL1	PDL2	PDL3	PDL4	PDL5	PDL6	PDL7	PDL8
	PDL9	PDL10	PDL11	PDL12	PDL13	PDL72	PDL73	PDL74
	PDL75	PDL76	PDL77	PDL78	PDL79	PDL80	PDL81	PDL95
	PDL96	PDL97	PDL98	PDL99	PDL100	PDL101	PDL102	PDL103
	PDL104	PDL105	PDL106	PDL107	PDL108	PDL109	PDL110	PDL111
	PDL112	PDL113	PDL114	PDL115	PDL116			
Citaro Artic	MA125	MA126	MA127	MA128	MA129	MA130	MA131	MA132
	MA133	MA134	MA135	MA136	MA137	MA138	MA139	MA140
	MA141	MA142	MA143	MA144	MA145	MA146	MA147	MA148
	MA149	MA150	MA151	MA152	MA153	MA154	MA155	MA156
	MA157							
Routemaster	RML901							
DB250	DLA125	DLA348	DLA349	DLA350	DLA351	DLA352	DLA353	DLA354
	DLA355	DLA356	DLA357	DLA358	DLA359	DLA360	DLA361	DLA362
	DLA363	DLA364	DLA365	DLA366	DLA367	DLA368	DLA369	

Enfield (Southbury Road, Ponders End) - E

Dart	PDL61	PDL64	PDL65	PDL66	PDL67	PDL68	PDL69	PDL70
	PDL71	PDL82	PDL83	PDL84	PDL85	PDL86	PDL87	PDL88
	PDL89	PDL90	PDL91	PDL92	PDL93	PDL94		
SB120	DWL23	DWL24	DWL25	DWL26	DWL27	DWL29	DWL56	
Routemaster	RM1124							
DB250	DLA72	DLA73	DLA74	DLA75	DLA76	DLA77	DLA78	DLA79
	DLA80	DLA81	DLA82	DLA83	DLA84	DLA85	DLA91	DLA92
	DLA93	DLA94	DLA95	DLA116	DLA117	DLA118	DLA119	DLA120
	DLA121	DLA122	DLA123	DLA124	DLA190	DLA191	DLA192	DLA193
	DLA194	DLA195	DLA196	DLA197	DLA198	DLA199	DLA200	DLA201
	DLA202	DLA203	DLA210	DLA211	DLA212	DLA225	DLA226	DLA237
	DLA238	DLA248	DLA249	DLA270	DLP15	DLP16	DLP17	DLP18
	DLP19	DLP20	DLP76	DLP77	DLP78	DLP79	DLP80	DLP81
	DLP82	DLP83	DLP84	DLP85	DLP86	DLP87	DLP88	DLP89
	DLP90	DLP91	DLP92	DLP93	DLP94	DLP95	DLP96	DLP97
	DLP98	DLP99	DLP100	DLP101	DLP102	DLP103	DLP104	DLP105
	DLP106	DLP107	DLP108	DLP109	DLP110			

Lea Valley (Leeside Road, Edmonton) - LV

Citaro Artic	MA1	MA2	MA3	MA4	MA5	MA6	MA7	MA8
	MA9	MA10	MA11	MA12	MA13	MA14	MA15	MA16
	MA17	MA18	MA19	MA20	MA21	MA22	MA23	MA24
	MA25	MA26	MA27	MA28	MA29	MA30	MA31	MA32
	MA33	MA34	MA35	MA36	MA37	MA38	MA39	MA40
	MA41	MA42	MA43	MA44	MA45	MA46	MA47	MA48
	MA49	MA50	MA51	MA52	MA53	MA54	MA55	MA56
	MA57	MA58	MA59	MA60	MA61	MA62	MA63	MA64
	MA65	MA66	MA67	MA68	MA69	MA70	MA71	MA72
	MA73	MA74	MA75	MA76				

Pictured here shortly after delivery, is Alexander Dennis Dart (ADL) PDL126, LJ56ARO. It is seen in Croydon's Windmill Road. *Mark Lyons*

Norwood (Ernest Avenue, West Norwood) - N

Routemaster	RM6	RM2217	RML2355	RML2360				
DB250	DLA112	DLA140	DLA141	DLA154	DLA155	DAL158	DLA159	DLA166
	DLA167	DLA168	DLA169	DLA170	DLA171	DLA172	DLA173	DLA174
	DLA204	DLA205	DLA236	DLA311	DLA318			
Volvo B7TL	VLA1	VLA2	VLA3	VLA4	VLA5	VLA6	VLA7	VLA8
	VLA9	VLA10	VLA11	VLA12	VLA13	VLA14	VLA15	VLA16
	VLA17	VLA18	VLA19	VLA20	VLA21	VLA22	VLA23	VLA24
	VLA25	VLA26	VLA27	VLA28	VLA29	VLA30	VLA31	VLA32
	VLA33	VLA34	VLA35	VLA36	VLA37	VLA38	VLA39	VLA40
	VLA41	VLA42	VLA43	VLA44	VLA45	VLA46	VLA47	VLA48
	VLA49	VLA50	VLA51	VLA52	VLA53	VLA54	VLA55	VLA70
	VLA71	VLA72	VLA73	VLA104	VLA105	VLA106	VLA107	VLA108
	VLA109	VLA110	VLA111	VLA112	VLA113	VLA114	VLA115	VLA116
	VLA117	VLA118	VLA119	VLA120	VLA121	VLA122	VLA123	VLA124
	VLA125	VLA126	VLA127	VLA128				

Stamford Hill (Rookwood Road) - SF

DB250	DLA96	DLA97	DLA98	DLA99	DLA100	DLA101	DLA102	DLA103
	DLA104	DLA105	DLA106	DLA107	DLA108	DLA109	DLA110	DLA111
	DLA113	DLA114	DLA115	DLA291	DLA292	DLA293	DLA294	DLA295
	DLA296	DLA297	DLA298	DLA299	DLA300	DLA301	DLA302	DLA303
	DLA304	DLA305	DLA306	DLA307	DLA309	DLA310	DLA316	DLA346
	DLA370	DLA371	DLA372	DLA373	DLA374	DLA375	DLA376	DLA377
	DLA378	DLA379	DLA380	DLA381	DLA382	DLA383	DLA384	DLA385
	DLA386	DLA387	DLA388					
Volvo B7TL	VLW140	VLW141	VLW142	VLW143	VLW144	VLW145	VLW146	VLW147
	VLW148	VLW149	VLW150	VLW151	VLW152	VLW153	VLW154	VLW155
	VLW156	VLW157	VLW158	VLW159	VLW160	VLW161	VLW162	VLW163
	VLW164	VLW165	VLW166	VLW167	VLW168			

Thornton Heath (719 London Road) - TH

Dart	DDL1	DDL2	DDL3	DDL4	DDL5	DDL6	DDL7	DDL8
	DDL9	DDL10	DDL11	DDL12	DDL13	DDL14	PDL50	PDL51
	PDL52	PDL53	PDL54	PDL55	PDL56	PDL57	PDL58	PDL59
	PDL60	PDL62						
DB250	DLA2	DLA3	DLA4	DLA5	DLA6	DLA7	DLA8	DLA9
	DLA10	DLA38	DLA39	DLA40	DLA41	DLA42	DLA43	DLA44
	DLA48	DLA49	DLA50	DLA51	DLA52	DLA53	DLA54	DLA55
	DLA56	DLA57	DLA58	DLA59	DLA60	DLA61	DLA62	DLA63
	DLA64	DLA126	DLA127	DLA128	DLA129	DLA130	DLA131	DLA132
	DLA272	DLA322	DLA323	DLA324	DLA325	DLA326	DLA327	DLA328
	DLA329	DLA330	DLA331	DLA332	DLA333	DLA334	DLA335	DLA336
	DLA337	DLA338	DLA339	DLA340	DLA341	DLA342	DLA343	DLA344
	DLA345	DLA347	DLA389					

Tottenham (Philip Lane) - AR

Dart	PDL14	PDL15	PDL16	PDL17	PDL18	PDL39	PDL40	PDL41
	PDL42	PDL43	PDL44	PDL45	PDL46	PDL47	PDL48	PDL49
Routemaster	RM5							
DB250	DLA230	DLA231	DLA232	DLA234	DLA235	DLA239	DLA240	DLA241
	DLA242	DLA243	DLA244	DLA245	DLA246	DLA247	DLA277	DLA278
	DLA279	DLA280	DLA281	DLA282	DLA283	DLA284	DLA285	DLA286
	DLA287	DLA288	DLA289					
Volvo B7TL	VLA74	VLA75	VLA76	VLA77	VLA78	VLA79	VLA80	VLA81
	VLA82	VLA83	VLA84	VLA85	VLA86	VLA87	VLA88	VLA89
	VLA90	VLA91	VLA92	VLA93	VLA94	VLA95	VLA96	VLA97
	VLA98	VLA99	VLA100	VLA101	VLA102	VLA103	VLW97	VLW98
	VLW99	VLW100	VLW101	VLW102	VLW103	VLW104	VLW117	VLW118
	VLW119	VLW120	VLW121	VLW122	VLW123	VLW124	VLW125	VLW126
	VLW127	VLW128	VLW129	VLW130	VLW131	VLW132	VLW133	VLW134
	VLW135	VLW136	VLW137	VLW138	VLW139	VLW169	VLW170	VLW171
	VLW172	VLW173	VLW174	VLW175	VLW176	VLW177	VLW178	VLW179
	VLW180	VLW181	VLW182	VLW183	VLW184	VLW185	VLW186	VLW187
	VLW188	VLW189	VLW190	VLW191	VLW192	VLW193	VLW194	VLW195
	VLW196	VLW197	VLW198	VLW199				
Training buses	M1075	M1124	M1126	M1130	M1136	M1140	M1231	M1248
	M1253	M1300	M1312	M1313	M1326	M1327	M1367	M1405

Wandsworth (High Road) - WD - Sightseeing depot

Volvo B7TL	VLA56	VLA57	VLA58	VLA59	VLA60	VLA61	VLA62	VLA63
	VLA64	VLA65	VLA66	VLA67	VLA68	VLA69		

Wood Green (High Road) - WN

Sub-depot: Regent's Avenue, Palmers Green

SB120	CW1	DWL30	DWL31	DWL32	DWL33	DWL34	DWL35	DWL36
	DWL37	DWL38	DWL39	DWL40	DWL41	DWL42	DWL43	DWL44
	DWL45	DWL46	DWL47	DWL48	DWL49	DWL50	DWL51	DWL52
	DWL53	DWL54	DWL55					
DB250	DLA1	DLA11	DLA12	DLA13	DLA14	DLA15	DLA16	DLA17
	DLA18	DLA19	DLA20	DLA21	DLA22	DLA23	DLA24	DLA25
	DAL26	DLA27	DLA28	DLA29	DLA30	DLA31	DLA32	DLA33
	DLA34	DLA35	DLA36	DLA37	DLA45	DLA46	DLA47	DLA214
	DLA227	DLA228	DLA229	DLA233	DLA273	DLA274	DLA275	DLP40
	DLP41	DLP42	DLP43	DLP44	DLP45	DLP46	DLP47	DLP48
	DLP49	DLP50	DLP51	DLP52	DLP53	DLP54	DLP55	DLP56
	DLP57	DLP58	DLP59	DLP60	DLP61	DLP62	DLP63	DLP64
	DLP65	DLP66	DLP67	DLP68	DLP69	DLP70	DLP71	DLP72
	DLP73	DLP74	DLP75					
Volvo B7TL	VLW1	VLW2	VLW3	VLW4	VLW5	VLW6	VLW7	VLW8
	VLW9	VLW10	VLW11	VLW12	VLW13	VLW14	VLW15	VLW16
	VLW17	VLW18	VLW19	VLW20	VLW21	VLW22	VLW23	VLW24
	VLW25	VLW26	VLW27	VLW28	VLW29	VLW30	VLW31	VLW32
	VLW33	VLW34	VLW35	VLW36	VLW37	VLW38	VLW39	VLW40
	VLW41	VLW42	VLW43	VLW44	VLW45	VLW46	VLW47	VLW48
	VLW49	VLW50	VLW51	VLW52	VLW53	VLW54	VLW55	VLW56
	VLW57	VLW58	VLW59	VLW60	VLW61	VLW62	VLW63	VLW64
	VLW65	VLW66	VLW67	VLW68	VLW70	VLW71	VLW72	VLW73
	VLW74	VLW75	VLW76	VLW77	VLW78	VLW79	VLW80	VLW81
	VLW82	VLW83	VLW84	VLW85				

Unallocated - u/w

Routemaster	RMC1453	RMC1454
DB250	DLA308	

The London Bus Handbook

ARRIVA - THE ORIGINAL TOUR

The Original Tour Ltd, Jews Road, Wandsworth, SW18 1TB

EMB763	D553YNO	MCW Metrobus DR115/4	MCW	PO61/35D	1987	New World FirstBus, 2001
EMB764	E964JAR	MCW Metrobus DR115/4	MCW	PO61/35D	1987	New World FirstBus, 2001
EMB765	E965JAR	MCW Metrobus DR115/4	MCW	PO61/35D	1987	New World FirstBus, 2001
EMB767	E767JAR	MCW Metrobus DR115/4	MCW	PO61/35D	1987	New World FirstBus, 2001
EMB768	E768JAR	MCW Metrobus DR115/4	MCW	PO61/35D	1987	New World FirstBus, 2001
EMB769	E769JAR	MCW Metrobus DR115/4	MCW	PO61/35D	1987	New World FirstBus, 2001
EMB770	E770JAR	MCW Metrobus DR115/4	MCW	PO61/35D	1987	New World FirstBus, 2001
EMB771	E771JAR	MCW Metrobus DR115/4	MCW	PO61/35D	1987	New World FirstBus, 2001
EMB772	E772JAR	MCW Metrobus DR115/4	MCW	PO61/35D	1987	New World FirstBus, 2001
EMB773	E773JAR	MCW Metrobus DR115/4	MCW	PO61/35D	1987	New World FirstBus, 2001
EMB775	D675YNO	MCW Metrobus DR115/4	MCW	PO61/35D	1987	New World FirstBus, 2001
EMB776	A737WEV	MCW Metrobus DR115/4	MCW	PO61/35D	1987	New World FirstBus, 2001
EMB777	A735WEV	MCW Metrobus DR115/4	MCW	PO61/35D	1987	New World FirstBus, 2001
MB500	GYE500W	MCW Metrobus DR101/14	MCW	PO43/28D	1980	Arriva London, 1999
MB525	GYE525W	MCW Metrobus DR101/14	MCW	PO43/28D	1981	London South, 1998
MB555	GYE555W	MCW Metrobus DR101/14	MCW	PO31/14F	1981	Arriva London, 2000
MB710	KYV710X	MCW Metrobus DR101/14	MCW	B43/28D	1981	Arriva London, 2000
MB840	OJD840Y	MCW Metrobus DR101/16	MCW	PO43/28D	1983	Cowie South London, 1996
MB863	OJD863Y	MCW Metrobus DR101/16	MCW	B43/28D	1983	Arriva London, 2000

2001 arrivals with Arriva's Original Tour fleet included two former Hong Kong Metrobuses, EMB776 and EMB777, the latter now registered A735WEV is seen here in Trafalgar Square. These are 12metre examples and arrived in London from the Australian operation of City Sightseeing. This fleet operates from the former tram depot at Wandsworth and uses an outstation at Purfleet. *Dave Heath*

Delivered new to Arriva's Stamford Hill depot in 1992 was a batch of Leyland Olympians with Alexander bodywork that served mainly route 253 for over ten years. Now replaced on this service they have been converted to either fully or partial open-top by Arriva at Beddington Farm or Enfield and have started to reappear in service reseated and repainted. OA331, J331BSH, is seen here in Park Lane passing the Queen Mother's Gate to Hyde Park in May 2006. *Ian Jordan*

MB895	A895SUL	MCW Metrobus DR101/16	MCW	PO43/28D	1983	Arriva London, 2000
MB927	A927SUL	MCW Metrobus DR101/16	MCW	PO43/28D	1983	London South, 1998
MB1227	B227WUL	MCW Metrobus DR101/17	MCW	PO43/28D	1983	Arriva London, 1999
MB1239	B239WUL	MCW Metrobus DR101/17	MCW	B43/28D	1983	Arriva London, 2002
MB1265	B265WUL	MCW Metrobus DR101/17	MCW	B43/28D	1983	Arriva London, 2002
MB1310	C310BUV	MCW Metrobus DR101/17	MCW	B43/28D	1983	Arriva London, 2002
ML11	B241LRA	MCW Metroliner DR130/7	MCW	O63/23F	1986	Dunn Line, Nottingham, 1994
ML12	A112KFX	MCW Metroliner DR130/5	MCW	O67/22F	1984	London Pride, 2001
ML17	C907GUD	MCW Metroliner DR130/21	MCW	O63/17F	1985	London Pride, 2001
ML25	B225VHW	MCW Metroliner DR130/3	MCW	O63/18F	1984	London Pride, 2001
ML27	A667XDA	MCW Metroliner DR130/6	MCW	O63/23F	1984	London Pride, 2001

DLP201-214

DAF DB250 10.6m   Plaxton President   O45/21F 1999

201	WD	V601LGC	**205**	WD	T205XBV	**209**	WD	T208XBV	**212**	WD	T212XBV
202	WD	T202XBV	**206**	WD	T206XBV	**210**	WD	T210XBV	**213**	WD	T213XBV
203	WD	T203XBV	**207**	WD	T207XBV	**211**	WD	T211XBV	**214**	WD	T214XBV
204	WD	T204XBV	**208**	WD	T208XBV						

OA315-352

Leyland Olympian ON2R50C13Z4 Alexander RH   PO43/25D* 1992 Arriva London, 2003-05
*seating varies, including some B43/25D and O43/25D

315	WD	J315BSH	**325**	WD	J325BSH	**335**	WD	J335BSH	**344**	WD	J344BSH
316	WD	J316BSH	**326**	WD	J326BSH	**336**	WD	J336BSH	**345**	WD	J345BSH
317	WD	J317BSH	**327**	WD	J327BSH	**337**	WD	J337BSH	**346**	WD	J346BSH
318	WD	J318BSH	**328**	WD	J328BSH	**338**	WD	J338BSH	**347**	WD	J347BSH
319	WD	J319BSH	**329**	WD	J329BSH	**339**	WD	J339BSH	**348**	WD	J348BSH
320	WD	J320BSH	**330**	WD	J330BSH	**340**	WD	J340BSH	**349**	WD	J349BSH
321	WD	J321BSH	**331**	WD	J331BSH	**341**	WD	J341BSH	**350**	WD	J350BSH
322	WD	J322BSH	**332**	WD	J332BSH	**342**	WD	J342BSH	**351**	WD	J351BSH
323	WD	J323BSH	**333**	WD	J433BSH	**343**	WD	J343BSH	**352**	WD	J352BSH
324	WD	J324BSH	**334**	WD	J334BSH						

Ten Volvo B7L with Ayats Bravo City open-top bodies were delivered to Arriva in 2005, the first buses supplied new for the London open-top service. While some carry the City Sightseeing livery, most carry the Arriva livery incorporating *The Original Tour* branding as shown here. VLY605, LX05HRO, is seen near St Paul's Cathedral on Ludgate Hill. *Dave Heath*

VLY601-610

		Volvo B7L 10.6m			Ayats Bravo City			O51/24F	2005		
601	WD	LX05GDV	604	WD	LX05GEJ	607	WD	LX05KNZ	609	WD	EU05DVW
602	WD	LX05GDY	605	WD	LX05HRO	608	WD	LX05KOA	610	WD	EU05DVX
603	WD	LX05GDZ	606	WD	LX05HSC						

Ancillary vehicle:

MB1152 B152WUL	MCW Metrobus DR101/17	MCW	TV	1983	Arriva London, 1999

Previous registrations:

A735WEV	CZ9920(HK)	E769JAR	DT7256 (HK)
A737WEV	DA2952(HK)	E770JAR	DU8506 (HK)
B241LRA	B904XJO, A4BOB	E771JAR	DT9187 (HK)
D553YNO	DV471 (HK)	E772JAR	DV2896 (HK)
D675YNO	DV3433(HK)	E773JAR	DU3481 (HK)
E767JAR	DU3460 (HK)	E964JAR	DT4549 (HK)
E768JAR	DU8346 (HK)	E965JAR	DV4883 (HK)

Depot: Jews Road, Wandsworth (WD)

ASHFORD LUXURY

Ashford Luxury - Windsorian

Ashford Luxury Coaches (Middlesex) Ltd; Windsorian Coaches Ltd
373 Hatton Road, Bedfont, Hounslow, TW14 9QS

AL	L227BUT	Dennis Javelin 10SDA2139	Plaxton Première 320	C35F	1994	
AL	L377NMV	Ford Transit	Ford	M11	1994	
WN	M777ASH	Dennis Javelin 12m	Plaxton Première 320	C53F	1995	
WN	S300ASH	Dennis Javelin 12m	Plaxton Première 320	C49FT	1998	
AL	S451WAT	Dennis Dart SLF	Plaxton Pointer MPD	N28F	1999	Plaxton demonstrator, 1999
AL	T200ALC	Mercedes-Benz Vario 0614	Mellor Opus	C16F	1999	
AL	T999ASH	Dennis Javelin	Plaxton Première 320	C53F	1999	
WN	W400ALC	Mercedes-Benz Vario 0814	Mellor Opus	C25F	2000	
WN	W555ASH	Volvo B7R	Plaxton Prima	C53F	2000	
WN	X444ASH	Dennis Javelin	Plaxton Prima	C57F	2001	
AL	Y111ASH	Dennis Javelin	Plaxton Première 320	C53F	2001	
AL	MC02ALC	Mercedes-Benz Vario 0814	Mellor Opus	C25F	2002	
WN	WN52ASH	Dennis R340	Plaxton Panther	C49FT	2002	
WN	WN03ASH	TransBus Javelin	TransBus Profile	C53F	2003	
AL	AL03ASH	TransBus Javelin	TransBus Profile	C53F	2003	
AL	AL04ASH	TransBus Javelin	TransBus Profile	C53F	2004	
AL	AL05ASH	ADL Dennis Javelin	Plaxton Profile	C53F	2005	
AL	AL06ASH	ADL Dennis Javelin	Plaxton Profile	C53F	2006	
WN	WN05ASH	ADL Dennis Javelin	Plaxton Profile	C53F	2005	
AL	MC06ASH	Irisbus EuroMidi CC80E	Indcar Maxim 2	C25F	2006	

AL - Ashford Luxury; WN - Windsorian.
Depots: Hatton Road, Bedfont and Downmill Road, Bracknell
Web: www.ashfordluxurycoaches.co.uk

**Ashford Luxury Coaches, together with Windsorian, operate a mix of vehicles from an eleven-seat Ford Transit
to those with fifty-three seat capacity. The full-size coach fleet consists, in the main, of Javelins with the sole
Volvo B7R, W555ASH shown here. Featuring a Plaxton Prima body, the coach is seen at Boxhill in May 2006.
The Royal Warrant insignia for service providers in England can be seen on the vehicle's side.** *Dave Heath*

THE BIG BUS COMPANY LTD

The Big Bus Company Ltd, Elms Ind Est, St Martin's Way, Wimbledon, SW17

Fleet	Reg	Chassis	Body	Seating	Year	History
853	PFN853	AEC Regent V	Park Royal	FO40/32F	1959	preservation, 1991
STD177	XMD47A	Leyland Titan PD2/12	Metro-Cammell Orion	O32/26RD	1956	preservation, 1991
RMF588	FPT588C	AEC Routemaster 3R2RH	Park Royal	O41/31F	1965	Blue Triangle, 1992
RMF592	FPT592C	AEC Routemaster 3R2RH	Park Royal	B41/31F	1965	preservation, 1995
RMF603	FPT603C	AEC Routemaster 3R2RH	Park Royal	B41/31F	1965	preservation, 1997
488	MLH488L	Daimler Fleetline CRL6	MCW	B44/24D	1973	London United, 1993
	MPJ206L	Leyland Atlantean PDR1A/1Rsp	MCW	O43/29F	1973	London Country NW, 1991
DM1117	GHV117N	Daimler Fleetline CRL6	Park Royal	PO44/27D	1975	St Ignatius College, 1997
DMS2376	OJD376R	Leyland Fleetline FE30ALRSp	Park Royal	O44/24D	1977	Garratt, Leicester, 1996
DMS2390	OJD390R	Leyland Fleetline FE30ALRSp	Park Royal	PO45/29F	1977	Wealden Beeline, 1995
DMS2412	OJD412R	Leyland Fleetline FE30ALRSp	Park Royal	O44/27D	1977	South London, 1992
DMS2545	THX545S	Leyland Fleetline FE30ALRSp	Park Royal	PO44/24D	1978	Motts, Stoke Mandeville, 1994
DMS2556	THX556S	Leyland Fleetline FE30ALRSp	Park Royal	O44/27D	1978	London Northern, 1993
-12	WYV12T	Leyland Titan TNLXB2RRSp	Park Royal	B44/26D	1980	Stagecoach, 2003
-25	WYV25T	Leyland Titan TNLXB2RRSp	Park Royal	B44/26D	1980	Stagecoach, 2003
-47	WYV47T	Leyland Titan TNLXB2RRSp	Park Royal	B44/26D	1980	Stagecoach, 2003
MB1173	CUL173V	Leyland Titan TNLXB2RRSp	Park Royal	O44/32F	1980	London Central, 2000
CRB4152	VLT125	Leyland Titan TNLXB2RR	Leyland	CO44/32F	1981	London Central, 2000
LB4384	KYV384X	Leyland Titan TNLXB2RR	Leyland	O44/24D	1981	London Central, 1998
LB4507	KYV507X	Leyland Titan TNLXB2RR	Leyland	O44/32F	1982	London Central, 1998
EM4676	OHV676Y	Leyland Titan TNLXB2RR	Leyland	PO44/32F	1983	London Central, 2000
-677	OHV677Y	Leyland Titan TNLXB2RR	Leyland	B44/32F	1983	London Central, 2003
LB4712	OHV712Y	Leyland Titan TNLXB2RR	Leyland	O45/32F	1983	London Central, 1998
CMB1720	OHV720Y	Leyland Titan TNLXB2RR	Leyland	CO44/32F	1983	London Central, 1998
CRM1722	OHV722Y	Leyland Titan TNLXB2RR	Leyland	O44/32F	1983	London Central, 1998
CRM1723	OHV723Y	Leyland Titan TNLXB2RR	Leyland	CO44/32F	1983	London Central, 1998
CRM4725	OHV725Y	Leyland Titan TNLXB2RR	Leyland	O45/32F	1983	London Central, 1998
EM1739	OHV739Y	Leyland Titan TNLXB2RR	Leyland	O44/32F	1983	London Central, 2000
CLB4742	OHV742Y	Leyland Titan TNLXB2RR	Leyland	O45/32F	1983	London Central, 1998
EM4759	OHV759Y	Leyland Titan TNLXB2RR	Leyland	O44/32F	1983	Stagecoach South, 2000
LB4763	OHV763Y	Leyland Titan TNLXB2RR	Leyland	O45/32F	1983	London Central, 1998
-774	OHV774Y	Leyland Titan TNLXB2RR	Leyland	B44/26D	1983	London Central, 2003
CMB4781	OHV781Y	Leyland Titan TNLXB2RR	Leyland	CO45/32F	1983	London Central, 1998
LB4786	OHV786Y	Leyland Titan TNLXB2RR	Leyland	O44/32F	1983	London Central, 1998
MB4788	OHV788Y	Leyland Titan TNLXB2RR	Leyland	O44/32F	1983	London Central, 1998
LB4792	OHV792Y	Leyland Titan TNLXB2RR	Leyland	O44/31F	1983	London Central, 1998
MB5803	OHV803Y	Leyland Titan TNLXB2RR	Leyland	O44/26D	1983	Go-Ahead London, 2004
CLB4808	OHV808Y	Leyland Titan TNLXB2RR	Leyland	CO44/32F	1983	London Central, 1998
EM2000	OHV811Y	Leyland Titan TNLXB2RR	Leyland	CO44/32F	1983	London Central, 1998
-831	A831SUL	Leyland Titan TNLXB2RR	Leyland	B44/32F	1983	London Central, 2003
-835	A835SUL	Leyland Titan TNLXB2RR	Leyland	B44/32F	1983	London Central, 2003
-839	A839SUL	Leyland Titan TNLXB2RR	Leyland	B44/32F	1983	London Central, 2003
-844	A844SUL	Leyland Titan TNLXB2RR	Leyland	B44/32F	1983	London Central, 2003
EM851	A851SUL	Leyland Titan TNLXB2RR	Leyland	O44/32F	1983	London Central, 2003
EM852	A852SUL	Leyland Titan TNLXB2RR	Leyland	O44/32F	1983	London Central, 1998
-870	A870SUL	Leyland Titan TNLXB2RR	Leyland	B44/32F	1983	London Central, 2003
-875	A875SUL	Leyland Titan TNLXB2RR	Leyland	B44/32F	1983	London Central, 2006
-919	A919SYE	Leyland Titan TNLXB2RR	Leyland	B44/32F	1984	London Central, 2003
-928	A928SYE	Leyland Titan TNLXB2RR	Leyland	O44/26D	1984	Go-Ahead London, 2004
-931	A931SYE	Leyland Titan TNLXB2RR	Leyland	B44/32F	1984	London Central, 2003
-956	A956SYE	Leyland Titan TNLXB2RR	Leyland	B44/32F	1984	London Central, 2003
EM991	A991SYE	Leyland Titan TNLXB2RR	Leyland	O44/32F	1984	London Central, 2003
CRM1056	A56THX	Leyland Titan TNLXB2RR	Leyland	CO45/32F	1984	London Central, 1998
-60	A60THX	Leyland Titan TNLXB2RR	Leyland	B44/26D	1984	Go-Ahead London, 2004
LB472	A72THX	Leyland Titan TNLXB2RR	Leyland	O44/26D	1984	Go-Ahead London, 2004
-73	A73THX	Leyland Titan TNLXB2RR	Leyland	B44/26D	1984	Go-Ahead London, 2004
-605	A605THV	Leyland Titan TNLXB2RR	Leyland	B44/26D	1984	Go-Ahead London, 2004
-614	A614THV	Leyland Titan TNLXB2RR	Leyland	B44/26D	1984	Go-Ahead London, 2004
MBH4624	A624THV	Leyland Titan TNLXB2RR	Leyland	PO44/32F	1984	London Central, 1998
CRM1638	A638THV	Leyland Titan TNLXB2RR	Leyland	CO44/32F	1984	London Central, 1998
EM4640	A640THV	Leyland Titan TNLXB2RR	Leyland	PO44/32F	1984	London Central, 2003
-644	A644THV	Leyland Titan TNLXB2RR	Leyland	B44/26D	1984	Nu Venture, Aylesford, 2003
EU003	E949JAR	MCW Metrobus DR115/4	MCW	PO61/39D	1987	New World First Bus, 2003
ML764	E764JAR	MCW Metrobus DR115/4	MCW	O61/39D	1987	New World First Bus, 2001
ML869	E869JAR	MCW Metrobus DR115/4	MCW	O61/39D	1987	New World First Bus, 2002

Still the only examples in Britain, The Big Bus Company's open-top buses with canvas roofs were converted in Berlin. New to London Buses in 1983, several Leyland Titans were purchased by The Big Bus Company in 1998 for further London service. Since its days as a standard London bus, CMB1720, OHV720Y, has received roof modifications, a new blind display, repaint and the removal of the centre door. Also most, if not all, Big Bus vehicles now have new Cummins Euro 3 engines. *Colin Lloyd*

ML881	E881JAR	MCW Metrobus DR115/4	MCW	PO61/39D	1987	New World First Bus, 2002
ML901	E901JAR	MCW Metrobus DR115/4	MCW	PO61/39D	1987	New World First Bus, 2002
ML16	B16BSS	MCW Metrobus DR115/5	MCW	O61/39D	1988	New World First Bus, 2001
ML20	B20DMS	MCW Metrobus DR115/5	MCW	O61/39D	1988	New World First Bus, 2001
ML69	F69SYE	MCW Metrobus DR115/5	MCW	O61/39D	1988	New World First Bus, 2006
ML153	F153UJN	MCW Metrobus DR115/5	MCW	O61/39D	1988	New World First Bus, 2006
ML326	F326UJN	MCW Metrobus DR115/5	MCW	O61/39D	1988	New World First Bus, 2002
ML355	F355UJN	MCW Metrobus DR115/5	MCW	O61/39D	1988	New World First Bus, 2002
D32	G32FWC	Dennis Condor DDA1702	Duple Metsec	O62/40D	1989	New World First Bus, 2003
HD34	G34FWC	Dennis Condor DDA1702	Duple Metsec	PO62/40D	1989	New World First Bus, 2003
HD42	G42FWC	Dennis Condor DDA1702	Duple Metsec	PO62/40D	1989	New World First Bus, 2003
HD43	G43FWC	Dennis Condor DDA1702	Duple Metsec	O62/40D	1989	New World First Bus, 2003
D59	F59SYE	Dennis Condor DDA1702	Duple Metsec	O62/40D	1989	New World First Bus, 2003
D67	F67SYE	Dennis Condor DDA1702	Duple Metsec	O62/40D	1989	New World First Bus, 2003
HD14	B14BUS	Dennis Condor DDA1702	Duple Metsec	O62/40D	1989	New World First Bus, 2006
D96	G96SGO	Dennis Condor DDA1702	Duple Metsec	O62/40D	1989	New World First Bus, 2003
HD159	G159FWC	Dennis Condor DDA1702	Duple Metsec	PO62/40D	1989	New World First Bus, 2003
D418	F418UJN	Dennis Condor DDA1702	Duple Metsec	PO62/40D	1989	New World First Bus, 2003
HD938	G938FVX	Dennis Condor DDA1702	Duple Metsec	PO62/40D	1989	New World First Bus, 2003
HD939	G939FVX	Dennis Condor DDA1702	Duple Metsec	PO62/40D	1989	New World First Bus, 2003
D943	G943FVX	Dennis Condor DDA1702	Duple Metsec	O62/40D	1989	New World First Bus, 2003
D952	G952FVX	Dennis Condor DDA1702	Duple Metsec	O62/40D	1989	New World First Bus, 2003
HD953	G953FVX	Dennis Condor DDA1702	Duple Metsec	PO62/40D	1989	New World First Bus, 2003
HD954	G954FVX	Dennis Condor DDA1702	Duple Metsec	PO62/40D	1989	New World First Bus, 2003
D956	G956FVX	Dennis Condor DDA1702	Duple Metsec	O62/40D	1989	New World First Bus, 2003
HD964	G964FVX	Dennis Condor DDA1702	Duple Metsec	PO62/40D	1989	New World First Bus, 2003
D969	G969FVX	Dennis Condor DDA1702	Duple Metsec	PO62/40D	1989	New World First Bus, 2003
D991	G991FVX	Dennis Condor DDA1702	Duple Metsec	PO62/40D	1989	New World First Bus, 2003
MBO336	E336NUV	Leyland Olympian	Alexander	O59/34D	1990	Kowloon Motor Bus, 2005
MBO337	E337NUV	Leyland Olympian	Alexander	O59/34D	1990	Kowloon Motor Bus, 2005
MBO338	E338NUV	Leyland Olympian	Alexander	O59/34D	1990	Kowloon Motor Bus, 2005
MBO340	E340NUV	Leyland Olympian	Alexander	PO59/34D	1990	Kowloon Motor Bus, 2005
MBO512	D512UGT	Leyland Olympian	Alexander	O59/34D	1990	Kowloon Motor Bus, 2005
MBO514	D514UGT	Leyland Olympian	Alexander	O59/34D	1990	Kowloon Motor Bus, 2005
MBO690	D690UGT	Leyland Olympian	Alexander	O59/34D	1990	Kowloon Motor Bus, 2005
MBO692	D692UGT	Leyland Olympian	Alexander	O59/34D	1990	Kowloon Motor Bus, 2005

The London Bus Handbook

The Big Bus Company operates exclusively on sightseeing tours, both in London and Dubai using a variety of double-deck buses. Although the majority of the fleet are Leyland Titans acquired from London operators, a growing number of buses have been imported from Hong Kong. These consist of Dennis Condors, MCW Metrobuses and Leyland Olympians, all originally built in Britain. Here, tri-axle Metrobus ML869, E869JAR, passes through Trafalgar Square in June 2006. *Colin Lloyd*

Previous registrations:

XMD47A	KCH106	F326UJN	DZ7095 (HK)
B14BUS	EG5851 (HK), G67FWC	F355UJN	DZ3401 (HK)
B16BSS	DZ3015 (HK), F164UJN	F418UJN	EF3349 (HK)
B20DMS	DZ7066 (HK), F159UJN	G32FWC	EJ2225 (HK)
D512UGT	DW7274(HK)	G34FWC	EG2166 (HK)
D514UGT	-	G42FWC	EH6321 (HK)
D690UGT	DT8317(HK)	G43FWC	EH7636 (HK)
D692UGT	DW3065(HK)	G96SGO	EF5328(HK)
E336NUV	DW4358(HK)	G159FWC	EH7436 (HK)
E337NUV	DW3683(HK)	G938FVX	EG9356 (HK)
E338NUV	-	G939FVX	EG857 (HK)
E340NUV	-	G943FVX	EH7098 (HK)
E764JAR	DU542 (HK)	G952FVX	EH9876 (HK)
E869JAR	DU194 (HK)	G953FVX	EG9386 (HK)
E881JAR	DU7765 (HK)	G954FVX	EH6884 (HK)
E901JAR	DU4314 (HK)	G956FVX	EH4324 (HK)
E949JAR	DT7029 (HK)	G964FVX	EG6964 (HK)
F59SYE	EF4079(HK)	G969FVX	EJ3811 (HK)
F67SYE	EF750(HK)	G991FVX	EG4627 (HK)
F69SYE	EA4389(HK)	VLT125	KYV336V
F153UJN	DY8172(HK)		

Where seating is shown above in brown, the vehicle is fitted with a folding canvas roof.

This operator also has vehicles in Dubai, UAE.

BLUE TRIANGLE

Blue Triangle Ltd, 3c Denver Industrial Estate, Ferry Lane, Rainham, RM13 9BU

SO1-5

Scania OmniDekka N94UB 10.6m East Lancs 4.4m   N45/27D   2005

1	BV55UCT	3	BV55UCW	4	BV55UCX	5	BV55UCY
2	BV55UCU						

DN181-188

Dennis Dart SLF 11m   Caetano Nimbus   N36D   2001   On loan to Armchair

181	Y181RCR	183	Y183RCR	185	Y185RCR	187	Y187RCR
182	Y182RCR	184	Y184RCR	186	Y186RCR	188	Y188RCR

DP189-192

Dennis Dart SLF 10.7m   Plaxton Pointer 2   N37F*   2003   *192 is N39D

189	EJ52WXC	190	EJ52WXD	191	EJ52WXE	192	EJ52WXF

DP193-205

TransBus Dart 10.7m   TransBus Pointer   N36D   2003-04

193	EU53PXY	197	EU53PYD	200	EU53PYH	203	EU53PYO
194	EU53PXZ	198	EU53PYF	201	EU53PYJ	204	EU53PYP
195	EU53PYA	199	EU53PYG	202	EU53PYL	205	BT04BUS
196	EU53PYB						

DP206	EU04BVD	TransBus Dart 10.7m	TransBus Pointer	N37F	2004	
DP207	EU04BVF	TransBus Dart 10.7m	TransBus Pointer	N37F	2004	
DP208	SN56AYC	ADL Dart 10.7m	ADL Pointer	N37F	2006	
DP209	SN56AYD	ADL Dart 10.7m	ADL Pointer	N37F	2006	
RT3062	KXW171	AEC Regent III 0961	Saunders	B30/26R	1950	Ensign Bus, 1993
RT3435	LYR854	AEC Regent III 0961	Weymann	O30/26R	1952	preservation, 2000
RT3871	LLU670	AEC Regent III 0961	Park Royal	B30/26R	1950	preservation, 1997
RM85	VLT85	AEC Routemaster R2RH	Park Royal	B36/28R	1959	Transport for London, 2006
RCL2260	CUV260C	AEC Routemaster R2RH/3	Park Royal	B36/29R	1965	Arriva London Tour, 1997
RM298	VLT298	AEC Routemaster R2RH	Park Royal	B36/28R	1960	preservation
RM346	SVS615	AEC Routemaster R2RH	Park Royal	B36/28R	1960	?, 2006
RM713	YSK270	AEC Routemaster R2RH	Park Royal	B36/28R	1960	Mike Nash, Cobham, 2006
RML899	215UXJ	AEC Routemaster R2RH1	Park Royal	B40/32R	1961	Ensign Bus, 2006
RML900	WLT900	AEC Routemaster R2RH1	Park Royal	B40/32R	1961	Clydeside 2000, 1995
RM1975	ALD975B	AEC Routemaster R2RH	Park Royal	B36/28R	1962	Mike Nash, Cobham, 2006
RTW75	KGK575	Leyland Titan PD2/3	Leyland	B30/26R	1949	preservation, 2004
MCW28	WYW28T	MCW Metrobus DR101/8	MCW	B43/28D	1979	London United, 1998

To commemorate the last days of Routemaster operation on many routes, Transport for London (TfL) allowed special vehicles to be used. On 1st April 2005, route 19 was one such, with many vintage buses employed by a number of London area operators. Operating an Arriva London route, Blue Triangle's RT3062 KXW171, is seen fully loaded rounding Highbury Corner. *Mark Lyons*

MCW271	BYX271V	MCW Metrobus DR101/12	MCW		B43/28D	1980	London General, 1999
MCW463	GYE463W	MCW Metrobus DR101/12	MCW		B43/28D	1980	London General, 1999
MCW468	GYE468W	MCW Metrobus DR101/12	MCW		B43/28D	1980	Metropolitan Omnibus, 2002
MCW693	KYV693X	MCW Metrobus DR101/14	MCW		B43/28D	1981	Metropolitan Omnibus, 2002
MCW801	KYV801X	MCW Metrobus DR101/14	MCW		B43/28D	1982	FE Thorpe, Wembley, 2003
MCW809	OJD809Y	MCW Metrobus DR101/16	MCW		B43/28D	1983	Metropolitan Omnibus, 2002
MCW981	A981SYF	MCW Metrobus DR101/17	MCW		B43/28D	1984	London United, 1999
MCW1200	B200WUL	MCW Metrobus DR101/17	MCW		B43/28D	1985	London United, 2002

T2-33

Leyland Titan TNLXB2RRSp — Park Royal — B44/24D — 1978-80 — Stagecoach, 2002

2	THX402S	8	WYV8T	11	WYV11T	23	WYV23T
4	WYV4T	9	WYV9T	22	WYV22T	33	WYV33T

T512	KYV512X	Leyland Titan TNLXB2RR	Leyland		B44/26D	1983	Stagecoach, 2005
T819	RYK819Y	Leyland Titan TNLXB2RR	Leyland		B44/26D	1983	Stagecoach, 2005
T820	RYK820Y	Leyland Titan TNLXB2RR	Leyland		B44/26D	1983	Stagecoach, 2005
T908	A908SYE	Leyland Titan TNLXB2RR	Leyland		B44/26D	1983	Stagecoach, 2002
T1095	B95WUV	Leyland Titan TNLXB2RR	Leyland		B44/24D	1984	Stagecoach, 2002
T1101	B101WUV	Leyland Titan TNLXB2RR	Leyland		B44/24D	1984	Stagecoach, 2002

TL901-909

Dennis Trident 10m — East Lancs Lolyne* — N45/21D* — 1999 — *905 2003 and NC46/20D

901	V901FEC	904	V904FEC	906	V906FEC	908	V908FEC
902	V902FEC	905	V905FEC	907	V907FEC	909	V909FEC
903	V903FEC						

TL910-923

Dennis Trident 10m — East Lancs Lolyne — N46/20D — 2001

910	PO51UMF	914	PO51UMK	918	PO51UMS	921	PO51UMW
911	PO51UMG	915	PO51UML	919	PO51UMT	922	PO51UMX
912	PO51UMH	916	PO51UMM	920	PO51UMV	923	PO51UMY
913	PO51UMJ	917	PO51UMR				

TPL924	V8AEC	Dennis Trident 10.5m	Plaxton President		N47/29F	2001	Pete's Travel, W Bromwich
TPL925	VLT110	Dennis Trident 10.5m	Plaxton President		N47/29F	2000	Pete's Travel, W Bromwich
TPL926	EY03FNK	TransBus Trident 10.5m	TransBus President		N45/23D	2003	
TPL927	EY03FNL	TransBus Trident 10.5m	TransBus President		N45/23D	2003	
TPL928	PO51UGF	Dennis Trident 10.5m	Plaxton President		N47/28F	2001	Liverpool Motor Services, 2004

Previous registrations:

215UXJ	WLT899		PO51WNH	
SVS615	WLT346	VLT110	VLT298	VLT298, WTS245A
V8AEC	00D88846, W81TJU	YSK270	WLT713	

Five East Lancs Scania OmniDekkas were purchased by Blue Triangle in 2005, the first non-Dennis/TransBus vehicles for this operator. SO5, BV55UCY, is seen on its usual haunt, route 474, in Manor Park during April 2006. *Mark Lyons*

CAVALIER

A W & D H Pagan, Armchair House, Commerce Road, Brentford, TW7 8LZ

FN52GUC	Irisbus EuroRider 391E.12.35	Beulas El Mundo	C51FT	2002
YP52CUJ	Scania K124IB4	Van Hool T9 Alizée	C49FT	2002
FY03WZT	Mercedes-Benz Atego 1223L	Ferqui/Optare Solera 2	C29F	2003
FX03GJJ	Mercedes-Benz Sprinter 413cdi	Ferqui/Optare Soroco	M16	2003
YO53OAD	Irisbus MidiRider 395E.9.27	Beulas MidiStar ε	C35F	2003
FX04EEP	Mercedes-Benz Sprinter 413cdi	Ferqui/Optare Soroco	M16	2004
BX04BJF	Toyota Coaster BB50R	Caetano Optimo V	C22F	2004
YN04AYD	Irisbus MidiRider 395E.9.27	Beulas MidiStar ε	C35F	2004
YN05BVC	Neoplan Euroliner N316 SHD	Neoplan	C49FT	2005
YN05BVD	Neoplan Euroliner N316 SHD	Neoplan	C49FT	2005
YN55WPD	Mercedes-Benz Sprinter 616cdi	Unvi/Esker Riada 616	C22F	2005

Web: www.cavaliercoaches.com

Operating from a base in Brentford, Cavalier has a mixed fleet of coaches ranging from full size to minicoaches. Representing the midi-coach within the group is YO53OAD, an Irisbus MidiRider with Beulas Midi-Star ε 35-seat body. One of a brace in the fleet, it is seen in Trafalgar Square in February 2006. *Colin Lloyd*

CHALFONT

Chalfont Coaches of Harrow Ltd, 200 Featherstone Road, Southall, UB2 5AQ

MNT595W	Volvo B58-56	Plaxton Supreme IV Express	C53F	1981	Vagg, Knockin Heath, 1983
V470RDN	LDV Convoy	Concept	M16	1999	
X579BYD	Volvo B10M-62	Van Hool T9 Alizée	C46FT	2000	
Y395KCB	LDV Convoy	Concept	M16	2001	
WA04MHJ	Volvo B12M	Van Hool T9 Alizée	C55F	2004	
WA04MHK	Volvo B12M	Van Hool T9 Alizée	C53FT	2004	
WA04MHL	Volvo B12M	Van Hool T9 Alizée	C53FT	2004	
WA54HXU	Volvo B12M	Van Hool T9 Alizée	C53FT	2004	
WA54HXV	Volvo B12M	Van Hool T9 Alizée	C53FT	2004	
WA54HXW	Volvo B12M	Van Hool T9 Alizée	C53FT	2004	
WA54HXX	Volvo B12M	Van Hool T9 Alizée	C53FT	2004	
WA06CDX	Volvo B12M	Van Hool T9 Alizée	C53FT	2006	
WA06CDY	Volvo B12M	Van Hool T9 Alizée	C53FT	2006	
WA06CDZ	Volvo B12M	Van Hool T9 Alizée	C53FT	2006	
WA56ENK	Volvo B12M	Van Hool T9 Alizée	C53FT	2006	
WA56ENL	Volvo B12M	Van Hool T9 Alizée	C53FT	2006	
WA56ENM	Volvo B12M	Van Hool T9 Alizée	C57F	2006	

Web: www.chalfontcoaches.co.uk

Apart from a pair of LDV minibuses, the whole of the Chalfont fleet comprises full-size Volvo coaches, all bar the oldest fitted with the Van Hool T9 Alizée body. Fourteen of this model are in the current fleet with recently replaced WA03EYK seen approaching Oxford Street while operating on National Express route 440. *Colin Lloyd*

CITY CIRCLE

City Circle UK Ltd, The West London Coach Centre, North Hyde Gardens, Hayes, Hillingdon, UB3 4QT

17	YN03AXF	Neoplan Euroliner N316SHD	Neoplan	C53F	2003
18	YN03AXG	Neoplan Euroliner N316SHD	Neoplan	C53F	2003
19	YN03AXH	Neoplan Euroliner N316SHD	Neoplan	C53F	2003
20	YN03AXJ	Neoplan Euroliner N316SHD	Neoplan	C53F	2003
21	YN03AXK	Neoplan Euroliner N316SHD	Neoplan	C53F	2003
22	BU04EZA	Setra S415 HD	Setra	C49FT	2004
23	BU04EZB	Setra S415 HD	Setra	C49FT	2004
24	BU04EZC	Setra S415 HD	Setra	C49FT	2004
25	BU04EZD	Setra S415 HD	Setra	C49FT	2004
26	BU04EZE	Setra S415 HD	Setra	C49FT	2004
27	BX05UVL	Setra S415 HD	Setra	C49FT	2005
28	BX05UVM	Setra S415 HD	Setra	C49FT	2005
29	BX05UVN	Setra S415 HD	Setra	C49FT	2005
30	BX05UVO	Setra S315 GT-HD	Setra	C53F	2005
31	BX05UVP	Setra S315 GT-HD	Setra	C53F	2005
32	YJ06LCX	VDL Bus SB4000	Van Hool T9 Alizée	C51FT	2006
33	YJ06LDL	VDL Bus SB4000	Van Hool T9 Alizée	C51FT	2006
34	YJ06LFV	VDL Bus SB4000	Van Hool T9 Alizée	C51FT	2006

Livery: White, red, grey and dark blue; white; red and grey (My Bus): BX05UVO/P; white and blue (Kuoni): BX05UVN, YJ06LFV
Web: www.citycircleuk.com

The age profile and specification of the City Circle fleet are impressive. Here, one of the older vehicles, Neoplan Euroliner 18, YN03AXG, is seen rounding Parliament Square in June 2006 while carrying a party of Japanese tourists. The latest coaches to join the fleet form a trio of Dutch-built VDL Bus SB4000s, with Van Hool T9 Alizée bodies. *Dave Heath*

CLARKES OF LONDON

E Clarke & Sons (Coaches) Ltd, Kangley Bridge Road, Lower Sydenham, SE26 5AT

R183LBC	Toyota Coaster BB50R	Caetano Optimo IV	C16F	1997
R892MTL	Setra S250	Setra Special	C53F	1998
R128NFE	Setra S250	Setra Special	C53F	1998
R173SUT	Volvo B10M-62	Jonckheere Mistral 50	C53F	1998
R177SUT	Volvo B10M-62	Jonckheere Mistral 50	C53F	1998
R179SUT	Volvo B10M-62	Jonckheere Mistral 50	C53F	1998
T200OCL	Setra S315 GT-HD	Setra	C49FT	1999
X474ROA	Setra S315 GT-HD	Setra	C49FT	2001
X477ROA	Setra S315 GT-HD	Setra	C49FT	2001
Y371UOM	Setra S315 GT-HD	Setra	C49FT	2001
Y372UOM	Setra S315 GT-HD	Setra	C49FT	2001
Y376UOM	Setra S315 GT-HD	Setra	C53F	2001
Y377UOM	Setra S315 GT-HD	Setra	C53F	2001
Y378UOM	Setra S315 GT-HD	Setra	C53F	2001
Y585TOV	Setra S315 GT-HD	Setra	C53F	2001
Y586TOV	Setra S315 GT-HD	Setra	C53F	2001
Y587TOV	Setra S315 GT-HD	Setra	C53F	2001
FP51EUR	Volvo B12B	Jonckheere Mistral 50	C49FT	2002
LV51ZHJ	Setra S315 GT-HD	Setra	C49FT	2002
LV51ZHK	Setra S315 GT-HD	Setra	C49FT	2002
LV51ZHL	Setra S315 GT-HD	Setra	C49FT	2002
LV51ZHM	Setra S315 GT-HD	Setra	C49FT	2002
LW52AKK	Setra S315 GT-HD	Setra	C49FT	2003
LW52AKN	Setra S315 GT-HD	Setra	C49FT	2003
BU03LYS	Setra S415 HD	Setra	C49FT	2003

For more than thirty years Clarkes of London have been operating coaches and are currently located at impressive, purpose-built premises in the Lower Sydenham area of south London. Clarkes' modern coaches are mostly full-size but there are a few mini-coaches based on the Toyota Coaster with Caetano Optimo bodywork. Shown entering Trafalgar Square in June 2006 is FJ06URB. *Colin Lloyd*

The recent supply of full-size coaches in the Clarkes of London fleet has been divided between Irizar-bodied Scania products and integral coaches from Setra's Neu Ulm factory. Supplied in 2002, LV51ZHK, is one of the Setra S315s and illustrates the fleet colours of turquoise and silver. It is seen in Victoria Street in June 2006. *Colin Lloyd*

GG04ONE	Scania K114EB4	Irizar Capacity	C53F	2004
GG04TWO	Scania K114EB4	Irizar Capacity	C53F	2004
YN04GHA	Scania K114IB4	Irizar Capacity	C53F	2004
YN04GHB	Scania K114IB4	Irizar Capacity	C53F	2004
YN04GHD	Scania K114IB4	Irizar Capacity	C53F	2004
YN04GHF	Scania K114IB4	Irizar Capacity	C53F	2004
YN04GHG	Scania K114IB4	Irizar Capacity	C53FT	2004
YN04GHH	Scania K114IB4	Irizar Capacity	C53F	2004
YN04GHJ	Scania K114IB4	Irizar Capacity	C53F	2004
YN04GHK	Scania K114IB4	Irizar Capacity	C53F	2004
YN04GHU	Scania K114IB4	Irizar Capacity	C53F	2004
YN04GHV	Scania K114IB4	Irizar Capacity	C53F	2004
YN04GHX	Scania K114IB4	Irizar Capacity	C53FT	2004
YN04GHY	Scania K114IB4	Irizar Capacity	C53F	2004
YN04GHZ	Scania K114IB4	Irizar Capacity	C53F	2004
BX05UVJ	Setra S315 GT-HD	Setra	C49FT	2005
BX05UVK	Setra S315 GT-HD	Setra	C49FT	2005
YN06NYO	Scania K114EB4	Irizar Century Style	C53F	2006
YN06NYV	Scania K114EB4	Irizar Century Style	C53F	2006
YN06NYW	Scania K114EB4	Irizar Century Style	C53F	2006
FJ06URB	Toyota Coaster BB50R	Caetano Optimo V	C18F	2006
FJ06URC	Toyota Coaster BB50R	Caetano Optimo V	C18F	2006
FJ06URD	Toyota Coaster BB50R	Caetano Optimo V	C18F	2006
FJ06URE	Toyota Coaster BB50R	Caetano Optimo V	C18F	2006

Web: www.clarkescoaches.co.uk

CT PLUS

Hackney Community Transport; CT Plus Ltd, Mare Street, Hackney, E8 4RH

DCS1-9

			TransBus Dart 8.9m			Caetano Slimbus		N30F	2003		
1	HK	KV03ZFE	4	HK	KV03ZFH	6	HK	HX03MGU	8	HK	HX03MGY
2	HK	KV03ZFF	5	HK	HX03MGV	7	HK	HX03MGJ	9	HK	HX03MGZ
3	HK	KV03ZFG									

HDC1-11

			Dennis Dart SLF 10.5m			Caetano Nimbus		N26D	2001		
1	HK	X584ORV	4	HK	X587ORV	7	HK	X591ORV	10	HK	X594ORV
2	HK	X585ORV	5	HK	X588ORV	8	HK	X592ORV	11	HK	X595ORV
3	HK	X586ORV	6	HK	X589ORV	9	HK	X593ORV			

HDC12	T432LGP	Dennis Dart SLF	Caetano Compass	N30D	1999	Travel London, 2006
HDC13	T431LGP	Dennis Dart SLF	Caetano Compass	N30D	1999	Travel London, 2006
HDC14	T433LGP	Dennis Dart SLF	Caetano Compass	N30D	1999	Travel London, 2006

HTL1-13

			Dennis Trident			East Lancashire Lolyne		N45/23D	2003		
1	HK	LR52LTO	5	HK	LR52LWE	8	HK	LR52LWH	11	HK	PF52TGZ
2	HK	LR52LTN	6	HK	LR52LTK	9	HK	LR52LWJ	12	HK	LR52LYC
3	HK	LR52LTJ	7	HK	LR52LWF	10	HK	PF52TFX	13	HK	LR52LYJ
4	HK	LR52LTF									

Depot: Ash Grove, Cambridge Heath (HK). A large fleet of minibuses is employed on welfare work.

Thirteen East Lancs Lolynes fitted with the Myllennium front option were purchased by Hackney Community Transport during 2002 and put to work in January 2003 on their, then, newly-won tendered route 388. The entire fleet of vehicles, both single and double-deck, are based on Dennis/TransBus products. HTL3, LR52LTJ, is seen in Queen Victoria Street in July 2006. *Mark Lyons*

DOCKLANDS MINIBUSES

Docklands Minibuses Ltd, Factory Road, Newham, London, E16 2AA

K131SRH	Dennis Dart 9SDL3024	Plaxton Pointer	B34F	1993	Stagecoach London, 2002
M35CHS	Mercedes-Benz 609D	Crystals	BC24F	1995	
N205YJM	Ford Transit VE6	Devon Conversions	BC16F	1996	
N208YJM	Ford Transit VE6	Devon Conversions	BC16F	1996	
R546KSG	Mercedes-Benz 614D	Onyx	C24F	1998	
R547KSG	Mercedes-Benz 614D	Onyx	C24F	1998	
S399WTU	Mercedes-Benz 614D	Onyx	C24F	1998	
T574KGB	Mercedes-Benz 614D	Onyx	C24F	1998	Reekie, Kinglassie, 2002
T45RJL	Mercedes-Benz Vario 0814	Autobus Classique	C33F	1999	Optare demonstrator, 1999
T705SUT	Toyota Coaster BB50R	Caetano Optimo IV	C21F	1999	Stothart, Holmfirth, 2000
T402OWA	Scania L94IB	Irizar Century 12.35	C49FT	1999	Bus Eireann, 2004
V278NAD	Mercedes-Benz Vario 0814	Onyx	C24F	2000	
W873GBX	Renault Master	Cymric	M16	2000	
W874GBX	Renault Master	Cymric	M16	2000	
W582WCA	Mercedes-Benz Sprinter 412D	Onyx	M16	2000	
W583WCA	Mercedes-Benz Sprinter 512D	Onyx	C20F	2000	
Y513HWE	Mercedes-Benz Sprinter 614D	Onyx	C24F	2001	
YN51KKP	Mercedes-Benz Sprinter 316CDi	Onyx	M12	2001	
HV02OZS	Dennis Dart SLF 10.5m	Caetano Nimbus	N31D	2002	
HV02OZT	Dennis Dart SLF 10.5m	Caetano Nimbus	N31D	2002	
HV02OZU	Dennis Dart SLF 10.5m	Caetano Nimbus	N31D	2002	
HV02OZW	Dennis Dart SLF 10.5m	Caetano Nimbus	N31D	2002	
HV02OZX	Dennis Dart SLF 10.5m	Caetano Nimbus	N31D	2002	
HV02PCO	Dennis Dart SLF 10.5m	Caetano Nimbus	N31D	2002	
HV02PCU	Dennis Dart SLF 10.5m	Caetano Nimbus	N31D	2002	
HV02PCX	Dennis Dart SLF 10.5m	Caetano Nimbus	N31D	2002	
HV02PCY	Dennis Dart SLF 10.5m	Caetano Nimbus	N31D	2002	
HV02PCZ	Dennis Dart SLF 10.5m	Caetano Nimbus	N31D	2002	
HV02PDK	Dennis Dart SLF 10.5m	Caetano Nimbus	N31D	2002	
HV02PDO	Dennis Dart SLF 10.5m	Caetano Nimbus	N31D	2002	
YM52TSV	Optare Solo M850	Optare	N29F	2002	We Care, Stevenage, 2003
YM52TSX	Optare Solo M850	Optare	N29F	2002	We Care, Stevenage, 2003
LX53NMV	BMC Probus 850	BMC	C35F	2004	
AE06HCA	ADL Dart 10.8m	MCV Evolution	N29D	2006	
AE06HCC	ADL Dart 10.8m	MCV Evolution	N29D	2006	
AE06HCD	ADL Dart 10.8m	MCV Evolution	N29D	2006	
AE06HCF	ADL Dart 10.8m	MCV Evolution	N29D	2006	
AE06HCG	ADL Dart 10.8m	MCV Evolution	N29D	2006	
AE06HCH	ADL Dart 10.8m	MCV Evolution	N29D	2006	
AE06HCJ	ADL Dart 10.8m	MCV Evolution	N29D	2006	
AE06HCK	ADL Dart 10.8m	MCV Evolution	N29D	2006	

Previous registration:
T402OWA   99D51545

Depots: Mecca Bingo, Dagenham; Factory Road, Newham; Naval Row, Poplar; Duthie Street, Poplar.

As we go to press, it has been announced that Go-Ahead London has acquired Docklands Minibuses which will shortly be integrated into the main Go-Ahead London fleet. A further eight ADL Darts with MCV Evolution bodies are on order.

EALING COMMUNITY TRANSPORT

Ealing Community Transport Ltd, 97 Bollo Lane, Acton, W3 8QN

101-113			TransBus Dart 10.5m			Caetano Nimbus		N32D	2003		
101	EA	KX03HZN	**105**	EA	KX03HZV	**108**	EA	KX03HZZ	**111**	EA	KX03HZE
102	EA	KX03HZP	**106**	EA	KX03HZS	**109**	EA	KX03HZR	**112**	EA	KX03HZG
103	EA	KX03HZT	**107**	EA	KX03HZW	**110**	EA	KX03HZY	**113**	EA	KX03HZF
104	EA	KX03HZU									
115	EA	KN05KFW	ADL Dart 10.5m			Caetano Nimbus		N32D	2005		

Depot: Greenford Road, Greenford (EA). A large fleet of minibuses is used on welfare and school duties.

An example of the newest buses in the Docklands Minibus fleet is AE06HCF, an Alexander-Dennis Dart with MCV Evolution bodywork. It was pictured in Chadwell Heath in April 2006. These buses were ordered on winning the tender for route 368 earlier in the year.
Dave Heath

Ealing Community Transport operates route 195 on tender to TfL in west London. With a Monday-Friday peak vehicle requirement (pvr) of eleven Darts, fourteen buses are owned. Number 110, KX03HZY, is seen in Hillingdon on a sunny March afternoon in 2006.
Mark Lyons

EAST LONDON BUS GROUP

East London - Selkent

East London Buses Ltd; South East London & Kent Bus Co Ltd,
2 Clements Road, Ilford, IG1 1BA

12024	WA	WLT324	AEC Routemaster R2RH	Park Royal	B36/28R	1963
12052	WA	WLT652	AEC Routemaster R2RH	Park Royal	B36/28R	1963
12071	WA	ALM71B	AEC Routemaster R2RH	Park Royal	B36/28R	1964
12133	WA	ALD933B	AEC Routemaster R2RH	Park Royal	B36/28R	1964
12141	WA	ALD941B	AEC Routemaster R2RH	Park Royal	B36/28R	1964
12168	WA	ALD968B	AEC Routemaster R2RH	Park Royal	B36/28R	1964
12250	WA	ALM50B	AEC Routemaster R2RH	Park Royal	B36/28R	1964
12260	WA	ALM60B	AEC Routemaster R2RH	Park Royal	B36/28R	1964
12271	WA	WLT871	AEC Routemaster R2RH	Park Royal	B36/28R	1963
12289	WA	ALM89B	AEC Routemaster R2RH	Park Royal	B36/28R	1964
16001	NS	P801GMU	Volvo Olympian YN2RV18Z4	Northern Counties Palatine	B49/31D	1996
16002	NS	P802GMU	Volvo Olympian YN2RV18Z4	Northern Counties Palatine	B49/31D	1996
16003	NS	P803GMU	Volvo Olympian YN2RV18Z4	Northern Counties Palatine	B49/31D	1996
16122	TB	R122EVX	Volvo Olympian	Alexander RL	B45/23D	1998
16123	TB	R123EVX	Volvo Olympian	Alexander RL	B45/23D	1998

17001-17098   Dennis Trident 10.5m   Alexander ALX400 4.2m   N51/22D*   1999   *17048/9 are N51/26F

17001	T	S801BWC	17082	U	T682KPU	17088	U	T688KPU	17094	U	T694KPU
17048	WA	T648KPU	17083	U	T683KPU	17089	U	T689KPU	17095	U	T695KPU
17049	WA	T649KPU	17084	U	T684KPU	17090	U	T690KPU	17096	U	T696KPU
17064	BK	T664KPU	17085	U	T685KPU	17091	U	T691KPU	17097	U	T697KPU
17065	BK	T665KPU	17086	U	T686KPU	17092	U	T692KPU	17098	U	T698KPU
17080	BK	T680KPU	17087	U	T687KPU	17093	U	T693KPU			

17099-17222   Dennis Trident 10.5m   Alexander ALX400 4.4m   N47/24D   1999-2000   *several N47/23D

17099	PD	VLT14	17130	PD	V130MEV	17162	PD	V162MEV	17193	PD	V193MEV
17100	PD	WLT491	17131	PD	V131MEV	17163	PD	V163MEV	17194	NS	V194MEV
17101	PD	WLT461	17132	NS	V132MEV	17164	PD	V164MEV	17195	PD	V195MEV
17102	PD	V102MEV	17133	PD	V133MEV	17165	U	V165MEV	17196	SD	V196MEV
17103	PD	V103MEV	17134	PD	V134MEV	17166	PD	V166MEV	17197	SD	V197MEV
17104	PD	V104MEV	17135	NS	V135MEV	17167	SD	V167MEV	17198	SD	V198MEV
17105	PD	V105MEV	17136	NS	V136MEV	17168	SD	V168MEV	17199	SD	V199MEV
17106	BK	V106MEV	17137	NS	V137MEV	17169	SD	V169MEV	17200	SD	V363OWC
17107	PD	V107MEV	17138	PD	V138MEV	17170	SD	V170MEV	17201	SD	V201MEV
17108	PD	V108MEV	17139	PD	V139MEV	17171	SD	V171MEV	17202	PD	V202MEV
17109	PD	V109MEV	17140	PD	V140MEV	17172	SD	V172MEV	17203	U	V203MEV
17110	PD	V476KJN	17141	PD	V141MEV	17173	SD	V173MEV	17204	U	V204MEV
17111	SD	V477KJN	17142	PD	V142MEV	17174	SD	V174MEV	17205	U	V205MEV
17112	PD	V112MEV	17143	TL	V143MEV	17175	SD	V175MEV	17206	U	V206MEV
17113	PD	V113MEV	17144	NS	V144MEV	17176	SD	V176MEV	17207	U	V207MEV
17114	NS	V114MEV	17145	PD	V145MEV	17177	SD	V177MEV	17208	U	V208MEV
17115	PD	V115MEV	17147	U	V147MEV	17178	SD	V178MEV	17209	U	V209MEV
17116	PD	V116MEV	17148	TL	V148MEV	17179	SD	V179MEV	17210	BK	V210MEV
17117	PD	V117MEV	17149	PD	V149MEV	17180	SD	W187CNO	17211	BK	V211MEV
17118	PD	V118MEV	17150	PD	V150MEV	17181	T	V181MEV	17212	BK	V212MEV
17119	PD	V119MEV	17151	PD	V151MEV	17182	T	V182MEV	17213	BK	V213MEV
17120	PD	V120MEV	17152	PD	V152MEV	17183	T	V183MEV	17214	PD	V214MEV
17121	PD	V478KJN	17153	PD	V153MEV	17184	T	V184MEV	17215	PD	V215MEV
17122	PD	V122MEV	17154	NS	V154MEV	17185	T	V185MEV	17216	PD	V216MEV
17123	PD	V479KJN	17155	TL	V155MEV	17186	T	V186MEV	17217	PD	V217MEV
17124	NS	V124MEV	17156	TL	V156MEV	17187	T	V362OWC	17218	PD	V218MEV
17125	PD	V125MEV	17157	NS	V157MEV	17188	T	V188MEV	17219	U	V219MEV
17126	PD	V126MEV	17158	T	V158MEV	17189	T	V189MEV	17220	U	V220MEV
17127	PD	V127MEV	17159	PD	V159MEV	17190	T	V190MEV	17221	PD	V221MEV
17128	PD	V128MEV	17160	SD	V160MEV	17191	T	V191MEV	17222	PD	V364OWC
17129	U	V129MEV	17161	PD	V161MEV	17192	NS	V192MEV			

17223-17260 Dennis Trident 9.9m Alexander ALX400 4.4m N43/21D* 2000 *some N43/20D

17223	NS	X361NNO	17233	U	X233NNO	17243	U	X243NNO	17252	U	X252NNO
17224	NS	X362NNO	17234	U	X234NNO	17244	SD	X369NNO	17253	U	X253NNO
17225	TL	X363NNO	17235	NS	X235NNO	17245	SD	X371NNO	17254	U	X254NNO
17226	U	X364NNO	17236	NS	X236NNO	17246	SD	X246NNO	17255	U	X373NNO
17227	U	X365NNO	17237	NS	X237NNO	17247	U	X247NNO	17256	U	X256NNO
17228	U	X366NNO	17238	U	X238NNO	17248	U	X248NNO	17257	U	X257NNO
17229	U	X229NNO	17239	SD	X239NNO	17249	U	X249NNO	17258	U	X258NNO
17230	NS	X367NNO	17240	SD	X368NNO	17250	U	X372NNO	17259	U	X259NNO
17231	U	X231NNO	17241	SD	X241NNO	17251	U	X251NNO	17260	U	WLT575
17232	U	X232NNO	17242	SD	X242NNO						

17261-17358 Dennis Trident 10.5m Alexander ALX400 4.4m N47/24D 2000

17261	BK	X261NNO	17286	TB	X286NNO	17311	PD	X311NNO	17335	TB	X335NNO
17262	BK	X262NNO	17287	TB	X287NNO	17312	PD	X312NNO	17336	TB	X336NNO
17263	BK	X263NNO	17288	TB	X288NNO	17313	PD	X313NNO	17337	TB	X337NNO
17264	BK	X264NNO	17289	TB	X289NNO	17314	PD	X314NNO	17338	TB	X338NNO
17265	BK	X265NNO	17290	TB	X379NNO	17315	PD	X315NNO	17339	TB	X339NNO
17266	BK	X266NNO	17291	U	X291NNO	17316	PD	X385NNO	17340	TB	X395NNO
17267	BK	X267NNO	17292	SD	X292NNO	17317	TL	X317NNO	17341	TB	X341NNO
17268	NS	X268NNO	17293	SD	X293NNO	17318	TL	X386NNO	17342	TB	X342NNO
17269	BK	X269NNO	17294	SD	X294NNO	17319	TL	X319NNO	17343	TB	X343NNO
17270	BK	X376NNO	17295	SD	X295NNO	17320	TL	X387NNO	17344	TB	X344NNO
17271	BK	X271NNO	17296	NS	X296NNO	17321	TL	X388NNO	17345	TB	X396NNO
17272	BK	X272NNO	17297	SD	X297NNO	17322	TL	X322NNO	17346	TB	X346NNO
17273	BK	X273NNO	17298	SD	X298NNO	17323	TL	X389NNO	17347	TB	X347NNO
17274	BK	X274NNO	17299	SD	X299NNO	17324	TB	X324NNO	17348	TB	X348NNO
17275	BK	X377NNO	17300	NS	X381NNO	17325	TL	X391NNO	17349	TB	X349NNO
17276	PD	X276NNO	17301	NS	X301NNO	17326	TL	X326NNO	17350	TL	X397NNO
17277	PD	X277NNO	17302	PD	X302NNO	17327	TL	X327NNO	17351	TB	X351NNO
17278	PD	X278NNO	17303	PD	X303NNO	17328	TL	X392NNO	17352	TB	X352NNO
17279	TB	X279NNO	17304	PD	X304NNO	17329	TL	X329NNO	17353	TB	X353NNO
17280	TB	X378NNO	17305	PD	X382NNO	17330	TL	X393NNO	17354	TB	X354NNO
17281	TB	X281NNO	17306	PD	X383NNO	17331	TL	X331NNO	17355	TB	X398NNO
17282	TB	X282NNO	17307	PD	X307NNO	17332	TL	X332NNO	17356	TB	X356NNO
17283	TB	X283NNO	17308	PD	X308NNO	17333	TL	X394NNO	17357	TB	X357NNO
17284	TB	X284NNO	17309	PD	X309NNO	17334	TB	X334NNO	17358	TB	X358NNO
17285	TB	X285NNO	17310	PD	X384NNO						

East London and Selkent are the two trading names of the East London Bus Group Limited. Acquired on privatisation by the Stagecoach Group in April 1989, they were sold to Macquarie Bank of Australia on Wednesday, 30 August 2006. Currently Stagecoach provide management support and the Stagecoach fleet numbers are to be retained. An early example without, Stagecoach names, is 17354, X354NNO.
Dave Heath

Seen in April 2006 still in service with Stagecoach names, Dennis Trident 17767, LX03BVC, displays the erstwhile livery of blue skirt and coloured swirls at the rear. It is seen on route 86 as it passes through Manor Park. *Mark Lyons*

17359-17435   Dennis Trident 10.5m   Alexander ALX400 4.4m   N45/23D*   2001   *17402 is N45/27F

17359	BK	Y359NHK	17379	BK	Y379NHK	17398	SD	Y368NHK	17418	T	LX51FJF
17360	BK	Y508NHK	17380	BK	Y512NHK	17399	SD	LX51FHP	17419	T	LX51FJJ
17361	BK	Y361NHK	17381	BK	Y381NHK	17400	SD	Y514NHK	17420	T	LX51FJK
17362	BK	Y362NHK	17382	BK	Y382NHK	17401	SD	Y401NHK	17421	T	LX51FJN
17363	BK	Y363NHK	17383	BK	LX51FPF	17403	SD	LX51FHS	17422	T	LX51FJO
17364	BK	Y364NHK	17384	BK	Y384NHK	17404	SD	Y404NHK	17423	T	LX51FJP
17365	BK	Y365NHK	17385	BK	Y385NHK	17405	SD	LX51FHT	17424	T	LX51FJV
17366	BK	Y366NHK	17386	BK	Y386NHK	17406	SD	Y517NHK	17425	T	LX51FJY
17367	BK	Y367NHK	17387	BK	LX51FPC	17407	SD	Y407NHK	17426	T	LX51FJZ
17368	BK	Y368NHK	17388	BK	Y388NHK	17408	SD	LX51FHU	17427	T	LX51FKA
17370	BK	Y509NHK	17389	BK	Y389NHK	17409	T	Y409NHK	17428	NS	LX51FKB
17371	BK	Y371NHK	17390	BK	LX51FPD	17410	T	LX51FHV	17429	NS	Y429NHK
17372	BK	Y372NHK	17391	BK	Y391NHK	17411	T	LX51FHW	17430	NS	LX51FKD
17373	BK	Y373NHK	17392	BK	Y392NHK	17412	T	LX51FHY	17431	NS	LX51FKE
17374	BK	Y374NHK	17393	BK	Y393NHK	17413	T	LX51FHZ	17432	NS	LX51FKF
17375	BK	Y511NHK	17394	BK	LX51FHN	17414	T	LX51FJA	17433	NS	LX51FKG
17376	BK	Y376NHK	17395	SD	Y395NHK	17415	T	LX51FJC	17434	NS	Y434NHK
17377	BK	Y377NHK	17396	SD	LX51FHO	17416	T	LX51FJD	17435	NS	LX51FKJ
17378	BK	Y378NHK	17397	SD	Y367NHK	17417	T	LX51FJE			

The London Bus Handbook

In 2005, many Stagecoach buses started to gain repaints which omitted the rear coloured swirls in accordance with the new TfL directive. Trident 17411, LX51FHW, approaches Walthamstow bus station in August 2005 while operating on Leyton depot's route 230. *Mark Lyons*

17436-17534   Dennis Trident 9.9m   Alexander ALX400   N43/19D   2001

17436	NS	Y436NHK	17461	NS	LX51FKW	17486	SD	LX51FME	17511	SD	LX51FNO
17437	NS	Y437NHK	17462	NS	Y462NHK	17487	U	LX51FMF	17512	SD	LX51FNP
17438	NS	Y438NHK	17463	NS	LX51FKZ	17488	U	LX51FMG	17513	SD	LX51FNR
17439	NS	LX51FKL	17464	NS	Y464NHK	17489	U	LX51FMJ	17514	SD	LX51FNS
17440	NS	Y522NHK	17465	NS	LX51FLB	17490	U	LX51FMK	17515	SD	LX51FNT
17441	NS	Y441NHK	17466	SD	LX51FLC	17491	U	LX51FML	17516	SD	LX51FNU
17442	NS	Y442NHK	17467	TL	LX51FLD	17492	U	LX51FMM	17517	SD	LX51FNV
17443	NS	Y443NHK	17468	TL	LX51FLE	17493	U	LX51FMO	17518	SD	LX51FNW
17444	NS	LX51FKO	17469	TL	LX51FLF	17494	U	LX51FMP	17519	SD	LX51FNY
17445	NS	Y445NHK	17470	TL	Y531NHK	17495	U	LX51FMU	17520	SD	LX51FNZ
17446	NS	Y446NHK	17471	TL	LX51FLG	17496	U	LX51FMV	17521	SD	LX51FOA
17447	NS	Y447NHK	17472	TL	LX51FLH	17497	U	LX51FMY	17522	SD	LX51FOC
17448	NS	Y448NHK	17473	TL	LX51FLJ	17498	U	LX51FMZ	17523	TL	LX51FOD
17449	NS	Y449NHK	17474	TL	LX51FLK	17499	U	LX51FNA	17524	TL	LX51FOF
17450	NS	Y524NHK	17475	TL	LX51FLL	17500	U	LX51FNC	17525	TL	LX51FOH
17451	NS	LX51FKR	17476	TL	LX51FLM	17501	U	LX51FND	17526	TL	LX51FOJ
17452	NS	Y452NHK	17477	TL	LX51FLN	17502	SD	LX51FNE	17527	TL	LX51FOK
17453	NS	Y453NHK	17478	TL	LX51FLP	17503	SD	LX51FNF	17528	TL	LX51FOM
17454	NS	Y454NHK	17479	TL	LX51FLR	17504	SD	LX51FNG	17529	TL	LX51FON
17455	NS	Y526NHK	17480	TL	LX51FLV	17505	SD	LX51FNH	17530	TL	LX51FOP
17456	NS	Y527NHK	17481	TL	LX51FLW	17506	SD	LX51FNJ	17531	TL	LX51FOT
17457	NS	LX51FKT	17482	TL	LX51FLZ	17507	SD	LX51FNK	17532	TL	LX51FOU
17458	NS	Y458NHK	17483	TL	LX51FMA	17508	SD	LX51FNL	17533	TL	LX51FOV
17459	NS	LX51FKU	17484	TL	LX51FMC	17509	SD	LX51FNM	17534	TL	LX51FPA
17460	NS	Y529NHK	17485	TL	LX51FMD	17510	SD	LX51FNN			

17535-17591 Dennis Trident 9.9m Alexander ALX400 N43/21D 2002

17535	U	LY02OAA	17550	BW	LY02OBB	17564	SD	LV52HDX	17578	TL	LV52HFL
17536	U	LY02OAB	17551	BW	LY02OBC	17565	SD	LV52HDY	17579	TL	LV52HFM
17537	BW	LY02OAC	17552	BW	LY02OBD	17566	SD	LV52HDZ	17580	TL	LV52HFN
17538	BW	LY02OAD	17553	BW	LY02OBE	17567	TL	LV52HEJ	17581	TL	LV52HFO
17539	BW	LY02OAE	17554	BW	LY02OBF	17568	TL	LV52HFU	17582	TL	LV52HFP
17540	BW	LY02OAG	17555	BW	LY02OBG	17569	TL	LV52HFA	17583	TL	LV52HFR
17541	BW	LY02OAN	17556	BW	LY02OBH	17570	TL	LV52HFB	17584	TL	LV52HFS
17542	BW	LY02OAO	17557	BW	LY02OBJ	17571	TL	LV52HFC	17585	TL	LV52HFT
17543	BW	LY02OAP	17558	BW	LY02OBK	17572	TL	LV52HFD	17586	TL	LV52HFU
17544	BW	LY02OAS	17559	BW	LY02OBL	17573	TL	LV52HFE	17587	TL	LV52HFW
17545	BW	LY02OAU	17560	BW	LY02OBM	17574	TL	LV52HFF	17588	TL	LV52HFX
17546	BW	LY02OAV	17561	TL	LV52USV	17575	TL	LV52HFH	17589	TL	LV52HFY
17547	BW	LY02OAW	17562	TL	LV52HDO	17576	TL	LV52HFJ	17590	TL	LV52HFZ
17548	BW	LY02OAX	17563	SD	LV52HDU	17577	TL	LV52HFK	17591	TL	LV52HGA
17549	BW	LY02OAZ									

17592-17611 Dennis Trident 10.5m Alexander ALX400 4.4m N51/23D 2002

17592	T	LV52HHA	17597	T	LV52HHF	17602	T	LV52HHM	17607	T	LV52HHS
17593	T	LV52HHB	17598	T	LV52HHG	17603	T	LV52HHN	17608	T	LV52HHT
17594	T	LV52HHC	17599	T	LV52HHJ	17604	T	LV52HHO	17609	T	LV52HHU
17595	T	LV52HHD	17600	T	LV52HHK	17605	T	LV52HHP	17610	T	LV52HHW
17596	T	LV52HHE	17601	T	LV52HHL	17606	T	LV52HHR	17611	T	LV52HHX

17731	SD	LV52HHY	Dennis Trident 10.5m	Alexander ALX400	N51/27D	2002
17732	SD	LV52HHZ	Dennis Trident 10.5m	Alexander ALX400	N51/27D	2002
17733	SD	LV52HJA	Dennis Trident 10.5m	Alexander ALX400	N51/27D	2002

17740-17854 TransBus Trident 10.5m TransBus ALX400 4.4m N51/27D 2003

17740	SD	LY52ZDX	17769	SD	LX03BVE	17798	T	LX03BWM	17827	T	LX03BYA
17741	SD	LY52ZDZ	17770	SD	LX03BVF	17799	T	LX03BWN	17828	T	LX03BYB
17742	SD	LY52ZFA	17771	SD	LX03BVG	17800	T	LX03BWP	17829	T	LX03BYC
17743	SD	LY52ZFB	17772	SD	LX03BVH	17801	T	LX03BWU	17830	T	LX03BYD
17744	SD	LY52ZFC	17773	SD	LX03BVJ	17802	T	LX03BWV	17831	T	LX03BYF
17745	SD	LY52ZFD	17774	SD	LX03BVK	17803	T	LX03BWW	17832	T	LX03BYG
17746	SD	LY52ZFE	17775	SD	LX03BVL	17804	T	LX03BWY	17833	T	LX03BYH
17747	SD	LY52ZFF	17776	SD	LX03BVM	17805	T	LX03BWZ	17834	U	LX03BYJ
17748	SD	LY52ZFG	17777	SD	LX03BVN	17806	T	LX03BXA	17835	U	LX03BYL
17749	SD	LY52ZFH	17778	SD	LX03BVP	17807	T	LX03BXB	17836	U	LX03BYM
17750	BW	LX03BTE	17779	T	LX03BVR	17808	T	LX03BXC	17837	U	LX03BYN
17751	BW	LX03BTF	17780	T	LX03BVS	17809	T	LX03BXD	17838	U	LX03BYP
17752	BW	LX03BTU	17781	T	LX03BVT	17810	T	LX03BXE	17839	U	LX03BYR
17753	BW	LX03BTV	17782	BW	LX03BVU	17811	T	LX03BXF	17840	U	LX03BYS
17754	BW	LX03BTY	17783	BW	LX03BVV	17812	T	LX03BXG	17841	U	LX03BYT
17755	BW	LX03BTZ	17784	BW	LX03BVW	17813	T	LX03BXH	17842	U	LX03BYU
17756	BW	LX03BUA	17785	BW	LX03BVY	17814	T	LX03BXJ	17843	U	LX03BYV
17757	BW	LX03BUE	17786	BW	LX03BVZ	17815	T	LX03BXK	17844	U	LX03BYW
17758	LNu	LX03BUF	17787	BW	LX03BWA	17816	T	LX03BXL	17845	U	LX03BYY
17759	SD	LX03BUH	17788	T	LX03BWB	17817	T	LX03BXM	17846	U	LX03BYZ
17760	SD	LX03BUJ	17789	T	LX03BWC	17818	T	LX03BXN	17847	U	LX03BZA
17761	SD	LX03BUP	17790	T	LX03BWD	17819	T	LX03BXP	17848	U	LX03BZB
17762	SD	LX03BUU	17791	T	LX03BWE	17820	T	LX03BXR	17849	U	LX03BZC
17763	SD	LX03BUV	17792	T	LX03BWF	17821	T	LX03BXS	17850	U	LX03BZD
17764	SD	LX03BUW	17793	T	LX03BWG	17822	T	LX03BXU	17851	PD	LX03BZE
17765	SD	LX03BVA	17794	T	LX03BWH	17823	T	LX03BXV	17852	PD	LX03BZF
17766	SD	LX03BVB	17795	T	LX03BWJ	17824	T	LX03BXW	17853	PD	LX03BZG
17767	SD	LX03BVC	17796	T	LX03BWK	17825	T	LX03BXY	17854	NS	LX03BZH
17768	SD	LX03BVD	17797	T	LX03BWL	17826	T	LX03BXZ			

The London Bus Handbook

Within weeks of the sale of the London operations to Macquarie Bank, a few buses appeared carrying their logos used prior to privatisation. Among recipients was TransBus Trident 17965, LX53JZH, a Bromley-based bus, which now carries the Selkent motif. It is seen on route 269 in the London Borough of Bromley while bound for Bexleyheath. *Mark Lyons*

17855-17933 TransBus Trident 10.5m TransBus ALX400 4.4m N51/27D 2003

17855	BK	LX03NEU	17876	PD	LX03NGE	17896	BK	LX03ORJ	17916	BW	LX03OSM
17856	BK	LX03NEY	17877	PD	LX03NGF	17897	BK	LX03ORK	17917	BW	LX03OSN
17857	BK	LX03NFA	17878	PD	LX03NGJ	17898	BK	LX03ORN	17918	BW	LX03OSP
17858	BK	LX03NFC	17879	BW	527CLT	17899	BK	LX03ORP	17919	BW	LX03OSR
17859	BK	LX03NFD	17880	BW	LX03NGU	17900	BK	LX03ORS	17920	BW	LX03OSU
17860	BK	LX03NFE	17881	BW	LX03NGV	17901	BK	LX03ORT	17921	BW	LX03OSV
17861	BK	LX03NFF	17882	BW	LX03NGY	17902	BK	LX03ORU	17922	BW	LX03OSW
17862	BK	LX03NFG	17883	BW	LX03NGZ	17903	U	LX03ORV	17923	BW	LX03OSY
17863	BK	LX03NFH	17884	BW	LX03NHA	17904	U	LX03ORW	17924	BW	LX03OSZ
17864	U	LX03NFJ	17885	BW	LX03OPT	17905	PD	LX03ORY	17925	BW	LX03OTA
17865	U	LX03NFK	17886	BW	LX03OPU	17906	PD	LX03ORZ	17926	BW	LX03OTB
17866	PD	LX03NFL	17887	BW	LX03OPV	17907	PD	LX03OSA	17927	BW	LX03OTC
17867	PD	LX03NFM	17888	BW	LX03OPW	17908	PD	LX03OSB	17928	BW	LX03OTD
17868	PD	LX03NFN	17889	U	LX03OPY	17909	BW	LX03OSC	17929	BW	LX03OTE
17869	PD	LX03NFP	17890	U	LX03OPZ	17910	BW	LX03OSD	17930	BW	LX03OTF
17870	PD	LX03NFR	17891	U	LX03ORA	17911	BW	LX03OSE	17931	BW	LX03OTG
17871	PD	LX03NFT	17892	BK	LX03ORC	17912	BW	LX03OSG	17932	BW	LX03OTH
17873	PD	LX03NFV	17893	BK	LX03ORF	17913	BW	LX03OSJ	17933	BW	LX03OTJ
17874	PD	LX03NFY	17894	BK	LX03ORG	17914	BW	LX03OSK			
17875	PD	LX03NFZ	17895	BK	LX03ORH	17915	BW	LX03OSL			

17934-17975 TransBus Trident 10.5m TransBus ALX400 N51/28D 2003

17934	PD	LX53JXU	17945	PD	LX53JYH	17956	PD	LX53JYW	17966	TB	LX53JZJ
17935	PD	LX53JXV	17946	PD	LX53JYJ	17957	PD	LX53JYY	17967	TB	LX53JZK
17936	PD	LX53JXW	17947	PD	LX53JYK	17958	PD	LX53JYZ	17968	TB	LX53JZL
17937	PD	LX53JXY	17948	PD	LX53JYL	17959	PD	LX53JZA	17969	TB	LX53JZM
17938	PD	LX53JYA	17949	PD	LX53JYN	17960	PD	LX53JZC	17970	TB	LX53JZN
17939	PD	LX53JYB	17950	PD	LX53JYO	17961	PD	LX53JZD	17971	TB	LX53JZO
17940	PD	LX53JYC	17951	PD	LX53JYP	17962	PD	LX53JZE	17972	TB	LX53JZP
17941	PD	LX53JYD	17952	PD	LX53JYR	17963	PD	LX53JZF	17973	TB	LX53JZR
17942	PD	LX53JYE	17953	PD	LX53JYT	17964	PD	LX53JZG	17974	TB	LX53JZT
17943	PD	LX53JYF	17954	PD	LX53JYU	17965	TB	LX53JZH	17975	TB	LX53JZU
17944	PD	LX53JYG	17955	PD	LX53JYV						

Initially built as a development vehicle for Alexander-Dennis, 18500, LX55HGC, was acquired by Stagecoach as a replacement for the Trident which was destroyed in the July 2005 bombings. Featuring the Trident 2 underframe, it was initially a development vehicle built by Alexander-Dennis as the prototype low-height Enviro400 body. This bus carries the legend *Spirit of London* to commemorate the London bombings. While the bus was earmarked to operate on route 30, occasional workings have occurred such as here on route 15 in September 2006, shortly after the Stagecoach motifs were removed. A further ten Enviro 400s are due later in December 2006. *Dave Heath*

17976-17999   TransBus Trident 9.9m   TransBus ALX400 4.4m   N43/21D   2004

17976	NS	LX53JZV	17982	NS	LX53KAU	17988	NS	LX53KBO	17994	NS	LX53KCC
17977	NS	LX53JZW	17983	NS	LX53KBE	17989	NS	LX53KBP	17995	NS	LX53KCE
17978	NS	LX53KAE	17984	NS	LX53KBF	17990	NS	LX53KBV	17996	NS	LX53KCF
17979	NS	LX53KAJ	17985	NS	LX53KBJ	17991	NS	LX53KBW	17997	NS	LX53KCG
17980	NS	LX53KAK	17986	NS	LX53KBK	17992	NS	LX53KBZ	17998	NS	LX53KCJ
17981	NS	LX53KAO	17987	NS	LX53KBN	17993	NS	LX53KCA	17999	NS	LX53KCK

18201-18265   TransBus Trident 10.5m   TransBus ALX400   N45/23D   2004

18201	BW	LX04FWL	18218	BW	LX04FXF	18234	BW	LX04FYA	18250	T	LX04FYT
18202	BW	LX04FWM	18219	BW	LX04FXG	18235	BW	LX04FYB	18251	T	LX04FYU
18203	BW	LX04FWN	18220	BW	LX04FXH	18236	BW	LX04FYC	18252	T	LX04FYV
18204	BW	LX04FWP	18221	BW	LX04FXJ	18237	BW	LX04FYD	18253	T	LX04FYW
18205	BW	LX04FWR	18222	BW	LX04FXK	18238	BW	LX04FYE	18254	T	LX04FYY
18206	BW	LX04FWS	18223	BW	LX04FXL	18239	T	LX04FYF	18255	T	LX04FYZ
18207	BW	LX04FWT	18224	BW	LX04FXM	18240	T	LX04FYG	18256	T	LX04FZA
18208	BW	LX04FWU	18225	BW	LX04FXP	18241	T	LX04FYH	18257	U	LX04FZB
18209	BW	LX04FWV	18226	BW	LX04FXR	18242	T	LX04FYK	18258	U	LX04FZC
18210	BW	LX04FWW	18227	BW	LX04FXS	18243	T	LX04FYL	18259	U	LX04FZD
18211	BW	LX04FWY	18228	BW	LX04FXT	18244	T	LX04FYM	18260	U	LX04FZE
18212	BW	LX04FWZ	18229	BW	LX04FXU	18245	T	LX04FYN	18261	U	LX04FZF
18213	BW	LX04FXA	18230	BW	LX04FXV	18246	T	LX04FYP	18262	U	LX04FZG
18214	BW	LX04FXB	18231	BW	LX04FXW	18247	T	LX04FYR	18263	U	LX04FZH
18215	BW	LX04FXC	18232	BW	LX04FXY	18248	T	LX04FYS	18264	U	LX04FZJ
18216	BW	LX04FXD	18233	BW	LX04FXZ	18249	T	LX04FYT	18265	U	LX04FZK
18217	BW	LX04FXE									

18266-18277   ADL Trident 10.5m   ADL ALX400   N51/28D   2005

18266	SD	LX05BVY	18269	SD	LX05BWB	18272	SD	LX05BWE	18275	SD	LX05BWH
18267	SD	LX05BVZ	18270	SD	LX05BWC	18273	SD	LX05BWF	18276	SD	LX05BWJ
18268	SD	LX05BWA	18271	SD	LX05BWD	18274	SD	LX05BWG	18277	SD	LX05BWK

Forty-seven Mercedes-Benz Citaro O530G (Gelenken or articulated) buses are allocated to Stratford depot for use on route 25 between Ilford and Oxford Circus. With a pvr of 42, this is one of the busiest routes in London. Seen on layover in Holles Street in August 2006, complete with the latest East London lettering, is 23044, LX04KZS. An interesting development took place in September 2006 with the sale of the first four Citaro buses from this fleet to First. *Mark Lyons*

18451-18499

		ADL Trident 10.5m		ADL ALX400			N51/28D		2005-06	
18451	NS	LX05LLM	18464	SD	LX55EPO	18476	SD	LX55ERZ	18488	TL	LX06AFY
18452	NS	LX05LLN	18465	SD	LX55EPP	18477	SD	LX55ESF	18489	TL	LX06AFZ
18453	NS	LX05LLO	18466	SD	LX55EPU	18478	SD	LX55ESG	18490	TL	LX06AGO
18454	NS	LX05LLP	18467	SD	LX55EPV	18479	SD	LX55ESN	18491	TL	LX06AGU
18455	NS	LX55EPA	18468	SD	LX55EPY	18480	SD	LX55ESO	18492	TL	LX06AGV
18456	NS	LX55EPC	18469	SD	LX55EPZ	18481	TL	LX06AFF	18493	TL	LX06AGY
18457	NS	LX55EPD	18470	SD	LX55ERJ	18482	TL	LX06AFJ	18494	TL	LX06AGZ
18458	NS	LX55EPE	18471	SD	LX55ERK	18483	TL	LX06AFK	18495	TL	LX06AHA
18459	NS	LX55EPF	18472	SD	LX55ERO	18484	TL	LX06AFN	18496	TL	LX06AHC
18460	NS	LX55EPJ	18473	SD	LX55ERU	18485	TL	LX06AFO	18497	TL	LX06AHD
18461	NS	LX55EPK	18474	SD	LX55ERV	18486	TL	LX06AFU	18498	TL	LX06AHE
18462	NS	LX55EPL	18475	SD	LX55ERY	18487	TL	LX06AFV	18499	TL	LX06AHF
18463	SD	LX55EPN									

18500	SD	LX55HGC	ADL Trident 2 10.5m		ADL Enviro 400		N51/30D	2006	ADL development vehicle

19131-19140

		ADL Trident 2 10.5m		ADL Enviro 400			N45/28D		2006	
19131	-	LX56EAF	19134	-	LX56EAK	19137	-	LX56EAP	19139	-	LX56EAY
19132	-	LX56EAG	19135	-	LX56EAM	19138	-	LX56EAW	19140	-	LX56EBA
19133	-	LX56EAJ	19136	-	LX56EAO						

23005-23035

		Mercedes-Benz Citaro O530G		Mercedes-Benz			AN49D		2003	
23005	PD	LV52VGA	23013	PD	LX03HCN	23021	PD	LX03HDE	23029	PD	LX03HDU
23006	PD	LX03HCE	23014	PD	LX03HCP	23022	PD	LX03HDF	23030	PD	LX03HDV
23007	PD	LX03HCF	23015	PD	LX03HCU	23023	PD	LX03HDG	23031	WA	LX03HDY
23008	PD	LX03HCG	23016	PD	LX03HCV	23024	PD	LX03HDH	23032	WA	LX03HDZ
23009	PD	LX03HCH	23017	PD	LX03HCY	23025	PD	LX03HDJ	23033	WA	LX03HEJ
23010	PD	LX03HCJ	23018	PD	LX03HCZ	23026	PD	LX03HDK	23034	WA	LX03HEU
23011	PD	LX03HCK	23019	PD	LX03HDC	23027	PD	LX03HDL	23035	WA	LX03HEV
23012	PD	LX03HCL	23020	PD	LX03HDD	23028	PD	LX03HDN			

A few of the Stratford-based articulated buses have gained all-over adverts. This view taken at Manor Park shows 23034, LX03HEU, advertising the University of London, en route to Oxford Circus. *Mark Lyons*

23036-23077 Mercedes-Benz Citaro O530G Mercedes-Benz AN49D 2004

23036	WA	LX04KZG	23047	WA	LX04KZV	23058	WA	LX04LBN	23068	WA	LX04LCG
23037	WA	LX04KZJ	23048	WA	LX04KZW	23059	WA	LX04LBP	23069	WA	LX04LCJ
23038	WA	LX04KZK	23049	WA	LX04KZY	23060	WA	LX04LBU	23070	WA	LX04LCK
23039	WA	LX04KZL	23050	WA	LX04KZZ	23061	WA	LX04LBV	23071	WA	LX04LCM
23040	WA	LX04KZM	23051	WA	LX04LBA	23062	WA	LX04LBY	23072	WA	LX04LCN
23041	WA	LX04KZN	23052	WA	LX04LBE	23063	WA	LX04LBZ	23073	WA	LX04LCP
23042	WA	LX04KZP	23053	WA	LX04LBF	23064	WA	LX04LCA	23074	WA	LX04LCT
23043	WA	LX04KZR	23054	WA	LX04LBG	23065	WA	LX04LCC	23075	WA	LX04LCU
23044	WA	LX04KZS	23055	WA	LX04LBJ	23066	WA	LX04LCE	23076	WA	WLT886
23045	WA	LX04KZT	23056	WA	LX04LBK	23067	WA	LX04LCF	23077	WA	VLT240
23046	WA	LX04KZU	23057	WA	LX04LBL						

34117	BK	V117MVX	Dennis Dart SLF 10.1m	Plaxton Pointer 2	N31D	1999

34147-34172 Dennis Dart SLF 9.3m Plaxton Pointer 2 N27D 1999-2000 *some N24D

34147	PD	V147MVX	34157	PD	V157MVX	34163	SD	V163MVX	34168	SD	V168MVX
34148	PD	V148MVX	34158	U	V158MVX	34164	SD	V164MVX	34169	SD	V169MVX
34149	PD	V149MVX	34159	SD	V159MVX	34165	SD	V165MVX	34170	SD	V170MVX
34150	PD	V150MVX	34161	SD	V161MVX	34166	SD	V166MVX	34171	SD	V171MVX
34152	TB	V152MVX	34162	SD	V162MVX	34167	SD	V167MVX	34172	SD	V172MVX
34156	PD	V156MVX									

34173-34203 Dennis Dart SLF 10.1m Plaxton Pointer 2 N31D 2000

34173	TL	W173DNO	34181	U	W181DNO	34188	WA	W188DNO	34196	WA	W196DNO
34174	U	W174DNO	34182	WA	W182DNO	34189	WA	W189DNO	34198	U	W198DNO
34175	U	W224DNO	34183	WA	W183DNO	34190	U	W231DNO	34199	BK	W199DNO
34176	U	W176DNO	34184	WA	W184DNO	34191	WA	W191DNO	34200	TL	W233DNO
34177	TL	W177DNO	34185	WA	W185DNO	34192	WA	W192DNO	34201	TL	W201DNO
34178	U	W178DNO	34186	WA	W186DNO	34193	WA	W193DNO	34202	BK	W202DNO
34179	U	W226DNO	34187	WA	W187DNO	34194	WA	W194DNO	34203	TL	W203DNO
34180	TL	W227DNO									

Many East London Group Darts carry their five digit numbers with a locally-applied suffix that denotes their length. The example shown here, 34367x, LV52HGD, is the short 8.8m Mini Pointer Dart version denoted by the 'x' suffix. When photographed in June 2006 at Greenwich, the vehicle was still carrying the rear coloured swirls from its time as a Stagecoach bus. *Richard Godfrey*

34204-34211

Dennis Dart SLF 9.3m   Plaxton Pointer 2   N27D   2000

34204	SD	W204DNO	34206	TB	W229DNO	34208	SD	W208DNO	34210	SD	W232DNO
34205	SD	W228DNO	34207	SD	W207DNO	34209	SD	W209DNO	34211	SD	W211DNO

34212-34223

Dennis Dart SLF 9.3m   Plaxton Pointer 2   N30F   2000

34215	PD	W215DNO	34218	TB	W218DNO	34222	PD	W236DNO	34223	PD	W223DNO
34216	PD	W216DNO	34219	TB	W219DNO						

34224-34236

Dennis Dart SLF 11.3m   Plaxton Pointer SPD   N37D*   2001   *Converting to N35D

34224	TB	X224WNO	34228	TB	X228WNO	34231	TB	X231WNO	34234	TB	X234WNO
34225	TB	X237WNO	34229	TB	X229WNO	34232	TB	X232WNO	34235	TB	X235WNO
34226	TB	X226WNO	34230	TB	X238WNO	34233	TB	X233WNO	34236	TB	X236WNO
34227	TB	X227WNO									

34237-34253

Dennis Dart SLF 9.4m   Alexander ALX200   N28F*   2001   *Converting to N26F

34237	TL	Y237FJN	34242	TL	Y242FJN	34246	TL	Y246FJN	34250	TL	Y349FJN
34238	TL	Y238FJN	34243	TL	Y243FJN	34247	TL	Y247FJN	34251	TL	Y251FJN
34239	TL	Y239FJN	34244	TL	Y244FJN	34248	PD	Y248FJN	34252	TL	Y252FJN
34240	PD	Y347FJN	34245	TL	Y348FJN	34249	TL	Y249FJN	34253	TL	Y253FJN
34241	TL	Y241FJN									

34254-34272

Dennis Dart SLF 10.2m   Alexander ALX200   N30D   2001

34254	BK	Y254FJN	34259	BK	Y259FJN	34264	BK	Y264FJN	34269	BK	Y269FJN
34255	BK	Y351FJN	34260	BK	Y352FJN	34265	BK	Y265FJN	34270	BK	Y353FJN
34256	BK	Y256FJN	34261	BK	Y261FJN	34266	BK	Y266FJN	34271	BK	Y271FJN
34257	BK	Y257FJN	34262	BK	Y262FJN	34267	BK	Y267FJN	34272	BK	Y272FJN
34258	BK	Y258FJN	34263	BK	Y263FJN	34268	BK	Y268FJN			

This Stratford-based Dart is one from a batch of 10.8m examples delivered in 2001. When this picture was taken in September 2006, 34335, Y335FJN, had recently undergone a repaint and its rear swirls had been removed, but it still retained the permitted blue skirt. Many of the earlier ALX200 buses have been transferred to Stagecoach provincial fleets in recent years. *Colin Lloyd*

34273-34327

			Dennis Dart SLF 10.2m			Alexander ALX200			N30D		2001
34273	BK	Y273FJN	34287	BK	Y287FJN	34301	BK	Y301FJN	34315	TL	LX51FGU
34274	BK	Y274FJN	34288	BK	Y671JSG	34302	BK	Y302FJN	34316	TL	LX51FGZ
34275	BK	Y354FJN	34289	BK	Y289FJN	34303	TL	LX51FGA	34317	TL	LX51FHG
34276	BK	Y276FJN	34290	BK	LX51FFW	34304	TL	LX51FGF	34318	TL	LX51FHB
34277	BK	Y277FJN	34291	BK	Y291FJN	34305	TL	LX51FGE	34319	TL	LX51FHA
34278	BK	LX51FPE	34292	BK	Y292FJN	34306	TL	LX51FGD	34320	TL	LX51FHC
34279	BK	Y279FJN	34293	BK	Y293FJN	34307	TL	LX51FGG	34321	TL	LX51FHD
34280	BK	Y356FJN	34294	BK	Y294FJN	34308	TL	LX51FGM	34322	TL	LX51FHE
34281	BK	Y281FJN	34295	BK	Y295FJN	34309	TL	LX51FGK	34323	TL	LX51FHF
34282	BK	Y282FJN	34296	BK	Y296FJN	34310	TL	LX51FGV	34324	TL	LX51FHK
34283	BK	Y283FJN	34297	BK	Y297FJN	34311	TL	LX51FGJ	34325	TL	LX51FHL
34284	BK	Y284FJN	34298	BK	Y298FJN	34312	TL	LX51FGN	34326	TL	LX51FHH
34285	BK	Y285FJN	34299	BK	Y299FJN	34313	TL	LX51FGO	34327	TL	LX51FHJ
34286	BK	Y286FJN	34300	BK	LX51FPJ	34314	TL	LX51FGP			

34328-34346

			Dennis Dart SLF 10.8m			Alexander ALX200			N33D		2001
34328	SD	Y371FJN	34333	SD	Y373FJN	34338	SD	Y338FJN	34343	SD	Y343FJN
34329	SD	Y329FJN	34334	SD	Y334FJN	34339	SD	Y339FJN	34344	SD	Y344FJN
34330	SD	Y372FJN	34335	SD	Y335FJN	34340	SD	Y374FJN	34345	SD	Y376FJN
34331	SD	Y331FJN	34336	SD	Y336FJN	34341	SD	LX51FFO	34346	SD	Y346FJN
34332	SD	Y332FJN	34337	SD	Y337FJN	34342	SD	Y342FJN			

34347-34365

			Dennis Dart SLF 10.2m			Plaxton Pointer 2			N30D		2002
34347	BK	LV52HJY	34352	BK	LV52HKD	34357	TB	LV52HKJ	34362	TB	LV52HKO
34348	BK	LV52HJZ	34353	BK	LV52HKE	34358	TB	LV52HKK	34363	TB	LV52HKP
34349	BK	LV52HKA	34354	TB	LV52HKF	34359	TB	LV52HKL	34364	TB	LV52HKT
34350	BK	LV52HKB	34355	TB	LV52HKG	34360	TB	LV52HKM	34365	TB	LV52HKU
34351	BK	LV52HKC	34356	TB	LV52HKH	34361	TB	LV52HKN			

Unusually, the 'm' suffix is not carried on this Barking-based Dart. The 'm' applies to the 10.1m examples and 34350, LV52HKB, is seen outside Barking station in March 2006. This is one of the batch of nineteen medium length TransBus Darts delivered during 2002. Due in December 2006 are the first Darts for the group with engines that meet the Euro 4 emission regulations and these will start a new number series within the Stagecoach system, at 36001. *Colin Lloyd*

34366-34376

Dennis Dart SLF 8.8m   Plaxton Pointer 2   N28F   2003

34366	PD	LV52HGC	34369	PD	LV52HGF	34372	PD	LV52HGK	34375	PD	LV52HGN
34367	PD	LV52HGD	34370	PD	LV52HGG	34373	PD	LV52HGL	34376	PD	LV52HGO
34368	PD	LV52HGE	34371	PD	LV52HGJ	34374	PD	LV52HGM			

34377-34386

TransBus Dart SLF 9.3m   Transbus Pointer   N30F   2003

34377	PD	LX03BZJ	34380	PD	LX03BZM	34383	PD	LX03BZR	34385	PD	LX03BZT
34378	PD	LX03BZK	34381	PD	LX03BZN	34384	PD	LX03BZS	34386	PD	LX03BZU
34379	PD	LX03BZL	34382	PD	LX03BZP						

34387-34397

TransBus Dart SLF 10.2m   TransBus Pointer   N31D   2003

34387	TL	LX03BZV	34390	TL	LX03CAA	34393	TL	LX03CAV	34396	TL	LX03CBV
34388	TL	LX03BZW	34391	TL	LX03CAE	34394	TL	LX03CBF	34397	TL	LX03CBY
34389	TL	LX03BZY	34392	TL	LX03CAU	34395	TL	LX03CBU			

34551-34560

TransBus Dart SLF 10.2m   TransBus Pointer   N31D   2003

34551	PD	LX53LGF	34554	PD	LX53LGK	34557	PD	LX53LGO	34559	PD	LX53LGV
34552	PD	LX53LGG	34555	PD	LX53LGL	34558	PD	LX53LGU	34560	PD	LX53LGW
34553	PD	LX53LGJ	34556	PD	LX53LGN						

36001-36008

ADL Dart E200 8.8m   ADL Enviro 200   N29F   2006

36001	-	LX56DZU	36003	-	LX56DZW	36005	-	LX56DZZ	36007	-	LX56EAC
36002	-	LX56DZV	36004	-	LX56DZY	36006	-	LX56EAA	36008	-	LX56EAE

52217	WA	SYC852	Volvo B10M-62	Plaxton Première 350	C53F	1995
52219	WA	CSU992	Volvo B10M-62	Plaxton Première 350	C53F	1995
52604	WA	S134KRM	Volvo B10M-62	Jonckheere Mistral 50	C44FT	1998
52615	WA	S905JHG	Volvo B10M-62	Jonckheere Mistral 50	C46FT	1998
52616	WA	S906JHG	Volvo B10M-62	Jonckheere Mistral 50	C46FT	1998

One of a trio of Special Event buses operated by East London is the last Routemaster built, 12760, SMK760F, which displays its original London Transport number RML2760. It is seen in its Heritage livery on route 15. *Mark Lyons*

Special Event vehicles:

10001	WA	THX401S	Leyland Titan TNLXB2RRSp	Park Royal	B44/26D	1978	*displays T1*
12665	WA	SMK665F	AEC Routemaster R2RH1	Park Royal	B40/32R	1968	*displays RML2665*
12760	WA	SMK760F	AEC Routemaster R2RH1	Park Royal	B40/32R	1968	*displays RML2760*

Ancillary vehicles:

26001	NSt	J401LKO	DAF SB220LC550	Optare Delta	TV	1991
26003	TBt	J403LKO	DAF SB220LC550	Optare Delta	TV	1991

26011-26034

			DAF SB220LC550	Optare Delta	TV	1992-93

26011	TBt	J711CYG	**26024**	TBt	J724CYG	**26029**	Ut	J729CYG	**26034**	PDt	K634HWX
26016	TLt	J716CYG									

28615-28630

		Scania N113CRL		Wright Pathfinder 320	N37D	1994

28615	PDt	RDZ6115	**28619**	Ut	RDZ6119	**28623**	TBt	RDZ6123	**28627**	BKt	RDZ6127
28616	Ut	RDZ6116	**28620**	TLt	RDZ6120	**28624**	BKt	RDZ6124	**28628**	WAt	RDZ6128
28617	PDt	RDZ6117	**28621**	Ut	RDZ6121	**28625**	NSt	RDZ6125	**28629**	BKt	RDZ6129
28618	Ut	RDZ6118	**28622**	TLt	RDZ6122	**28626**	BKt	RDZ6126	**28630**	WAt	RDZ6130

Previous registrations:

527CLT	LX03NGN		WLT461	V475KJN
CSU992	M409BFG		WLT491	V474KJN
SYC852	M407BFG		WLT575	X374NNO
VLT14	V473KJN		WLT886	LX04LCV
VLT240	LX04LCW			

The London Bus Handbook

Depots and allocations:

Barking (Longbridge Road) - BK

Trident	17064	17065	17080	17106	17210	17211	17212	17213
	17261	17262	17263	17264	17265	17266	17267	17269
	17270	17271	17272	17273	17274	17275	17296	17359
	17360	17361	17362	17363	17364	17365	17366	17367
	17368	17370	17371	17372	17373	17374	17375	17376
	17377	17378	17379	17380	17381	17382	17383	17384
	17385	17386	17387	17388	17389	17390	17391	17392
	17393	17394	17855	17856	17857	17858	17859	17860
	17861	17862	17863	17892	17893	17894	17895	17896
	17897	17898	17899	17900	17901	17902		
Dart SLF	34173	34177	34180	34199	34200	34201	34202	34254
	34255	34256	34257	34258	34259	34260	34261	34262
	34263	34264	34265	34266	34267	34268	34269	34270
	34271	34272	34273	34274	34275	34276	34277	34278
	34279	34280	34281	34282	34283	34284	34285	34286
	34287	34288	34289	34290	34291	34292	34293	34294
	34295	34296	34297	34298	34299	34300	34301	34302
	34347	34348	34349	34350	34351	34352	34353	
Ancillary	28624	28626	28627	28629				

Bow (Fairfield Road) - BW

Trident	17430	17431	17432	17433	17434	17435	17558	17750
	17751	17752	17753	17754	17755	17756	17757	17782
	17783	17784	17785	17786	17787	17879	17880	17881
	17882	17883	17884	17885	17886	17887	17888	17909
	17911	17912	17913	17914	17915	17916	17917	17918
	17919	17920	17921	17922	17923	17924	17925	17926
	17927	17928	17929	17930	17931	17932	17933	18201
	18202	18203	18204	18205	18206	18207	18208	18209
	18210	18211	18212	18213	18214	18215	18216	18217
	18218	18219	18220	18221	18222	18223	18224	18225
	18226	18227	18228	18229	18230	18231	18232	18233
	18234	18235	18236	18237	18238	18266	18267	18268
	18269	18270	18271	18272	18273	18274	18275	18276
	18277							

Bromley (Hastings Road) - TB

Olympian	16122	16123						
Trident	17279	17280	17281	17282	17283	17284	17285	17286
	17287	17288	17289	17290	17324	17334	17335	17336
	17337	17338	17339	17340	17341	17342	17343	17344
	17345	17346	17347	17348	17349	17351	17352	17353
	17354	17355	17356	17357	17358	17965	17966	17967
	17968	17969	17970	17971	17972	17973	17974	17975
Dart SLF	34224	34225	34226	34227	34228	34229	34230	34231
	34232	34233	34234	34235	34236	34310	34311	34312
	34354	34355	34356	34357	34358	34359	34360	34361
	34362	34363	34364	34365				
Ancillary	26003	26011	26024	28623				

Driver training buses with East London are now mainly in the hands of Wright-bodied Scanias, although a few Optare Delta trainers remain. Green liveried 26003, J403LKO, shows the eye-catching Learn & Earn logos. It is still carrying its former fleet number which is a rare instance within London having been acquired from a provincial operator, in this case, Stagecoach South East. *Colin Lloyd*

Catford (Bromley Road) - TL

Trident	17152	17154	17155	17156	17157	17225	17317	17318
	17319	17320	17321	17322	17323	17325	17326	17327
	17328	17329	17330	17331	17332	17333	17350	17467
	17468	17469	17470	17471	17472	17473	17474	17475
	17476	17477	17478	17479	17480	17481	17482	17483
	17484	17485	17523	17524	17525	17526	17527	17528
	17529	17530	17531	17532	17533	17534	17561	17562
	17567	17568	17569	17570	17571	17572	17573	17574
	17575	17576	17577	17578	17579	17580	17581	17582
	17583	17584	17585	17586	17587	17588	17589	17590
	17591	18481	18482	18483	18484	18485	18486	18487
	18488	18489	18490	18491	18492	18493	18494	18495
	18496	18497	18498	18499				
Dart	34237	34238	34239	34241	34242	34243	34244	34245
	34246	34247	34249	34250	34251	34252	34253	34313
	34314	34315	34316	34317	34318	34319	34320	34321
	34322	34323	34324	34325	34326	34327	34387	34388
	34389	34390	34391	34392	34393	34394	34395	34396
	34397	34551	34552	34553	34554	34555	34556	34557
	34558	34559	34560					
Ancillary	26016	28620	28622					

The London Bus Handbook

Leyton (High Road) - T

Trident

17001	17158	17181	17182	17183	17184	17185	17186
17187	17188	17189	17190	17191	17409	17410	17411
17412	17413	17414	17415	17416	17417	17418	17419
17420	17421	17422	17423	17424	17425	17426	17427
17592	17593	17594	17595	17596	17597	17598	17599
17600	17601	17602	17603	17604	17605	17606	17607
17608	17609	17610	17611	17779	17780	17781	17788
17789	17790	17791	17792	17793	17794	17795	17796
17797	17798	17799	17800	17801	17802	17803	17804
17805	17806	17807	17808	17809	17810	17811	17812
17813	17814	17815	17816	17817	17818	17819	17820
17821	17822	17823	17824	17825	17826	17827	17828
17829	17830	17831	17832	17833	18239	18240	18241
18242	18243	18244	18245	18246	18247	18248	18249
18250	18251	18252	18253	18254	18255	18256	

Plumstead (Pettman Crescent) - PD

Trident

17099	17100	17101	17102	17103	17104	17105	17107
17108	17109	17110	17112	17113	17115	17116	17117
17118	17119	17120	17121	17122	17123	17125	17126
17127	17128	17130	17131	17133	17134	17138	17140
17141	17142	17143	17145	17148	17149	17150	17151
17153	17159	17161	17162	17163	17164	17166	17193
17195	17214	17215	17216	17217	17218	17221	17222
17276	17277	17278	17302	17303	17304	17305	17306
17307	17308	17309	17310	17311	17312	17313	17314
17315	17316	17851	17852	17853	17866	17867	17868
17869	17870	17871	17873	17874	17875	17876	17877
17878	17905	17906	17907	17908	17934	17935	17936
17937	17938	17939	17940	17941	17942	17943	17944
17945	17946	17947	17948	17949	17950	17951	17952
17953	17954	17955	17956	17957	17958	17959	17960
17961	17962	17963	17964				

Only five Olympians remain with Selkent and East London, two for special contracts from Bromley depot and three for private hire duties based at Stratford. The latter are represented here by 16001, P801GMU, seen in Parliament Square in June 2006 the modified livery used by Stagecoach London. *Colin Lloyd*

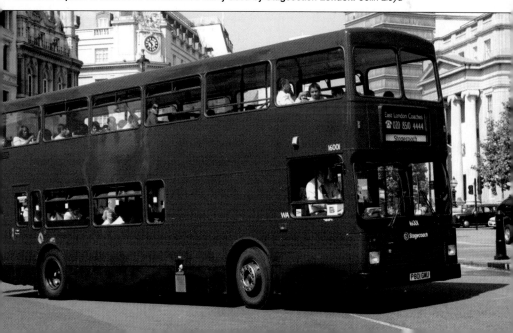

Citaro Artic	23005	23006	23007	23008	23009	23010	23011	23012
	23013	23014	23015	23016	23017	23018	23019	23020
	23021	23022	23023	23024	23025	23026	23027	23028
	23029	23030						
Dart SLF	34147	34148	34149	34150	34152	34156	34157	34206
	34222	34223	34240	34248	34366	34367	34368	34369
	34370	34371	34372	34373	34377	34378	34379	34380
	34381	34382	34383	34384	34385	34386		
Ancillary	26034	28615	28617					

Romford (North Street) - NS

Trident	17114	17124	17132	17135	17136	17137	17144	17192
	17194	17223	17224	17230	17235	17236	17237	17268
	17300	17301	17428	17429	17436	17437	17438	17439
	17440	17441	17442	17443	17444	17445	17446	17447
	17448	17449	17450	17451	17452	17453	17454	17455
	17456	17457	17458	17459	17460	17461	17462	17463
	17464	17465	17537	17538	17539	17540	17541	17542
	17543	17544	17854	17976	17977	17978	17979	17980
	17981	17982	17983	17984	17985	17986	17987	17988
	17989	17990	17991	17992	17993	17994	17995	17996
	17997	17998	17999	18451	18452	18453	18454	18455
	18456	18457	18458	18459	18460	18461	18462	
Dart	34303	34304	34305	34306	34308	34309		
Ancillary	26001	28625						

Stratford (Stability Works, Waterden Road) - SD

Trident	17111	17160	17167	17168	17169	17170	17171	17172
	17173	17174	17175	17176	17177	17178	17179	17180
	17196	17197	17198	17199	17200	17201	17202	17239
	17240	17241	17242	17244	17245	17246	17292	17293
	17294	17295	17297	17298	17299	17395	17396	17397
	17398	17399	17400	17401	17403	17404	17405	17406
	17407	17408	17466	17486	17502	17503	17504	17505
	17506	17507	17508	17509	17510	17511	17512	17513
	17514	17515	17516	17517	17518	17519	17520	17521
	17522	17559	17560	17563	17564	17565	17566	17731
	17732	17733	17740	17741	17742	17743	17744	17745
	17746	17747	17748	17749	17759	17760	17761	17762
	17763	17764	17765	17766	17767	17768	17769	17770
	17771	17772	17773	17774	17775	17776	17777	17778
	18463	18464	18465	18466	18467	18468	18469	18470
	18471	18472	18473	18474	18475	18476	18477	18478
	18479	18480						
Enviro 400	18500							
Dart SLF	34159	34161	34162	34163	34164	34165	34166	34167
	34168	34169	34170	34171	34172	34204	34205	34207
	34208	34209	34210	34211	32328	32329	32330	32331
	32332	32333	32334	32335	32336	32337	32338	32339
	32340	32341	32342	32343	32344	32345	32346	

The London Bus Handbook

Stratford (44 Waterden Road) - WA

Routemaster	12024	12052	12071	12133	12141	12168	12250	12260
	12271	12289						
Titan	10001							
Olympian	16001	16002	16003					
Citaro Artic	23031	23032	23033	23034	23035	23036	23037	23038
	23039	23040	23041	23042	23043	23044	23045	23046
	23047	23048	23049	23050	23051	23052	23053	23054
	23055	23056	23057	23058	23059	23060	23061	23062
	23063	23064	23065	23066	23067	23068	23069	23070
	23071	23072	23073	23074	23075	23076	23077	
Dart	34182	34183	34184	34185	34186	34187	34188	34189
	34191	34192	34193	34194	34195	34196		
Volvo B10M coach	52217	52219	52604	52615	52616			
Ancillary	28616	28618	28619	28624	28628	28630		

Upton Park (Redclyffe Road) - U

Trident	17082	17083	17084	17085	17086	17087	17088	17089
	17090	17091	17092	17093	17094	17095	17096	17097
	17098	17129	17147	17165	17203	17204	17205	17206
	17207	17208	17209	17219	17220	17234	17243	17247
	17248	17249	17250	17251	17252	17253	17254	17255
	17256	17257	17258	17259	17260	17291	17487	17488
	17489	17490	17491	17492	17493	17494	17495	17496
	17497	17498	17499	17500	17501	17535	17536	17834
	17835	17836	17837	17838	17839	17840	17841	17842
	17843	17844	17845	17846	17847	17848	17849	17850
	17864	17865	17889	17890	17891	17903	17904	18257
	18258	18259	18260	18261	18262	18263	18264	18265
Dart	34133	34158	34174	34175	34176	34178	34179	34181
	34190	34198						
Ancillary	26029	28616	28618	28619	28621			

One of the early recipients of the Selkent name is Mercedes-Benz Citaro 23025, LX03HDJ, seen approaching Westminster Bridge. *Mark Lyons*

EAST THAMES BUSES

London Buses Ltd, 172 Buckingham Palace Road, Victoria, SW1W 9TN

DC15	BV	T553HNH	Dennis Dart SLF 8.8m	Plaxton Pointer MPD	N26F	1999

DW1-12
DAF SB120 — Wrightbus Cadet 2 — N23D — 2003

1	MA	LF52TKJ	4	MA	LF52TJY	7	MA	LF52TKO	10	MA	LF52TKE
2	MA	LF52TKC	5	MA	LF52TJV	8	MA	LF52TKK	11	MA	LF52TKN
3	MA	LF52TKD	6	MA	LF52TJX	9	MA	LF52TKT	12	MA	LF52TKA

DWL13-37
VDL Bus SB120 10.8m — Wrightbus Merit — N30D — 2004

13	MA	BX04BXP	20	MA	FJ54ZDU	26	BV	FJ54ZFA	32	BV	FJ54ZUA
14	MA	BX04BXL	21	MA	FJ54ZDV	27	BV	FJ54ZTU	33	BV	FJ54ZUC
15	MA	BX04BXM	22	BV	FJ54ZDW	28	BV	FJ54ZTW	34	BV	FJ54ZUD
16	MA	BX04BXN	23	BV	FJ54ZDX	29	BV	FJ54ZTX	35	BV	FJ54ZVA
17	MA	FJ54ZDR	24	BV	FJ54ZDY	30	BV	FJ54ZTY	36	BV	FJ54ZVB
18	MA	FJ54ZDP	25	BV	FJ54ZDZ	31	BV	FJ54ZTZ	37	BV	FJ54ZDC
19	MA	FJ54ZDT									

ELS1-14
Scania N94UB 10.6m — East Lancashire Myllennium — N32D — 2002

1	MA	YU02GHG	5	MA	YU02GHD	9	MA	YR52VFJ	12	MA	YR52VFL
2	MA	YU02GHH	6	MA	YU02GHA	10	MA	YR52VFH	13	MA	YR52VFM
3	MA	YU02GHJ	7	MA	YU02GHN	11	MA	YR52VFK	14	MA	YR52VFN
4	MA	YU02GHK	8	MA	YU02GHO						

Fourteen East Lancs-bodied Scanias were delivered to East Thames Buses in 2002 for route 42 that links Denmark Hill with Liverpool Street. However, here we see ELS8, YU02GHO, at the Elephant & Castle in April 2006 unusually on route 1 which is normally double-deck operated. *Colin Lloyd*

Delivered new to East Thames in 2004, VWL34, BX04AZU, shows to great effect the all-red livery which is now the standard requirement on all new and repainted buses on TfL tendered routes. Lewisham is the backdrop to this Wrightbus Eclipse Gemini-bodied Volvo B7TL seen on route 180. *Mark Lyons*

VP1-20

Volvo B7TL 10m — Plaxton President — N41/23D — 2001 — Easylink, 2003

1	BV	X149FBB	6	BV	X157FBB	11	BV	X163FBB	16	BV	X168FBB
2	BV	X151FBB	7	BV	X158FBB	12	BV	X164FBB	17	BV	X169FBB
3	BV	X152FBB	8	BV	X159FBB	13	BV	X165FBB	18	BV	X171FBB
4	BV	X153FBB	9	BV	X161FBB	14	BV	X166FBB	19	BV	X172FBB
5	BV	X154FBB	10	BV	X162FBB	15	BV	X167FBB	20	BV	X173FBB

VWL1-31

Volvo B7TL 10.6m — Wrightbus Eclipse Gemini — N43/23D — 2002

1	MA	LB02YWX	10	MA	LB02YXH	18	MA	LB02YXH	25	BV	LF52THN
2	MA	LB02YWY	11	MA	LB02YXJ	19	MA	LF52TGV	26	BV	LF52THU
3	MA	LB02YWZ	12	MA	LB02YXK	20	MA	LF52TGX	27	BV	LF52THV
4	MA	LB02YXA	13	MA	LB02YXL	21	MA	LF52TGY	28	BV	LF52THX
6	MA	LB02YXD	14	MA	LB02YXM	22	MA	LF52TGZ	29	BV	LF52THZ
7	MA	LB02YXE	15	MA	LB02YXN	23	MA	LF52THG	30	BV	LF52TJO
8	MA	LB02YXF	16	MA	LF52TGN	24	BV	LF52THK	31	BV	LF52TJU
9	MA	LB02YXG	17	MA	LF52TGO						

VWL32-44

Volvo B7TL 10.6m — Wrightbus Eclipse Gemini — N43/23D — 2004

32	BV	BX04AZW	36	BV	BX04BAA	39	BV	BX04BBE	42	BV	BX04BKL
33	BV	BX04AZV	37	BV	BX04BAU	40	BV	BX04BBF	43	BV	BX04BKK
34	BV	BX04AZU	38	BV	BX04BAV	41	BV	BX04BBJ	44	BV	BX04BKJ
35	BV	BX04AZZ									

Ancillary vehicles:

DC16	MA	JDZ2407	Dennis Dart 9m	Wright Handybus	Staff	1990	London United, 2002
DC17	MA	JDZ2408	Dennis Dart 9m	Wright Handybus	Staff	1990	London United, 2002
317	MA	OJD831Y	MCW Metrobus DR101/16	MCW	TV	1983	London United, 2001
318	MA	OJD832Y	MCW Metrobus DR101/16	MCW	TV	1983	London United, 2001
M1010	BV	A710THV	MCW Metrobus DR101/18	MCW	Staff	1984	London United, 2001

Depots and allocations:

Belvedere (Burt's Wharf, Crabtree Manorway North) - BV

Dart	DC15							
DAF/VDL SB120	DWL22	DWL23	DWL24	DWL25	DWL26	DWL27	DWL28	DWL29
	DWL30	DWL31	DWL32	DWL33	DWL34	DWL35	DWL36	DWL37
Volvo B7TL	VP1	VP2	VP3	VP4	VP5	VP6	VP7	VP8
	VP9	VP10	VP11	VP12	VP13	VP14	VP15	VP16
	VP17	VP18	VP19	VP20	VWL24	VWL25	VWL26	VWL27
	VWL28	VWL29	VWL30	VWL31	VWL32	VWL33	VWL34	VWL35
	VWL36	VWL37	VWL38	VWL39	VWL40	VWL41	VWL42	VWL43
	VWL44							
Ancillary	M1010							

Southwark (Mandela Way) - MA

Dart	DC16	DC17						
DAF/VDL SB120	DW1	DW2	DW3	DW4	DW5	DW6	DW7	DW8
	DW9	DW10	DW11	DW12	DWL13	DWL14	DWL15	DWL16
	DWL17	DWL18	DWL19	DWL20	DWL21			
Scania N94	ELS1	ELS2	ELS3	ELS4	ELS5	ELS6	ELS7	ELS8
	ELS9	ELS10	ELS11	ELS12	ELS13	ELS14		
Volvo B7TL	VWL1	VWL2	VWL3	VWL4	VWL5	VWL6	VWL7	VWL8
	VWL9	VWL10	VWL11	VWL12	VWL13	VWL14	VWL15	VWL16
	VWL17	VWL18	VWL19	VWL20	VWL21	VWL22	VWL23	
Ancillary	DC16	DC17	317	318				

The DWL class operated by East Thames is based on the VDL Bus SB120 chassis, the successor to the DAF SB120 model. These vehicles carry the longer Wrightbus Cadet 2 10.8m bodywork, which when sold by Volvo is marketed as the Merit. Here, DWL15, BX04BXN, is pictured at Stratford in August 2005 while showing the destination Lewisham on route 108. This remains the only bus route to pass beneath the River Thames using the Blackwall Tunnel. *Colin Lloyd*

P & J ELLIS Ltd.

P & J Ellis Ltd, 3 Radford Estate, Old Oak Lane, North Acton, London, NW10 6UA

FL02ZXR	Volvo B12M	Jonckheere Mistral 50	C51FT	2002
FL02ZXT	Volvo B12M	Jonckheere Mistral 50	C51FT	2002
FJ03ABU	Volvo B12M	Jonckheere Mistral 50	C51FT	2003
FJ03ACU	Volvo B12M	Jonckheere Mistral 50	C51FT	2003
FJ03ACY	Volvo B12M	Jonckheere Mistral 50	C51FT	2003
FP53JYO	Volvo B12M	Jonckheere Mistral 50	C53F	2004
FJ04ERK	Volvo B12B	VDL Jonckheere Mistral 50	C51FT	2004
FJ04ERU	Volvo B12B	VDL Jonckheere Mistral 50	C51FT	2004
FJ04ETZ	Volvo B12B	VDL Jonckheere Mistral 50	C51FT	2004
YJ04HHS	VDL Bus SB4000XF	Van Hool T9 Alizée	C49FT	2004
FJ05AOA	Volvo B12B	VDL Jonckheere Mistral 50	C51FT	2005
FJ05AOB	Volvo B12B	VDL Jonckheere Mistral 50	C51FT	2005
FJ06BOF	Volvo B12B	VDL Jonckheere Mistral 50	C53F	2006
FJ06BOH	Volvo B12B	VDL Jonckheere Mistral 50	C53F	2006

Web: www.pjellis.co.uk

Since the last edition of this Handbook, the P & J Ellis fleet has seen significant changes with nine new vehicles acquired while seven have departed. With the exception of one Van Hool bodied VDL Bus SB4000, all the new coaches have been further Jonckheere Mistrals. August 2005 finds FJ05AOA in Trafalgar Square. *Colin Lloyd*

EPSOM COACHES

Epsom Coaches - Quality Line

H R Richmond Ltd, Blenheim Road, Epsom, KT19 9AF

Quality Line

MB16	QL	S452LGN	Mercedes-Benz Vario 0814	Plaxton Beaver 2	B27F	1998

MCL1-7 — Mercedes-Benz O530 — Mercedes-Benz Citaro — N38D — 2003

1	QL	BW03ZMZ	3	QL	BU53AXA	5	QL	BU53AWX	7	QL	BW03ZMY
2	QL	BU53AWZ	4	QL	BU53AWY	6	QL	BU53AWW			

OP1-11 — Optare Solo M850 — Optare — N28F — 2002

1	QL	YE52FHH	4	QL	YE52FHL	7	QL	YE52FHO	10	QL	YE52FHS
2	QL	YE52FHJ	5	QL	YE52FHM	8	QL	YE52FHP	11	QL	YE52FGU
3	QL	YE52FHK	6	QL	YE52FHN	9	QL	YE52FHR			

OP12	QL	YN03ZXF	Optare Solo M850	Optare	N28F	2003
OP13	QL	YN53SWF	Optare Solo M850	Optare	N28F	2003

OP14-21 — Optare Solo M850 — Optare — N28F — 2004

14	QL	YN53SUF	16	QL	YN53SVL	18	QL	YN53SVP	20	QL	YN53ZXA
15	QL	YN53SVK	17	QL	YN53SVO	19	QL	YN53SVR	21	QL	YN53ZXB

SD1	QL	K321GEW	Dennis Dart 9.8m	Marshall C27	B40F	1993	
SD13	QL	S459LGN	Dennis Dart SLF 8.8m	Plaxton Pointer MPD	N29F	1998	
SD14	QL	S460LGN	Dennis Dart SLF 8.8m	Plaxton Pointer MPD	N29F	1998	
SD18	QL	S464LGN	Dennis Dart SLF 8.8m	Plaxton Pointer MPD	N29F	1998	
SD22	QL	V943DNB	Dennis Dart SLF 8.8m	Plaxton Pointer MPD	N29F	2000	Safeguard, Guildford, 2001

SD23-28 — Dennis Dart SLF 8.9m — Alexander ALX200 — N28F — 2000

23	QL	W871VGT	25	QL	W873VGT	27	QL	W875VGT	28	QL	W876VGT
24	QL	W872VGT	26	QL	W874VGT						

There are now no Volvo coaches and only one Dennis remaining in the Epsom fleet because, since 2002, the company has chosen new Setra integral coaches. Here the remaining Javelin GX 808, T808TGP, is seen passing along Buckingham Palace Road in Victoria while on a Terravision working (route A50) from Stansted Airport. *Colin Lloyd*

Pictured in North Cheam is Epsom's SD42, PL05PLX. The bus is a 9-metre ADL Dart fitted with East Lancs Myllennium Spryte bodywork. The company use the Quality Line logo for its bus services. *Mark Lyons*

SD29-36

											Dennis Dart SLF 8.9m		Alexander ALX200	N29F	2002	

| 29 | QL | SN51UCM | **31** | QL | SN51UCH | **33** | QL | SN51UCO | **35** | QL | SN51UCR |
| 30 | QL | SN51UCL | **32** | QL | SN51UCJ | **34** | QL | SN51UCP | **36** | QL | SN51UCS |

SD37	QL	T76JBA		Dennis Dart SLF 8.8m		Plaxton Pointer MPD	N29F	1999	Redby, Sunderland, 2002

SD38-42

						ADL Dart 9m		East Lancs Myllennium	N26F	2005

| **38** | QL | PL05PLN | **40** | QL | PL05PLU | **41** | QL | PL05PLV | **42** | QL | PL05PLX |
| **39** | QL | PL05PLO | | | | | | | | | |

Epsom Coaches

4	EC	HY06CJO	Ford Excursion	Executive Coachbuilders	M13	2006
406	EC	LB51OCL	Volkswagen Caravelle	Volkswagen	M8	2001
502	EC	A9HRR	Iveco EuroMidi CC80E	Indcar Maxim	C27F	2000
601	EC	LX06FFA	Mercedes-Benz Sprinter 413cdi	Mercedes-Benz	M16	2006
602	EC	LX06FFB	Mercedes-Benz Sprinter 413cdi	Mercedes-Benz	M16	2006
716	EC	BU04EXV	Setra S315 GT-HD	Setra	C53F	2004
717	EC	BU04EXW	Setra S315 GT-HD	Setra	C53F	2004
718	EC	BU04EXX	Setra S315 GT-HD	Setra	C53F	2004
719	EC	BX54ECF	Setra S315 GT-HD	Setra	C53F	2005
720	EC	BX54ECJ	Setra S315 GT-HD	Setra	C53F	2005
808	EC	T808TGP	Dennis Javelin GX	Berkhof Axial 50	C49FT	1999
811	EC	BX02CMO	Setra S315 GT-HD	Setra	C49FT	2002
812	EC	BX02CMU	Setra S315 GT-HD	Setra	C49FT	2002
813	EC	BU53ZWN	Setra S315 GT-HD	Setra	C48FT	2004
814	EC	BU53ZWP	Setra S315 GT-HD	Setra	C48FT	2004
815	EC	BU53ZWR	Setra S315 GT-HD	Setra	C48FT	2004
816	EC	BU04EXT	Setra S315 GT-HD	Setra	C48FT	2004
901	EC	BU06CSF	Setra S416 GT-HD	Setra	C49FT	2006
902	EC	BU06CSO	Setra S416 GT-HD	Setra	C49FT	2006

Previous registration:

A9HRR	W813AAY

Web: www.epsomcoaches.com
On order: Eleven Alexander-Dennis E200s with East Lancs Esteem bodywork (SD43/4 9m; SD45-53 9.3m)
Depot: Blenheim Road, Epsom

EXCALIBUR

Excalibur - Phoenix

Excalibur Coach Company Ltd; Phoenix Travel (London) Ltd, 709 Old Kent Road, New Cross, SE15 1JS

P	F137FCC	Volvo B10M-60	Plaxton Paramount 3500 III	C49F	1989	KMP, Llanberis, 1998
P	N950RBC	Volvo B10M-62	Plaxton Premiere 350	C49FT	1996	Harrison, Morecambe, 2002
E	Y177JSH	Scania K124IB4	Van Hool T9 Alizee	C49FT	2001	Allan, Gorebridge, 2005
E	EO02NVW	Irisbus DailyBus 50C13	Indcar	C16F	2002	
P	YP52CTY	Scania K124IB4	Irizar PB	C49FT	2003	Scania demonstrator, 2003
E	YN03WPV	Scania K114IB4	Irizar Capacity 12.35	C53F	2003	
E	YN03WPX	Scania K114IB4	Irizar Century 12.35	C49FT	2003	
E	YN03WPY	Scania K124EB4	Irizar PB	C49FT	2003	
E	YN03WPZ	Scania K124EB4	Irizar PB	C49FT	2003	
E	YN04UKB	Scania K114IB4	Irizar Capacity 12.35	C53F	2004	
E	YN04UKC	Scania K114IB4	Irizar Capacity 12.35	C53F	2004	
E	YN04UKD	Scania K114IB4	Irizar Capacity 12.35	C53F	2004	
E	FJ55BXR	Volvo B12B	Caetano Enigma	C53F	2005	
E	FJ55BXS	Volvo B12B	Caetano Enigma	C53F	2005	
E	YN06CHJ	Scania K114EB4	Irizar Century Style	C53F	2006	
E	YN06CHK	Scania K114EB4	Irizar Century Style	C53F	2006	
E	YN06CHL	Scania K114EB4	Irizar Century Club	C49FT	2006	
E	YN06CKG	Scania K114EB4	Irizar Century Club	C49FT	2006	
E	YN06JXS	Scania K114EB4	Irizar Century Style	C53F	2006	

Previous registrations:
F137FCC   F717EUG, A7KMP   Y177JSH   B12DWA

Liveries: Blue (Excalibur); blue, white and red (Golden Tours): YN04UKB; white, pink and dark blue (Terravision): YN04UKC, YN04UKD, FJ55BXR; white (Phoenix): F137FCC, N950RBC; maroon (Phoenix): YP52CTY
Web: www.excalibur-coach-hire.com

Excalibur operates fifteen full-size coaches with a mix of Caetano, Irizar and Van Hool bodywork thirteen of which are based on Scania chassis, the other two on Volvo. With the rear-engined Volvo B12B chassis coupled to a Caetano Enigma body, FJ55BXS represents one of the 2005 intake and is seen in Artillery Row in Victoria. *Colin Lloyd*

FIRST LONDON

First Capital East Ltd, First Capital North Ltd,
Centrewest London Buses Ltd,
Macmillan House, Paddington Station, London, W2 1TY

11000	WJ	BX54EBC	Mercedes-Benz Citaro O530G	Mercedes-Benz		AN49T	2004	Evobus, 2006

EA11001-11032 — Mercedes-Benz Citaro O530G — Mercedes-Benz — AN49T — 2003

11001	WJ	LK53FAA	11009	WJ	LK53FBC	11017	WJ	LK53FBO	11025	WJ	LK53FCD
11002	WJ	LK53FAF	11010	WJ	LK53FBD	11018	WJ	LK53FBU	11026	WJ	LK53FCE
11003	WJ	LK53FAJ	11011	WJ	LK53FBE	11019	WJ	LK53FBV	11027	WJ	LK53FCM
11004	WJ	LK53FAM	11012	WJ	LK53FBF	11020	WJ	LK53FBX	11028	WJ	LK53FCN
11005	WJ	LK53FAO	11013	WJ	LK53FBG	11021	WJ	LK53FBY	11029	WJ	LK53FCO
11006	WJ	LK53FAU	11014	WJ	LK53FBJ	11022	WJ	LK53FBZ	11030	WJ	LK53FCP
11007	WJ	LK53FBA	11015	WJ	LK53FBL	11023	WJ	LK53FCA	11031	WJ	LK53FCU
11008	WJ	LK53FBB	11016	WJ	LK53FBN	11024	WJ	LK53FCC	11032	WJ	LK53FCV

EA11039-11065 — Mercedes-Benz Citaro O530G — Mercedes-Benz — AN49T — 2005

11039	HS	LK54FKX	11046	HS	LK05FDG	11053	HS	LK05FCO	11060	HS	LK05FCZ
11040	HS	LK54FKW	11047	HS	LK05FDL	11054	HS	LK05FCP	11061	HS	LK05FDD
11041	HS	LK05FDC	11048	HS	LK05EZW	11055	HS	LK05FCU	11062	HS	LK05FBZ
11042	HS	LK05FDD	11049	HS	LK05EZX	11056	HS	LK05FCV	11063	HS	LK05FCA
11043	HS	LK05FDE	11050	HS	LK05EZZ	11057	HS	LK05FBY	11064	HS	LK05FCB
11044	HS	LK05FDF	11051	HS	LK05FCM	11058	HS	LK05FCX	11065	HS	LK05FCC
11045	HS	LK05FDJ	11052	HS	LK05FCN	11059	HS	LK05FCY			

EA11066-11069 — Mercedes-Benz Citaro O530G — Mercedes-Benz — AN49T — 2002 — East London Buses, 2006

11066	WJ	LV52VFW	11067	WJ	LV52VFX	11068	WJ	LV52VFY	11069	WJ	LV52VFZ

21090	DM	M290FAE	Dennis Javelin GX 12m	Plaxton Expressliner 2	C49FT	1995
21121	DM	N821KWS	Dennis Javelin GX 12m	Plaxton Expressliner 2	C46FT	1996
21122	DM	N822KWS	Dennis Javelin GX 12m	Plaxton Expressliner 2	C49FT	1995
32052	ON	X578RJW	Volvo B7TL 10.2m	East Lancs Vyking	N41/22D	2000

A sunny High Street in Acton finds First London's EA11056, LK05FCV, on its usual haunt, route 207. This Mercedes-Benz Citaro O530G is one of twenty-seven of the type to operate from Hayes depot. The route is one of two routes worked by First's articulated buses in west London, the other being the 18 from Sudbury to Euston rail station with vehicles provided by Willesden Junction depot. *Mark Lyons*

Low-floor, double-deck buses for the First London fleets have been a mix of Dennis Trident and Volvo B7TL chassis. Bodywork came from Alexander with the ALX400 and Plaxton with the President, both of which later became TransBus products, and appeared on both chassis types with First. 32108, LT02ZCY, with locally applied class prefix VN is seen in High Street Bromley and thus identified as a Volvo B7TL with President bodywork. *Mark Lyons*

VN32100-32112   Volvo B7TL 10m   Plaxton President 4.4m   N39/20D   2002

32100	Y	LT02ZCJ	32104	Y	LT02ZCO	32107	Y	LT02ZCX	32110	Y	LT02ZDJ
32101	Y	LT02ZCK	32105	Y	LT02ZCU	32108	Y	LT02ZCY	32111	Y	LT02ZDK
32102	Y	LT02ZCL	32106	Y	LT02ZCV	32109	Y	LT02ZDH	32112	Y	LT02ZDL
32103	Y	LT02ZCN									

VNL32200-32228   Volvo B7TL 10.6m   TransBus President 4.4m   N42/23D   2002

32200	ON	LT52WTE	32208	ON	LT52WTO	32215	ON	LT52WTY	32222	NP	LT52WVG
32201	ON	LT52WTF	32209	ON	LT52WTP	32216	ON	LT52WTZ	32223	NP	LT52WVH
32202	ON	LT52WTG	32210	ON	LT52WTR	32217	ON	LT52WVA	32224	NP	LT52WVJ
32203	ON	LT52WTJ	32211	ON	LT52WTU	32218	ON	LT52WVB	32225	NP	LT52WVK
32204	ON	LT52WTK	32212	ON	LT52WTV	32219	ON	LT52WVC	32226	NP	LT52WVL
32205	ON	LT52WTL	32213	ON	LT52WTW	32220	ON	LT52WVD	32227	NP	LT52XAL
32206	ON	LT52WTM	32214	ON	LT52WTX	32221	NP	LT52WVE	32228	NP	LT52XAM
32207	ON	LT52WTN									

VNL32249-32276   Volvo B7TL 10.6m   TransBus ALX400 4.4m   N45/21D   2003

32249	X	LT52WVM	32256	X	LT52WWB	32263	X	LT52WWJ	32270	X	LT52WWR
32250	X	LT52WVN	32257	X	LT52WWC	32264	X	LT52WWK	32271	X	LT52WWS
32251	X	LT52WVO	32258	X	LT52WWD	32265	X	LT52WWL	32272	X	LT52WWU
32252	X	LT52WVP	32259	X	LT52WWE	32266	X	LT52WWM	32273	X	LT52WXC
32253	X	LT52WVY	32260	X	LT52WWF	32267	X	LT52WWN	32274	X	LT52WXD
32254	X	LT52WVZ	32261	X	LT52WWG	32268	X	LT52WWO	32275	X	LT52WXE
32255	X	LT52WWA	32262	X	LT52WWH	32269	X	LT52WWP	32276	X	LT52WXF

VNL32294-32327   Volvo B7TL 10.6m   TransBus President 4.4m   N42/23D   2003

32294	NP	LK03NGJ	32303	NP	LK03NHC	32312	NP	LK03NHN	32320	NP	LK03NJF
32295	NP	LK03NGN	32304	NP	LK03NHD	32313	NP	LK03NHP	32321	NP	LK03NJJ
32296	NP	LK03NGU	32305	NP	LK03NHE	32314	NP	LK03NHT	32322	NP	LK03NJN
32297	NP	LK03NGV	32306	NP	LK03NHF	32315	NP	LK03NHV	32323	NP	LK03NJV
32298	NP	LK03NGX	32307	NP	LK03NHG	32316	NP	LK03NHX	32324	NP	LK03NJX
32299	Y	LK03NGY	32308	NP	LK03NHH	32317	NP	LK03NHY	32325	NP	LK03NJY
32300	NP	LK03NGZ	32309	NP	LK03NHJ	32318	NP	LK03NHZ	32326	NP	LK03NJZ
32301	NP	LK03NHA	32310	NP	LK03NHL	32319	NP	LK03NJE	32327	NP	LK03NKA
32302	NP	LK03NHB	32311	NP	LK03NHM						

Commencing with 2003 deliveries, several Volvo B7TLs have been supplied with Wrightbus Eclipse Gemini bodywork. A large number of these vehicles are based at Westbourne Park depot where they see use on various routes. Routemaster operated route 28 was controversially converted to 'pay as you board' using minibuses, although Dennis Darts soon replaced these, and these in turn were replaced by low-floor Darts and finally the Gemini deckers. VNW32414, LK04JBV, seen in High Street in Kensington, illustrates the most suitable type for this busy route since the withdrawal of the Routemasters. *Mark Lyons*

VNZ32328-32348

Volvo B7TL 10.6m   Wrightbus Eclipse Gemini   N41/24D   2003

32328	ON	LK53LYH	32334	ON	LK53LYU	32339	ON	LK53LYZ	32344	ON	LK53LZE
32329	ON	LK53LYJ	32335	ON	LK53LYV	32340	ON	LK53LZA	32345	ON	LK53LZF
32330	ON	LK53LYO	32336	ON	LK53LYW	32341	ON	LK53LZB	32346	ON	LK53LZG
32331	ON	LK53LYP	32337	ON	LK53LYX	32342	ON	LK53LZC	32347	ON	LK53LZH
32332	ON	LK53LYR	32338	ON	LK53LYY	32343	ON	LK53LZD	32348	ON	LK53LZL
32333	ON	LK53LYT									

VNW32349-32370

Volvo B7TL 10.1m   Wrightbus Eclipse Gemini   N38/21D   2004

32349	ON	LK53LZM	32355	ON	LK53LZU	32361	ON	LK04HYN	32366	ON	LK04HYY
32350	ON	LK53LZN	32356	ON	LK53LZV	32362	ON	LK04HYM	32367	ON	LK04HYA
32351	ON	LK53LZO	32357	ON	LK53LZW	32363	ON	LK04HYW	32368	ON	LK04HYS
32352	ON	LK53LZP	32358	ON	LK53LZX	32364	ON	LK04HYT	32369	ON	LK04HYU
32353	ON	LK53LZR	32359	ON	LK53MBF	32365	ON	LK04HYX	32370	ON	LK04HYV
32354	ON	LK53LZT	32360	ON	LK04HYP						

VNW32371-32430

Volvo B7TL 10.1m   Wrightbus Eclipse Gemini   N41/21D   2004

32371	X	LK04HZA	32386	X	LK04HZU	32401	X	LK04HXL	32416	X	LK04JBY
32372	X	LK04HZB	32387	X	LK04HZV	32402	X	LK04HXM	32417	X	LK04JBZ
32373	X	LK04HZC	32388	X	LK04HZW	32403	X	LK04HXN	32418	X	LK04JCJ
32374	X	LK04HZD	32389	X	LK04HZX	32404	X	LK04HXP	32419	X	LK04JCU
32375	X	LK04HZE	32390	X	LK04HZY	32405	X	LK04HXR	32420	X	LK04JCV
32376	X	LK04HZF	32391	X	LK04HZZ	32406	X	LK04HXS	32421	X	LK04JCX
32377	X	LK04HZG	32392	X	LK04HXA	32407	X	LK04HXT	32422	X	LK04HYZ
32378	X	LK04HZH	32393	X	LK04HXB	32408	X	LK04HXU	32423	X	LK04JCZ
32379	X	LK04HZJ	32394	X	LK04HXC	32409	X	LK04HXV	32424	X	LK04HYB
32380	X	LK04HZL	32395	X	LK04HXD	32410	X	LK04HXW	32425	X	LK04HYC
32381	X	LK04HZM	32396	X	LK04HXE	32411	X	LK04HXX	32426	X	LK04HYF
32382	X	LK04HZN	32397	X	LK04HXF	32412	X	LK04JBE	32427	X	LK04HYG
32383	X	LK04JBU	32398	X	LK04HXG	32413	X	LK04HZP	32428	X	LK04HYH
32384	X	LK04HZS	32399	X	LK04HXH	32414	X	LK04JBV	32429	X	LK04HYJ
32385	X	LK04HZT	32400	X	LK04HXJ	32415	X	LK04JBX	32430	X	LK04HYL

Apart from the few exceptions that use short-length Dennis Darts, all TfL routes specify the use of dual-doorway buses. Illustrating this layout is TN32992, Y992NLP, a Dennis Trident with Plaxton President bodywork, seen passing through High Street, Cranford en route to Heathrow Airport. *Mark Lyons*

VNZ32495-32502   Volvo B7TL 10.1m   Wrightbus Eclipse Gemini   N38/21D   2004

32495	ON	LK54FLA	**32497**	ON	LK54FLC	**32499**	ON	LK54FLE	**32501**	ON	LK54FLG
32496	ON	LK54FLB	**32498**	ON	LK54FLD	**32500**	ON	LK54FLF	**32502**	ON	LK54JFF

VNW32657-32668   Volvo B7TL 10.1m   Wrightbus Eclipse Gemini   N41/21D   2005

32657	DM	LX55ACO	**32660**	DM	LX55AAF	**32663**	DM	LX55AAU	**32666**	DM	LX55AAY
32658	DM	LX55ACU	**32661**	DM	LX55AAJ	**32664**	DM	LX55AAV	**32667**	DM	LX55AAZ
32659	DM	LX55AAE	**32662**	DM	LX55AAN	**32665**	DM	LX55AAX	**32668**	DM	LX55ABF

TN32801-32818   Dennis Trident 9.9m   Plaxton President 4.4m   N39/20D   1999

32801	X	T801LLC	**32807**	X	T807LLC	**32813**	NP	T813LLC	**32816**	NP	T816LLC
32804	NP	T804LLC	**32809**	G	T809LLC	**32814**	NP	T814LLC	**32818**	X	T818LLC
32806	X	T806LLC	**32810**	NP	T810LLC	**32815**	NP	T815LLC			

TN32838-32853   Dennis Trident 9.9m   Plaxton President 4.4m   N39/20D   1999

32838	NP	T838LLC	**32842**	NP	T842LLC	**32847**	NP	T847LLC	**32851**	NP	T851LLC
32839	NP	T839LLC	**32843**	NP	T843LLC	**32849**	NP	T849LLC	**32852**	NP	T852LLC
32840	NP	T840LLC	**32844**	NP	T844LLC	**32850**	NP	T850LLC	**32853**	NP	T853LLC
32841	NP	T841LLC	**32845**	NP	T845LLC						

TN32854-32887   Dennis Trident 9.9m   Plaxton President 4.4m   N39/20D   1999

32854	NP	T854KLF	**32863**	NP	V863HBY	**32872**	NP	V872HBY	**32880**	NP	T880KLF
32855	NP	V855HBY	**32864**	NP	T864KLF	**32873**	NP	T873KLF	**32881**	NP	T881KLF
32856	NP	V856HBY	**32865**	NP	T865KLF	**32874**	NP	V874HBY	**32882**	NP	V882HBY
32857	NP	T857HBY	**32866**	NP	T866KLF	**32875**	NP	T875KLF	**32883**	NP	T883KLF
32858	NP	V858HBY	**32867**	NP	V867HBY	**32876**	NP	T876KLF	**32884**	NP	T884KLF
32859	NP	V859HBY	**32868**	NP	T868KLF	**32877**	NP	V877HBY	**32885**	NP	T885KLF
32860	NP	V860HBY	**32869**	NP	V869HBY	**32878**	NP	T878KLF	**32886**	NP	V886HBY
32861	NP	V861HBY	**32870**	NP	T870KLF	**32879**	NP	T879KLF	**32887**	NP	V887HBY
32862	NP	V862HBY	**32871**	NP	T871KLF						

The batches of Dennis Tridents used in the First London operations are a mix of the two lengths 9.9 and 10.5 metres. By far the majority have President bodywork, represented here on this 10.5 metre long example by TNL32911, W896VLN, at Uxbridge. First's earlier Tridents, including this example, have glazing bonded directly to the body structure. *Mark Lyons*

TNL32888-32930   Dennis Trident 10.5m   Plaxton President 4.4m   N43/24D   2000

32888	UX	V988HLH	32899	G	V899HLH	32910	AT	W895VLN	32921	AT	W921VLN
32889	UX	V889HLH	32900	G	V990HLH	32911	AT	W896VLN	32922	AT	W922VLN
32890	UX	V890HLH	32901	X	W901VLN	32912	AT	W912VLN	32923	AT	W923VLN
32891	UX	V891HLH	32902	X	W902VLN	32913	AT	W913VLN	32924	AT	W924VLN
32892	UX	V892HLH	32903	X	W903VLN	32914	AT	W914VLN	32925	AT	W898VLN
32893	UX	V893HLH	32904	X	W904VLN	32915	AT	W915VLN	32926	AT	W926VLN
32894	G	V894HLH	32905	X	W905VLN	32916	AT	W916VLN	32927	AT	W927VLN
32895	UX	V895HLH	32906	AT	W906VLN	32917	AT	W917VLN	32928	AT	W928VLN
32896	UX	V896HLH	32907	UX	W907VLN	32918	AT	W918VLN	32929	AT	W929VLN
32897	G	V897HLH	32908	AT	W908VLN	32919	AT	W919VLN	32930	AT	W899VLN
32898	G	V898HLH	32909	AT	W909VLN	32920	AT	W897VLN			

TNA32931-32952   Dennis Trident 10.5m   Alexander ALX400 4.4m   N45/24D   2000

32931	X	W931ULL	32937	X	W937ULL	32942	X	W942ULL	32949	X	W949ULL
32934	X	W934ULL	32939	X	W939ULL	32946	X	W946ULL	32950	X	W132VLO
32935	X	W935ULL	32940	X	W840VLO	32947	X	W947ULL	32951	X	W951ULL
32936	X	W936ULL	32941	X	W941ULL	32948	X	W948ULL	32952	X	W952ULL

TN32954-32983   Dennis Trident 9.9m   Plaxton President 4.4m   N39/23D   2001

32954	G	X954HLT	32962	X	X962HLT	32970	NP	X613HLT	32977	NP	X977HLT
32955	G	X611HLT	32963	X	X963HLT	32971	NP	X971HLT	32978	NP	X978HLT
32956	X	X956HLT	32964	X	X964HLT	32972	NP	X972HLT	32979	NP	Y224NLF
32957	NP	X957HLT	32965	X	X965HLT	32973	NP	X973HLT	32980	NP	X614HLT
32958	X	X958HLT	32966	X	X966HLT	32974	NP	X974HLT	32981	NP	X981HLT
32959	X	X959HLT	32967	NP	X967HLT	32975	NP	X975HLT	32982	NP	Y346NLF
32960	X	X612HLT	32968	NP	X968HLT	32976	NP	Y223NLF	32983	NP	Y344NLF
32961	X	X961HLT	32969	NP	X969HLT						

TN32984-33000 Dennis Trident 9.9m Plaxton President 4.4m N39/20D 2001

32984	G	Y984NLP	32989	G	Y989NLP	32993	G	Y993NLP	32997	G	Y997NLP
32985	G	Y985NLP	32990	G	Y932NLP	32994	G	Y994NLP	32998	G	Y998NLP
32986	G	Y986NLP	32991	G	Y991NLP	32995	G	Y995NLP	32999	G	Y933NLP
32987	G	Y987NLP	32992	G	Y992NLP	32996	G	Y996NLP	33000	G	Y934NLP
32988	G	Y988NLP									

TNL33001-33036 Dennis Trident 10.5m Plaxton President 4.4m N42/23D 2001

33001	NP	LK51UZO	33010	H	LK51UZH	33019	H	LK51UYW	33028	H	LK51UYJ
33002	NP	LK51UZP	33011	H	LK51UZJ	33020	H	LK51UYX	33029	DM	LK51UYL
33003	NP	LK51UZS	33012	H	LK51UZL	33021	H	LK51UYY	33030	DM	LK51UYM
33004	NP	LK51UZT	33013	H	LK51UZM	33022	H	LK51UYZ	33031	DM	LK51UYN
33005	NP	LK51UZC	33014	H	LK51UZN	33023	H	LK51UZA	33032	H	LK51UYO
33006	H	LK51UZD	33015	H	LK51UYS	33024	H	LK51UZB	33033	H	LK51UYP
33007	H	LK51UZE	33016	H	LK51UYT	33025	H	LK51UYF	33034	H	LK51UYR
33008	H	LK51UZF	33017	H	LK51UYU	33026	H	LK51UYG	33035	H	LK51UYD
33009	H	LK51UZG	33018	H	LK51UYV	33027	H	LK51UYH	33036	DM	LK51UYE

TN33037-33071 Dennis Trident 9.9m Plaxton President 4.4m N39/20D 2001

33037	UX	LN51DWA	33046	G	LN51DVL	33055	DM	LN51GKO	33064	DM	LN51GKY
33038	LNu	LN51DWC	33047	DM	LN51DVM	33056	DM	LN51GKP	33065	DM	LN51GKZ
33039	DM	LN51DWD	33048	DM	LN51GKD	33057	DM	LN51GJJ	33066	DM	LN51GLF
33040	X	LN51DWE	33049	DM	LN51GKE	33058	DM	LN51GJK	33067	DM	LN51GLJ
33041	DM	LN51DWF	33050	X	LN51GKF	33059	UX	LN51GJO	33068	DM	LN51GLK
33042	DM	LN51DWG	33051	DM	LN51GKG	33060	DM	LN51GJU	33069	DM	LN51GLV
33043	DM	LN51DVG	33052	DM	LN51GKJ	33061	DM	LN51GKU	33070	DM	LN51GLY
33044	DM	LN51DVH	33053	DM	LN51GKK	33062	DM	LN51GKV	33071	DM	LN51GKA
33045	DM	LN51DVK	33054	DM	LN51GKL	33063	DM	LN51GKX			

TNL33072-33099 Dennis Trident 10.5m Plaxton President 4.4m N42/23D 2002

33072	DM	LN51GOC	33079	DM	LN51GNK	33086	DM	LN51GMG	33093	NP	LN51NRJ
33073	DM	LN51GOE	33080	DM	LN51GNP	33087	DM	LN51GMO	33094	DM	LN51NRK
33074	DM	LN51GOH	33081	DM	LN51GNU	33088	DM	LN51GMU	33095	DM	LN51NRL
33075	DM	LN51GOJ	33082	DM	LN51GNV	33089	X	LN51GMV	33096	X	LN51GNY
33076	DM	LN51GOK	33083	DM	LN51GNX	33090	H	LN51GMX	33097	X	LN51GNZ
33077	DM	LN51GNF	33084	DM	LN51GME	33091	NP	LN51GMY	33098	X	LN51GOA
33078	DM	LN51GNJ	33085	DM	LN51GMF	33092	NP	LN51GMZ	33099	DM	LN51GLZ

TN33113-33129 Dennis Trident 9.9m Plaxton President 4.4m N39/20D 2002

33113	NP	LT02NVX	33118	NP	LT02NWA	33122	NP	LT02NVL	33126	NP	LT02NVO
33114	NP	LT02NVW	33119	NP	LT02NWB	33123	NP	LT02NVK	33127	NP	LT02NVP
33115	NP	LT02NVV	33120	NP	LT02NWC	33124	NP	LT02NVM	33128	NP	LT02NVR
33116	NP	LT02NVU	33121	NP	LT02NWD	33125	NP	LT02NVN	33129	NP	LT02NVS
33117	NP	LT02NVZ									

TNL33130-33140 Dennis Trident 10.5m Plaxton President 4.4m N42/23D 2002

33130	UX	LT02ZCZ	33133	UX	LT02ZBZ	33136	UX	LT02ZCF	33139	UX	LT02ZFL
33131	UX	LT02ZBX	33134	UX	LT02ZCA	33137	UX	LT02ZFJ	33140	UX	LT02ZFM
33132	UX	LT02ZBY	33135	UX	LT02ZCE	33138	UX	LT02ZFK			

TN33141-33154 Dennis Trident 9.9m Plaxton President 4.4m N39/20D 2002

33141	G	LR02LWW	33145	G	LR02LXA	33149	G	LR02LXH	33152	G	LR02LXL
33142	G	LR02LWX	33146	G	LR02LXB	33150	G	LR02LXJ	33153	G	LR02LXM
33143	G	LR02LWY	33147	G	LR02LXC	33151	G	LR02LXK	33154	G	LR02LXN
33144	G	LR02LWZ	33148	G	LR02LXG						

Another Trident seen in Uxbridge, albeit on local route U4, is a 9.9 metre example. TN33340, LK03UFV is from the last batch of Tridents to have President bodywork for First London. Later batches, such as this, reverted to using glazing mounted in traditional rubber gaskets. While the Wigan facility that assembled the President was acquired from the administrators of TransBus by Alexander Dennis, that unit was closed shortly afterwards. *Mark Lyons*

TN33155-33199   Dennis Trident 9.9m   Plaxton President 4.4m   N39/20D   2002

33155	G	LR02LXO	33167	G	LR02LYF	33178	X	LR02LYX	33189	X	LT52WVE
33156	G	LR02LXP	33168	G	LR02LYG	33179	X	LR02LYY	33190	X	LT52XAA
33157	G	LR02LXS	33169	G	LR02LYJ	33180	X	LR02LYZ	33191	X	LT52XAB
33158	G	LR02LXT	33170	G	LR02LYK	33181	X	LR02LZA	33192	X	LT52XAC
33159	G	LR02LXU	33171	G	LR02LYO	33182	X	LR02LZB	33193	X	LT52XAD
33160	G	LR02LXV	33172	G	LR02LYP	33183	X	LR02LZC	33194	X	LT52XAE
33161	G	LR02LXW	33173	G	LR02LYS	33184	X	LR02LZD	33195	X	LT52XAF
33162	G	LR02LXX	33174	G	LR02LYT	33185	X	LR02LZE	33196	X	LT52XAG
33163	G	LR02LXZ	33175	G	LR02LYU	33186	X	LT52WVB	33197	X	LT52XAH
33164	G	LR02LYA	33176	G	LR02LYV	33187	X	LT52WVC	33198	X	LT52XAJ
33165	G	LR02LYC	33177	G	LR02LYW	33188	X	LT52WVD	33199	X	LT52XAK
33166	G	LR02LYD									

TN33229-33248   Dennis Trident 9.9m   Plaxton President 4.4m   N39/20D   2002-03

33229	X	LT52WXG	33234	X	LT52WWX	33239	X	LT52WVH	33244	X	LT52WUV
33230	X	LT52WXH	33235	X	LT52WWY	33240	X	LT52WVJ	33245	X	LT52WUW
33231	X	LT52WXJ	33236	X	LT52WWZ	33241	X	LT52WVK	33246	X	LT52WUX
33232	X	LT52WXK	33237	X	LT52WVF	33242	X	LT52WVL	33247	X	LT52WUY
33233	X	LT52WWV	33238	X	LT52WVG	33243	X	LT52WUU	33248	X	LT52WVA

TN33277-33293   Dennis Trident 9.9m   Plaxton President 4.4m   N39/20D   2003

33277	G	LK03NKC	33282	G	LK03NKP	33286	G	LK03NKU	33290	G	LK03NLA
33278	G	LK03NKD	33283	G	LK03NKR	33287	G	LK03NKW	33291	G	LK03NLC
33279	G	LK03NKE	33284	G	LK03NKS	33288	G	LK03NKX	33292	G	LK03NLP
33280	G	LK03NKF	33285	G	LK03NKT	33289	G	LK03NKZ	33293	G	LK03NLR
33281	G	LK03NKG									

TN33328-33342   TransBus Trident 9.9m   TransBus President 4.4m   N39/20D   2003

33328	UX	LK03UFD	33332	UX	LK03UFL	33336	UX	LK03UFR	33340	UX	LK03UFV
33329	UX	LK03UFE	33333	UX	LK03UFM	33337	UX	LK03UFS	33341	UX	LK03UFW
33330	UX	LK03UFG	33334	UX	LK03UFN	33338	UX	LK03UFT	33342	UX	LK03UFX
33331	UX	LK03UFJ	33335	UX	LK03UFP	33339	UX	LK03UFU			

TNA33343-33386   TransBus Trident 10.5m   TransBus ALX400 4.4m   N42/21D   2003

33343	X	LK53EZV	33354	X	LK53FDA	33365	X	LK53EYF	33376	X	LK53EYV
33344	X	LK53EZW	33355	X	LK53EXT	33366	X	LK53EYG	33377	X	LK53EYW
33345	X	LK53EZX	33356	X	LK53EXU	33367	X	LK53EYH	33378	X	LK53EYX
33346	X	LK53EZZ	33357	X	LK53EXV	33368	X	LK53EYJ	33379	X	LK53EYY
33347	X	LK53FCF	33358	X	LK53EXW	33369	X	LK53EYL	33380	X	LK53EYZ
33348	X	LK53FCG	33359	X	LK53EXX	33370	X	LK53EYM	33381	X	LK53EZA
33349	X	LK53FCJ	33360	X	LK53EXZ	33371	X	LK53EYO	33382	X	LK53EZB
33350	X	LK53FCL	33361	X	LK53EYA	33372	X	LK53EYP	33383	X	LK53EZC
33351	X	LK53FCX	33362	X	LK53EYB	33373	X	LK53EYR	33384	X	LK53EZD
33352	X	LK53FCY	33363	X	LK53EYC	33374	X	LK53EYT	33385	X	LK53EZE
33353	X	LK53FCZ	33364	X	LK53EYD	33375	X	LK53EYU	33386	X	LK53EZF

34215	NP	S215LLO	Volvo Olympian	Northern Counties Palatine	B47/27D	1998	
34216	R	S216LLO	Volvo Olympian	Northern Counties Palatine	B47/27D	1998	
34218	NP	S218LLO	Volvo Olympian	Northern Counties Palatine	B47/27D	1998	

VDN34329-34344   Leyland Olympian ON2R50C13Z4 Northern Counties   B47/30F   1990-91   London Buses, 1994

34329	DM	H129FLX	34336	DM	H136FLX	34339	DM	H139FLX	34344	DM	H144FLX
34330	DM	H130FLX	34337	DM	H137FLX					

39804	X	204CLT	AEC Routemaster R2RH	Park Royal/Marshall	B36/28R	1962	*Operated for London Buses*
39813	X	ALD913B	AEC Routemaster R2RH	Park Royal/Marshall	B36/28R	1964	*Operated for London Buses*
39818	X	218CLT	AEC Routemaster R2RH	Park Royal/Marshall	B36/28R	1962	*Operated for London Buses*
39827	X	627DYE	AEC Routemaster R2RH	Park Royal/Marshall	B36/28R	1963	*Operated for London Buses*
39835	X	735DYE	AEC Routemaster R2RH	Park Royal/Marshall	B36/28R	1963	*Operated for London Buses*
39840	X	640DYE	AEC Routemaster R2RH	Park Royal/Marshall	B36/28R	1963	*Operated for London Buses*
39850	X	640DYE	AEC Routemaster R2RH	Park Royal/Marshall	B36/28R	1963	*Operated for London Buses*
39862	X	562CLT	AEC Routemaster R2RH	Park Royal/Marshall	B36/28R	1962	*Operated for London Buses*
39876	X	776CLT	AEC Routemaster R2RH	Park Royal/Marshall	B36/28R	1962	*Operated for London Buses*
39880	X	280CLT	AEC Routemaster R2RH	Park Royal/Marshall	B36/28R	1962	*Operated for London Buses*

DM41229-41234   Dennis Dart SLF 9.3m   Marshall Capital   N22D   1998

41229	H	R229TLM	41232	H	R232TLM	41233	H	R233TLM	41234	H	R234TLM
41230	H	R230TLM								

DML41235-41256   Dennis Dart SLF 10.2m   Marshall Capital   N29D   1998   41237-9 are N37F

41235	UX	S235KLM	41240	UX	S240KLM	41245	UX	S245KLM	41253	UX	S253JLP
41236	UX	S236KLM	41241	UX	S241KLM	41246	UX	S246KLM	41254	UX	S254JLP
41237	UX	S237KLM	41242	UX	S242KLM	41247	UX	S247KLM	41255	UX	S255JLP
41238	UX	S238KLM	41243	UX	S243KLM	41248	UX	S248KLM	41256	UX	S256JLP
41239	UX	S239KLM	41244	UX	S244KLM					

DMS41257-41263   Dennis Dart SLF 8.9m   Marshall Capital   N25F   1999

41257	G	T257JLD	41259	G	T259JLD	41261	G	T261JLD	41263	G	T263JLD
41258	G	T258JLD	41260	G	T260JLD	41262	G	T262JLD			

DM41264-41306   Dennis Dart SLF 9.3m   Marshall Capital   N22D   1999

41264	NP	T264JLD	41275	H	T275JLD	41286	ON	T286JLD	41297	ON	T297JLD
41265	H	T265JLD	41276	H	T276JLD	41287	ON	T287JLD	41298	ON	T298JLD
41266	H	T266JLD	41277	H	T277JLD	41288	G	T288JLD	41299	ON	T299JLD
41267	NP	T267JLD	41278	H	T278JLD	41289	ON	T289JLD	41300	ON	T430JLD
41268	Y	T268JLD	41279	H	T279JLD	41290	ON	T290JLD	41301	ON	T301JLD
41269	H	T269JLD	41280	H	T280JLD	41291	ON	T291JLD	41302	G	T302JLD
41270	H	T270JLD	41281	H	T281JLD	41292	ON	T292JLD	41303	ON	T303JLD
41271	H	T271JLD	41282	H	T282JLD	41293	ON	T293JLD	41304	ON	T304JLD
41272	H	T272JLD	41283	H	T283JLD	41294	ON	T294JLD	41305	ON	T305JLD
41273	H	T273JLD	41284	H	T284JLD	41295	ON	T295JLD	41306	ON	T306JLD
41274	H	T274JLD	41285	H	T285JLD	41296	ON	T296JLD			

Note: *The Heritage service Routemasters display their former London Buses numbers.*

DML41307-41329
Dennis Dart SLF 10.2m — Marshall Capital — N28D — 1999

41307	H	V307GBY	41313	H	V313GBY	41319	ON	V319GBY	41325	ON	V325GBY
41308	H	V308GBY	41314	H	V314GBY	41320	H	V320GBY	41326	ON	V326GBY
41309	H	V309GBY	41315	H	V315GBY	41321	H	V421HBY	41327	ON	V327GBY
41310	H	V310GBY	41316	H	V316GBY	41322	H	V322GBY	41328	H	V328GBY
41311	H	V311GBY	41317	H	V317GBY	41323	H	V323GBY	41329	H	V329GBY
41312	H	V312GBY	41318	ON	V318GBY	41324	Y	V324GBY			

41336	DM	T336ALR

Dennis Dart SLF 10.2m — Marshall Capital — N33F — 1999

DMS41337-41361
Dennis Dart SLF 8.9m — Marshall Capital — N25F — 1999

41337	G	T337ALR	41344	G	T344ALR	41350	Y	V350DLH	41356	NP	V356DLH
41338	G	T338ALR	41345	G	V345DLH	41351	Y	V351DLH	41357	NP	V357DLH
41339	G	T339ALR	41346	G	V346DLH	41352	NP	V352DLH	41358	Y	V358DLH
41340	G	T340ALR	41347	G	V347DLH	41353	NP	V353DLH	41359	NP	V359DLH
41341	G	T341ALR	41348	G	V348DLH	41354	Y	V354DLH	41360	Y	V360DLH
41342	G	T342ALR	41349	NP	V349DLH	41355	Y	V355DLH	41361	Y	V361DLH
41343	G	T343ALR									

DML41362-41380
Dennis Dart SLF 10.2m — Marshall Capital — N28D — 2000

41362	Y	W362VLN	41367	Y	W367VLN	41372	Y	W372VLN	41377	Y	W377VLN
41363	Y	W363VLN	41368	Y	W368VLN	41373	Y	W373VLN	41378	Y	W378VLN
41364	Y	W364VLN	41369	Y	W369VLN	41374	Y	W374VLN	41379	Y	W379VLN
41365	Y	W365VLN	41370	Y	W358VLN	41375	Y	W359VLN	41380	Y	W361VLN
41366	Y	W366VLN	41371	Y	W371VLN	41376	Y	W376VLN			

DML41381-41402
Dennis Dart SLF 10.2m — Marshall Capital — N28D — 2000

41381	G	X381HLR	41387	G	X387HLR	41393	G	X393HLR	41398	G	X398HLR
41382	G	X382HLR	41388	G	X388HLR	41394	G	X394HLR	41399	G	X399HLR
41383	G	X383HLR	41389	G	X389HLR	41395	G	X395HLR	41400	G	X79HLR
41384	ON	X384HLR	41390	G	X78HLR	41396	ON	X396HLR	41401	ON	X401HLR
41385	G	X385HLR	41391	G	X391HLR	41397	G	X397HLR	41402	H	X402HLR
41386	G	X386HLR	41392	G	X392HLR						

DML41403-41431
Dennis Dart SLF 10.2m — Marshall Capital — N28D — 2001

41403	UX	133CLT	41411	Y	LK51JYJ	41418	WJ	LK51DXB	41425	WJ	LK51DWJ
41404	UX	292CLT	41412	Y	LK51JYL	41419	WJ	LK51DXC	41426	WJ	LK51DWK
41405	UX	503CLT	41413	Y	LK51JYN	41420	WJ	LK51DXD	41427	WJ	LK51DWL
41406	UX	WLT659	41414	WJ	LK51JYO	41421	WJ	LK51DXE	41428	WJ	LK51DWM
41407	UX	676DYE	41415	WJ	LK51DWY	41422	WJ	LK51DXF	41429	WJ	LK51DWO
41408	UX	809DYE	41416	WJ	LK51DWZ	41423	WJ	LK51DXG	41430	WJ	LK51DWP
41409	UX	810DYE	41417	WJ	LK51DXA	41424	WJ	LK51DXH	41431	WJ	LK51DWU
41410	UX	811DYE									

Marshall's worked closely with First London to develop the low-floor Capital body style and were rewarded with large orders for the model in 8.9 (DMS), 9.3 (DM) and 10.2 metre (DML) lengths. DML41729, X729HLF, shown this styling as the vehicle passes along Highbury Vale. *Mark Lyons*

DML41432-41449 — Dennis Dart SLF 9.3m — Marshall Capital — N24D — 2001

41432	WJ	LN51DWV	41437	WJ	LN51DVY	41442	WJ	LN51DVT	41446	WJ	LN51DUJ
41433	WJ	LN51DWW	41438	WJ	LN51DVZ	41443	WJ	LN51DVV	41447	WJ	LN51DUU
41434	WJ	LN51DWX	41439	WJ	LN51DVO	41444	WJ	LN51DUA	41448	WJ	LN51DUV
41435	WJ	LN51DVW	41440	WJ	LN51DVP	41445	WJ	LN51DUH	41449	WJ	LN51DUY
41436	WJ	LN51DVX	41441	WJ	LN51DVR						

DML41450-41473 — Dennis Dart SLF 8.9m — Marshall Capital — N25F — 2002

41450	Y	LN51DVA	41456	Y	LN51SBU	41462	Y	LT02ZDR	41468	Y	LT02ZDA
41451	Y	LN51DVB	41457	Y	LN51SBV	41463	Y	LT02ZDS	41469	Y	LT02ZDC
41452	Y	LN51DVC	41458	Y	LT02ZDM	41464	Y	LT02ZDU	41470	Y	LT02ZDD
41453	Y	LN51DVF	41459	Y	LT02ZDN	41465	Y	LT02ZDV	41471	Y	LT02ZDE
41454	Y	LN51RZZ	41460	Y	LT02ZDO	41466	Y	LT02ZDW	41472	Y	LT02ZDF
41455	Y	LN51SBO	41461	Y	LT02ZDP	41467	Y	LT02ZDX	41473	Y	LT02ZDG

DMS41474-41491 — TransBus Dart 8.9m — Marshall Capital — N25F — 2002

41474	DM	LT02NUK	41479	DM	LT02NUV	41484	DM	LT02NVJ	41488	G	LT02ZDZ
41475	DM	LT02NUM	41480	DM	LT02NVE	41485	Y	LT52WUM	41489	G	LT02ZFA
41476	DM	LT02NUO	41481	DM	LT52WUP	41486	Y	LT52WUR	41490	G	LT02ZFB
41477	DM	LT02NUP	41482	DM	LT52WUO	41487	G	LT02ZDY	41491	G	LT02ZFC
41478	DM	LT02NUU	41483	DM	LT02NVH						

DMC41492-41514 — TransBus Dart 10.5m — Caetano Nimbus — N29D — 2003

41492	DM	LK03LMJ	41498	DM	LK03NLN	41504	DM	LK03NLF	41510	DM	LK03NFY
41493	DM	LK03LLX	41499	DM	LK03LNV	41505	DM	LK03NLG	41511	DM	LK03NFZ
41494	DM	LK03LLZ	41500	DM	LK03LNW	41506	DM	LK03NLJ	41512	DM	LK03NGE
41495	DM	LK03LME	41501	DM	LK03LNX	41507	DM	LK03NLL	41513	DM	LK03NGF
41496	DM	LK03LMF	41502	DM	LK03NLD	41508	DM	LK03NLM	41514	DM	LK03NGG
41497	DM	LK03LNU	41503	DM	LK03NLE	41509	DM	LK03NLT			

DM41520-41544 — TransBus Dart 10.5m — Caetano Nimbus — N29D — 2003

41520	DM	LK03UEX	41527	DM	LK53FDD	41533	UX	LK53FDN	41539	UX	LK53FDY
41521	DM	LK03UEY	41528	UX	LK53FDE	41534	UX	LK53FDO	41540	UX	LK53FDZ
41522	UX	LK03UEZ	41529	UX	LK53FDF	41535	UX	LK53FDP	41541	UX	LK53FEF
41523	DM	LK03UFA	41530	UX	LK53FDG	41536	UX	LK53FDU	41542	UX	LK53FEG
41524	DM	LK03UFB	41531	UX	LK53FDJ	41537	UX	LK53FDV	41543	UX	LK53FEH
41525	DM	LK03UFC	41532	UX	LK53FDM	41538	UX	LK53FDX	41544	UX	LK53FEJ
41526	UX	LK53FDC									

DM41681-41690 — Dennis Dart SLF 9.3m — Marshall Capital — N24D — 2000

41681	H	W681ULL	41684	H	W684ULL	41687	H	W687ULL	41689	H	X689HLF
41682	H	W682ULL	41685	H	W685ULL	41688	H	X688HLF	41690	H	X501JLO
41683	H	W683ULL	41686	H	W686ULL						

DM41697-41700 — Dennis Dart SLF 9.3m — Marshall Capital — N24D — 2000

41697	H	X697HLF	41698	H	X698HLF	41699	H	X699HLF	41700	H	X502JLO

DM41718-41738 — Dennis Dart SLF 10.2m — Marshall Capital — N28D — 2000

41718	H	W718ULL	41724	H	W724ULL	41729	H	X729HLF	41734	H	X734HLF
41719	H	W719ULL	41725	H	W425VLO	41730	H	X503JLO	41735	H	X735HLF
41720	H	W133VLO	41726	H	W726ULL	41731	H	X731HLF	41736	H	X736HLF
41721	H	W721ULL	41727	H	W727ULL	41732	H	X732HLF	41737	H	X737HLF
41722	H	W722ULL	41728	H	W728VLO	41733	H	X733HLF	41738	H	X738HLF
41723	H	W723ULL									

41740-41745 — Dennis Dart SLF 10.2m — Marshall Capital — N28D — 2000

41740	H	X504JLO	41742	H	X742HLF	41744	H	X744HLF	41745	H	X745HLF
41741	H	X741HLF	41743	H	X743HLF						

41746	H	X746JLO	Dennis Dart SLF 9.3m	Marshall Capital	N24D	2000
41747	H	X747JLO	Dennis Dart SLF 9.3m	Marshall Capital	N24D	2000
41748	H	X748JLO	Dennis Dart SLF 9.3m	Marshall Capital	N24D	2000

Following cessation of bus body building by Marshall's in Cambridge, First London looked for an alternative source to supply bodywork on the Dart. With a history including the names of Wadham Stringer and UVG, the Waterlooville factory continues to build buses, currently under Caetano ownership. Several Darts with the Nimbus model of bodywork have been supplied to First, including two batches to the London operations. Chadwell Heath sees regular visits of the type, as witnessed by DMC41501, LK03LNX, shown passing along Station Road. *Mark Lyons*

DML41751-41772

Dennis Dart SLF 10.2m　　Marshall Capital　　N28D　　2000-01

41751	H	X751HLR	41757	H	X757HLR	41763	H	X763HLR
41752	H	X752HLR	41758	H	X758HLR	41764	H	X764HLR
41753	H	X753HLR	41759	H	X759HLR	41765	H	X508HLR
41754	H	X754HLR	41760	H	X507HLR	41766	H	X766HLR
41755	H	X506HLR	41761	H	X761HLR	41767	UX	X767HLR
41756	H	X756HLR	41762	H	X762HLR			

41768	Y	X768HLR
41769	ON	X769HLR
41770	H	X509HLR
41771	DM	X771HLR
41772	DM	X772HLR

DM41773-41788

Dennis Dart SLF 9.3m　　Marshall Capital　　N28D　　2001

41773	NP	X773HLR	41777	NP	X512HLR	41781	NP	X781HLR	41785	NP	X785HLR
41774	NP	X774HLR	41778	NP	X778HLR	41782	NP	X782HLR	41786	NP	X514HLR
41775	NP	X511HLR	41779	NP	X779HLR	41783	NP	X783HLR	41787	NP	X787HLR
41776	NP	X776HLR	41780	NP	X513HLR	41784	NP	X784HLR	41788	NP	X788HLR

DM41790-41795

Dennis Dart SLF 9.3m　　Marshall Capital　　N24D　　2001

41790	DM	LN51GJV	41792	DM	LN51GJY	41794	H	LN51GOP
41791	DM	LN51GJX	41793	DM	LN51GJZ	41795	DM	LN51GOU

DMS42401-42406

Dennis Dart SLF 10.1m　　Plaxton Pointer　　N34F　　1996

42401	UX	P401MLA	42403	UX	P403MLA	42405	UX	P405MLA
42402	UX	P402MLA	42404	UX	P404MLA	42406	UX	P406MLA

42515-42519

TransBus Dart 10.5m　　Caetano Nimbus　　N29D　　2003

42515	DM	LK03NKH	42517	DM	LK03NKL	42518	DM	LK03NKM	42519	DM	LK03NKN
42516	DM	LK03NKJ						

46104	DM	K904CVW	Dennis Dart 9m	Plaxton Pointer	B35F	1992
46106	R	K906CVW	Dennis Dart 9m	Plaxton Pointer	B35F	1992
46852	DM	N852CPU	Dennis Dart 9m	Marshall C36	BC17FL	1995
46853	DM	N853CPU	Dennis Dart 9m	Marshall C36	BC17FL	1995
46854	DM	N854CPU	Dennis Dart 9m	Marshall C36	BC17FL	1995

OOL53101-53111
Optare Solo M850 — Optare — N26F — 2002

53101	DM	EO02FLA	**53104**	DM	EO02FLD	**53107**	DM	EO02FLG	**53110**	DM	EO02FLK
53102	DM	EO02FLB	**53105**	DM	EO02FLE	**53108**	DM	EO02FLH	**53111**	DM	EO02FKZ
53103	DM	EO02FLC	**53106**	DM	EO02FLF	**53109**	DM	EO02FLJ			

OOS53701-53706
Optare Solo M780SL — Optare — N21F — 2005

53701	H	LK05DYO	**53703**	H	LK05DXR	**53705**	H	LK05DXT	**53706**	H	LK05DXU
53702	H	LK05DXP	**53704**	H	LK05DXS						

62666	DM	J916WVC	Leyland Lynx LX2R11V18Z4S	Leyland Lynx 2	B51F	1992	Volvo demonstrator, 1992

EC64001-64011
Mercedes-Benz O530 — Mercedes-Benz Citaro — N36D — 2003

64001	H	LT02NTV	**64004**	H	LT02NUA	**64007**	H	LT02NUE	**64010**	H	LT02NUJ
64002	H	LT02NTX	**64005**	H	LT02NUB	**64008**	H	LT02NUF	**64011**	H	LT02NVY
64003	H	LT02NTY	**64006**	H	LT02NUC	**64009**	H	LT02NUH			

64991	H	LK53MBO	Mercedes-Benz O530 Fuel Cell	Mercedes-Benz Citaro	N30D	2003	
64992	H	LK53MBU	Mercedes-Benz O530 Fuel Cell	Mercedes-Benz Citaro	N30D	2003	
64993	H	LK53MBV	Mercedes-Benz O530 Fuel Cell	Mercedes-Benz Citaro	N30D	2003	
67296	DM	M796MPM	Dennis Lance	Alexander PS	B46F	1992	Dennis demonstrator, 1998

Ancillary Vehicles:

32822	DMt	T822LLC	Dennis Trident 9.9m	Plaxton President 4.4m	N39/20D	1999	
34331	DMt	J131YRM	Leyland Olympian ON2R50C13Z4	Northern Counties	TV	1990	London Buses, 1994
34335	ONt	J135YRM	Leyland Olympian ON2R50C13Z4	Northern Counties	TV	1990	London Buses, 1994
34340	ONt	H140FLX	Leyland Olympian ON2R50C13Z4	Northern Counties	TV	1991	London Buses, 1994
34342	ONt	H142FLX	Leyland Olympian ON2R50C13Z4	Northern Counties	TV	1991	London Buses, 1994
34345	NP	H145FLX	Leyland Olympian ON2R50C13Z4	Northern Counties	TV	1991	London Buses, 1994
34346	DMt	J135PVC	Leyland Olympian ON2R50C13Z4	Leyland	TV	1991	Volvo demonstrator, 1991
35359	u	OJD859Y	MCW Metrobus DR101/16	MCW	TV	1983	
41649	ON	R649TLM	Dennis Dart SLF 10.2m	Marshall Capital	TV	1998	
47065	ONt	N605XJM	Dennis Dart 9.8m	Plaxton Pointer	TV	1996	
50186	Y	N119DWE	Mercedes-Benz 709D	Plaxton Beaver	Staff	1996	
59991	Y	H392MAR	Mercedes-Benz 709D	Reeve Burgess Beaver	Staff	1991	First Essex, 2003
90162	ONt	B260WUL	MCW Metrobus DR101/17	MCW	TV	1985	
90163	ONt	C328BUV	MCW Metrobus DR101/17	MCW	TV	1985	
90164	ONt	C335BUV	MCW Metrobus DR101/17	MCW	TV	1985	
90168	ONt	C384BUV	MCW Metrobus DR101/17	MCW	TV	1985	
90169	ONp	C412BUV	MCW Metrobus DR101/17	MCW	TV	1985	
90170	ONp	C418BUV	MCW Metrobus DR101/17	MCW	TV	1985	
90173	ONt	C422BUV	MCW Metrobus DR101/17	MCW	TV	1985	
90176	DMt	H135FLX	Leyland Olympian ON2R50C13Z4	Northern Counties	TV	1990	
90178	Y	F601XMS	Mercedes-Benz 811D	Alexander Sprint	Staff	1988	

Special Event vehicles:

RF326	u	MLL963	AEC Regal IV 9821LT	Metro-Cammell	B39F	1952	preservation, 1996
39735	X	SMK735F	AEC Routemaster R2RH1	Park Royal	B40/32R	1967	*displays RML2735*
38809	NP	SSL609	AEC Routemaster R2RH	Park Royal	O36/28R	1959	*displays RM120*
39810	X	510CLT	AEC Routemaster R2RH1	Park Royal	O32/25R	1962	*displays RM1510*

Previous Registrations:

SSL609	VLT120		V860HBY	T860KLF

Depots and allocations:

Acton (Uxbridge Road) - AT

Trident	32906	32908	32909	32910	32911	32912	32913	32914
	32915	32916	32917	32918	32919	32920	32921	32922
	32923	32924	32925	32926	32927	32928	32929	32930

The London Bus Handbook

Alperton (Ealing Road) - ON

Volvo B7TL	32052	32200	32201	32202	32203	32204	32205	32206
	32207	32208	32209	32210	32211	32212	32213	32214
	32215	32216	32217	32218	32219	32220	32271	32272
	32273	32274	32275	32276	32328	32329	32330	32331
	32332	32333	32334	32335	32336	32337	32338	32339
	32340	32341	32342	32343	32344	32345	32346	32347
	32348	32349	32350	32351	32352	32353	32354	32355
	32356	32357	32358	32359	32361	32362	32363	32364
	32365	32366	32367	32368	32369	32370	32495	32496
	32497	32498	32499	32500	32501	32502		
Dart	41286	41287	41289	41290	41291	41292	41293	41294
	41295	41296	41297	41298	41299	41300	41301	41303
	41304	41305	41306	41318	41319	41325	41326	41327
	41384	41396	41401	41769				
Ancillary	34335	34340	34342	41649	47065	90162	90163	90164
	90168	90169	90170	90173				

Dagenham (Chequers Lane) - DM

Solo	53101	53102	53103	53104	53105	53106	53107	53108
	53109	53110	53111					
Javelin	21090	21121	21122					
Olympian	34329	34330	34336	34337	34339	34341	34344	
Volvo B7TL	32657	32658	32659	32660	32661	32662	32663	32664
	32665	32666	32667	32668				
Trident	33029	33030	33031	33036	33039	33041	33042	33043
	33044	33045	33047	33048	33049	33051	33052	33053
	33054	33055	33056	33057	33058	33060	33061	33062
	33063	33064	33065	33066	33067	33068	33069	33070
	33071	33072	33073	33074	33075	33076	33077	33078
	33079	33080	33081	33082	33083	33084	33085	33086
	33087	33088	33094	33095	33099			
Dart	41336	41474	41475	41476	41477	41478	41479	41480
	41481	41482	41483	41484	41492	41493	41494	41495
	41496	41497	41498	41499	41500	41501	41502	41503
	41504	41505	41506	41507	41508	41509	41510	41511
	41512	41513	41514	41520	41521	41523	41524	41525
	41527	41771	41772	41790	41791	41792	41793	41795
	42515	42516	42517	42518	42519	46852	46853	46854
Lance	67296							
Ancillary	32822	34331	34346	90176				

Greenford (Greenford Road) - G

Trident	32809	32894	32897	32898	32899	32954	32955	32984
	32985	32986	32987	32988	32989	32990	32991	32992
	32993	32994	32995	32996	32997	32998	32999	33000
	33046	33141	33142	33143	33144	33145	33146	33147
	33148	33149	33150	33151	33152	33153	33154	33155
	33156	33157	33158	33159	33160	33161	33162	33163
	33164	33165	33166	33167	33168	33169	33170	33171
	33172	33173	33174	33175	33176	33177	33277	33278
	33279	33280	33281	33282	33283	33284	33285	33286
	33287	33288	33289	33290	33291	33292	33293	
Dart	41257	41258	41259	41260	41261	41262	41263	41288
	41302	41337	41338	41339	41340	41341	41342	41343
	41344	41345	41346	41347	41348	41381	41382	41383
	41385	41386	41387	41388	41389	41390	41391	41392
	41393	41394	41395	41397	41398	41399	41400	41487
	41488	41489	41490	41491				

This view of 39862, 562CLT, displaying its original London Transport number RM1562, majestically sweeping through Trafalgar Square shows that the age of proper buses has yet to die. A handful of these classic icons remain in service in London and they are the only surviving step-floor buses to be found on TfL services. Heritage Routemasters on routes 9 and 15 can still be savoured among some of London's tourist hot-spots. *Mark Lyons*

Hayes (Rigby Lane) - HS

Citaro O530G	11039	11040	11041	11042	11043	11044	11045	11046
	11047	11048	11049	11050	11051	11052	11053	11054
	11055	11056	11057	11058	11059	11060	11061	11062
	11063	11064	11065					

Orpington (Faraday Way) - Y

Volvo B7TL	32100	32101	32102	32103	32104	32105	32106	32107
	32108	32109	32110	32111	32112	32299		
Dart	41268	41324	41350	41351	41354	41355	41358	41360
	41361	41362	41363	41365	41366	41367	41368	41369
	41370	41371	41372	41373	41374	41375	41376	41377
	41378	41379	41380	41411	41412	41413	41450	41451
	41452	41453	41454	41455	41456	41457	41458	41459
	41460	41461	41462	41463	41464	41465	41466	41467
	41468	41469	41470	41471	41472	41473	41485	41486
	41768							
Ancillary	50186	59991						

Stratford (Waterden Road, Hackney Wick) - H

Trident	33006	33007	33008	33009	33010	33011	33012	33013
	33014	33015	33016	33017	33018	33019	33020	33021
	33022	33023	33024	33025	33026	33027	33028	33032
	33033	33034	33035	33090				
Dart	41229	41230	41232	41233	41234	41265	41266	41269
	41270	41271	41272	41273	41274	41275	41276	41277
	41278	41279	41280	41281	41282	41283	41284	41285
	41307	41308	41309	41310	41311	41312	41313	41314
	41315	41316	41317	41320	41321	41322	41323	41328
	41329	41402	41681	41682	41683	41684	41685	41686
	41687	41688	41689	41690	41697	41698	41699	41700
	41718	41719	41720	41721	41722	41723	41724	41725
	41726	41727	41728	41729	41730	41731	41732	41733
	41734	41735	41736	41737	41738	41740	41741	41742
	41743	41744	41745	41746	41747	41748	41751	41752
	41753	41754	41755	41756	41757	41758	41759	41760
	41761	41762	41763	41764	41765	41766	41770	41794
Solo	53701	53702	53703	53704	53705	53706		
MB Citaro O530	64001	64002	64003	64004	64005	64006	64007	64008
	64009	64010	64011	64991	64992	64993		

Tottenham (Marsh Lane, Northumberland Park) - NP

Routemaster	39809							
Olympian	34215	34218						
Trident	32804	32810	32813	32814	32815	32816	32838	32839
	32840	32841	32842	32843	32844	32845	32847	32849
	32850	32851	32852	32853	32854	32855	32856	32857
	32858	32859	32860	32861	32862	32863	32864	32865
	32866	32867	32868	32869	32870	32871	32872	32873
	32874	32875	32876	32877	32878	32879	32880	32881
	32882	32883	32884	32885	32886	32887	32957	32967
	32968	32969	32970	32971	32972	32973	32974	32975
	32976	32977	32978	32979	32980	32981	32982	32983
	33001	33002	33003	33004	33005	33029	33091	33092
	33093	33113	33114	33115	33116	33117	33118	33119
	33120	33121	33122	33123	33124	33125	33126	33127
	33128	33129						
Volvo B7TL	32221	32222	32223	32224	32225	32226	32227	32228
	32294	32295	32296	32297	32298	32300	32301	32302
	32303	32304	32305	32306	32307	32308	32309	32310
	32311	32312	32313	32314	32315	32316	32317	32318
	32319	32320	32321	32322	32323	32324	32325	32326
	32327							
Dart	41264	41267	41349	41352	41353	41356	41357	41359
	41773	41774	41775	41776	41777	41778	41779	41780
	41781	41782	41783	41784	41785	41786	41787	41788
Ancillary	34345							

Uxbridge (Bakers Road) - UX

Trident	32888	32889	32890	32891	32892	32893	32895	32896
	32907	33037	33059	33130	33131	33132	33133	33134
	33135	33136	33137	33138	33139	33140	33328	33329
	33330	33331	33332	33333	33334	33335	33336	33337
	33338	33339	33340	33341	33342			
Dart	41235	41236	41237	41238	41239	41240	41241	41242
	41243	41244	41245	41246	41247	41248	41253	41254
	41255	41256	41403	41404	41405	41406	41407	41408
	41409	41410	41522	41526	41528	41529	41530	41531
	41532	41533	41534	41535	41536	41537	41538	41539
	41540	41541	41542	41543	41544	41767	42401	42402
	42403	42404	42405	42406				

Westbourne Park (Great Western Road) - X

Outstation: - Ariel Way, White City.

Routemaster	39725	39804	39810	39813	39818	39827	39835	39849
	39850	38762	39876	39880	*(these display their former London Buses numbers)*			
Trident	32801	32806	32807	32818	32900	32901	32902	32903
	32904	32905	32931	32934	32935	32936	32937	32939
	32940	32941	32942	32946	32947	32948	32949	32950
	32951	32952	32956	32958	32959	32960	32961	32962
	32963	32964	32965	32966	33040	33050	33089	33096
	33097	33098	33151	33178	33179	33180	33181	33182
	33183	33184	33185	33186	33187	33188	33189	33190
	33191	33192	33193	33194	33195	33196	33197	33198
	33199	33229	33230	33231	33232	33233	33234	33235
	33236	33237	33238	33239	33240	33242	33244	33245
	33246	33247	33248	33343	33344	33345	33346	33347
	33348	33349	33350	33351	33352	33353	33354	33355
	33356	33357	33358	33359	33360	33361	33362	33363
	33364	33365	33366	33367	33368	33369	33370	33371
	33372	33373	33374	33375	33376	33377	33378	33379
	33380	33381	33382	33383	33384	33385	33386	
Volvo B7TL	32249	32250	32251	32252	32253	32254	32255	32256
	32257	32258	32259	32260	32261	32262	32263	32264
	32265	32266	32267	32268	32269	32270	32271	32272
	32273	32274	32275	32276	32371	32372	32373	32374
	32375	32376	32377	32378	32379	32380	32381	32382
	32383	32384	32385	32386	32387	32388	32389	32390
	32391	32392	32393	32394	32395	32396	32397	32398
	32399	32400	32401	32402	32403	32404	32405	32406
	32407	32408	32409	32410	32411	32412	32413	32414
	32415	32416	32417	32418	32419	32420	32421	32422
	32423	32424	32425	32426	32427	32428	32429	32430

Despite London's fleet of articulated buses being dominated by the Mercedes-Benz Citaro, the rigid version where the product choice is larger is currently less common in Britain. In association with First, London has seen the use of three Citaro buses powered by experimental Fuel-Cells. One of the standard O530 models is EC64007, LT02NUE seen crossing London Bridge. Its modest route branding above the windows includes names of some of the sights it passes. *Mark Lyons*

Willesden Junction (Station Road) - WJ

Citaro G	11001	11002	11003	11004	11005	11006	11007	11008
	11009	11010	11011	11012	11013	11014	11015	11016
	11017	11018	11019	11020	11021	11022	11023	11024
	11025	11026	11027	11028	11029	11030	11031	11032
Dart	41402	41415	41416	41417	41418	41419	41420	41421
	41422	41423	41424	41425	41426	41427	41428	41429
	41430	41431	41432	41433	41434	41435	41436	41437
	41438	41439	41440	41441	41442	41443	41444	41445
	41446	41447	41448	41449				

Unallocated and stored:

Regal	RF326
Metrobus	35359

FROG TOURS - DUCK TOURS

London Duck Tours Ltd, 55 York Road, Waterloo, SE1 7NJ

VSL143	General Motors DUKW	Tanmill	-30R	1944	Frog Tours, 2006
ESL636	General Motors DUKW	Tanmill	-30R	1944	Frog Tours, 2002
ESL660	General Motors DUKW	Tanmill	-30R	1944	Frog Tours, 2002
ESL679	General Motors DUKW	Tanmill	-30R	1944	Frog Tours, 2002
RSL602	General Motors DUKW	Tanmill	-30R	1944	Frog Tours, 2002
TSL931	General Motors DUKW	Tanmill	-30R	1944	Frog Tours, 2002

Named vehicles: ESL636, *Mistress Quickly*; ESL660, *Beatrice*; ESL679, *Cleopatra*; RSL602, *Titania*.
Depot: Westminster Bridge Road, Waterloo.

Originally built in 1944 for service in World War Two, some examples of the DUKW (Duck) have been converted for use as amphibious sightseeing vehicles. This example is VSL143 'Desdemona' seen negotiating Parliament Square in June 2006 and is operated by London Duck Tours Ltd. *Dave Heath*

GO-AHEAD LONDON

London Central Bus Co Ltd; London General Transport Services Ltd
18 Merton High Street, London, SW19 1DN

AVL1-46 — Volvo B7TL — Alexander ALX400 — N43/17D — 1999-2000

1	Q	V101LGC	13	Q	V113LGC	25	PM	V125LGC	36	PM	V136LGC
2	Q	V102LGC	14	Q	V114LGC	26	PM	V126LGC	37	PM	V137LGC
3	Q	V103LGC	15	Q	V115LGC	27	PM	V127LGC	38	PM	V138LGC
4	Q	V104LGC	16	Q	V116LGC	28	PM	V128LGC	39	PM	V139LGC
5	Q	V105LGC	17	Q	V117LGC	29	PM	V129LGC	40	PM	V140LGC
6	Q	V106LGC	18	Q	V118LGC	30	PM	V130LGC	41	PM	V141LGC
7	Q	V107LGC	19	Q	V119LGC	31	PM	V131LGC	42	PM	V142LGC
8	Q	V108LGC	20	Q	V120LGC	32	PM	V132LGC	43	PM	V143LGC
9	Q	V109LGC	21	Q	V221LGC	33	PM	V133LGC	44	PM	V144LGC
10	Q	V110LGC	22	PM	V122LGC	34	PM	V134LGC	45	PM	V145LGC
11	Q	V211LGC	23	PM	V223LGC	35	PM	V135LGC	46	PM	V146LGC
12	Q	V112LGC	24	PM	V124LGC						

B9 — SW — BX06BTF — Volvo B9TL — Wrightbus Gemini Eclipse — N41/21D — 2006

DML1-20 — Dennis Dart SLF 9.3m — Marshall Capital — N31F — 1999

1	BX	T401AGP	5	BX	T455AGP	11	BX	T411AGP	17	BX	T417AGP
2	BX	T402AGP	6	BX	T406AGP	12	BX	T412AGP	18	BX	T418AGP
3	BX	T403AGP	8	BX	T408AGP	14	BX	T414AGP	19	BX	T419AGP
4	BX	T404AGP	10	BX	T410AGP	15	BX	T415AGP	20	BX	T392AGP

DMS6-9 — Dennis Dart SLF 8.9m — Marshall Capital — N29F — 1999

6	BX	T106KGP	7	BX	T107KGP	8	BX	T108KGP	9	BX	T109KGP

In May 2006, the first E class double-deckers arrived at London General's Stockwell Garage. Initially allocated to route 196, these Alexander-Dennis Enviro400 bodied Trident 2s soon started intermixing within the large Stockwell allocation and can now be seen on most routes. Kennington Lane is the background for E4, SN06BNE, pictured shortly after entering service. *Mark Lyons*

The order for the Enviro 400 placed by Go-Ahead London has since been increased to fifty-six vehicles. Initially based on the Euro 4 version of the Trident 2 the product is being sold as a unit. Future developments will see the Enviro bodywork on other chassis while the Trident 2 will be bodied by other coachbuilders, including East Lancs. Illustrating the nearside layout which features more seated passengers than comparable models is E7, SN06BNK. *Mark Lyons*

E1-39

		ADL Trident 2			ADL Enviro 400			N41/26D	2006
1	SW	SN06BNA	11	SW	SN06BNV	21	PM	LX06EZR	31	PM	LX06EZF
2	SW	SN06BNB	12	SW	SN06BNX	22	PM	LX06EZS	32	PM	LX06EZG
3	SW	SN06BND	13	SW	SN06BNY	23	PM	LX06EZT	33	PM	LX06EZH
4	SW	SN06BNE	14	SW	SN06BNZ	24	PM	LX06EYY	34	PM	LX06ECT
5	SW	SN06BNF	15	SW	SN06BOF	25	PM	LX06EYZ	35	PM	LX06ECV
6	SW	SN06BNJ	16	PM	LX06EZL	26	PM	LX06EZA	36	PM	LX06FKL
7	SW	SN06BNK	17	PM	LX06EZM	27	PM	LX06EZB	37	SW	LX06FKM
8	SW	SN06BNL	18	PM	LX06EZN	28	PM	LX06EZC	38	SW	LX06FKN
9	SW	SN06BNO	19	PM	LX06EZO	29	PM	LX06EZD	39	SW	LX06FKO
10	SW	SN06BNU	20	PM	LX06EZP	30	PM	LX06EZE			

E40-56

		ADL Trident 2			ADL Enviro 400			N41/26D	On order
40	-	-	45	-	-	49	-	-	53	-	-
41	-	-	46	-	-	50	-	-	54	-	-
42	-	-	47	-	-	51	-	-	55	-	-
43	-	-	48	-	-	52	-	-	56	-	-
44	-	-									

EVL1-52

		Volvo B7TL 10.4m			East Lancs Vyking			N45/23D	2002
1	A	PL51LGA	14	A	PL51LGX	27	A	PN02XCL	40	A	PJ02PYX
2	A	PL51LGC	15	A	PN02XCB	28	A	PN02XCM	41	A	PJ02PYY
3	A	PL51LGD	16	A	PN02XCC	29	A	PN02XCO	42	A	PJ02PYZ
4	A	PL51LGE	17	A	PN02XCD	30	A	PN02XCP	43	A	PJ02PZA
5	A	PL51LGF	18	A	PN02XCE	31	A	PN02XCR	44	A	PJ02PZB
6	A	PL51LGG	19	A	PL51LFE	32	A	PN02XCS	45	A	PJ02PZC
7	A	PL51LGJ	20	A	PN02XCF	33	A	PN02XCT	46	A	PJ02PZD
8	A	PL51LGK	21	A	PL51LFG	34	A	PN02XBX	47	A	PJ02PZE
9	A	PL51LGN	22	A	PN02XCG	35	A	PN02XBY	48	A	PJ02PZF
10	A	PL51LGO	23	A	PL51LFJ	36	A	PN02XBZ	49	A	PJ02PZG
11	A	PL51LGU	24	A	PN02XCH	37	A	PJ02PYU	50	A	PJ02PZH
12	A	PN02XCA	25	A	PN02XCJ	38	A	PJ02PYV	51	A	PJ02PZK
13	A	PL51LGW	26	A	PN02XCK	39	A	PJ02PYW	52	A	PJ02PZL

Since being delivered to Sutton in 2002, the East Lancs Vyking with the Myllennium front, has been the double-deck mainstay of Go-Ahead London's most southerly garage. EVL2, PL51LGC, seen at the Cromwell Road bus station in Kingston, is about to start its return trip to Sutton depot on route 213. *Mark Lyons*

LDP1-16

Dennis Dart SLF 9.2m			Plaxton Pointer			N32F		1996				

1	A	P501RYM	4	NX	P504RYM	7	BX	P507RYM	14	A	P514RYM
2	SW	P502RYM	5	BX	P505RYM	8	A	P508RYM	16	u	P516RYM
3	Q	P503RYM	6	BX	P506RYM	9	A	P509RYM			

LDP37-44

Dennis Dart SLF 10m			Plaxton Pointer			N36F		1996		

37	A	P737RYL	41	A	P741RYL	43	A	P743RYL	44	A	P744RYL
40	A	P740RYL	42	A	P742RYL						

LDP45-89

Dennis Dart SLF 10m			Plaxton Pointer			N35F*		1997	*61 is N36F	

45	A	R445LGH	57	BX	R457LGH	67	Q	R467LGH	78	AL	R478LGH
46	A	R446LGH	58	w	R458LGH	68	BX	R468LGH	81	Q	R481LGH
47	A	R447LGH	59	AL	R459LGH	69	BX	R469LGH	82	Q	R482LGH
48	A	R448LGH	60	AL	R460LGH	70	BX	R470LGH	83	Q	R483LGH
49	A	R449LGH	61	AL	R461LGH	71	Q	R471LGH	84	Q	R484LGH
51	A	R451LGH	62	AL	R462LGH	72	Q	R472LGH	85	AL	R485LGH
52	A	R452LGH	63	u	R463LGH	73	w	R473LGH	86	Q	R486LGH
53	A	R453LGH	64	Q	R464LGH	74	A	R474LGH	87	Q	R487LGH
54	AL	R454LGH	65	A	R465LGH	76	NX	R476LGH	88	w	R488LGH
55	AL	R455LGH	66	w	R466LGH	77	BX	R477LGH	89	AL	R489LGH
56	AL	R456LGH									

LDP90-128

Dennis Dart SLF 10.1m			Plaxton Pointer 2			N30D*		1998-99	*118-128 are N32D	

90	AL	S638JGP	101	AL	S101EGK	111	BX	S954JGX	120	BX	T120KGP
91	AL	S91EGK	102	AL	S102EGK	112	BX	S112EGK	121	BX	T521AGP
92	AL	S92EGK	103	AL	S103EGK	113	BX	S113EGK	122	BX	T122KGP
93	AL	S93EGK	104	AL	S104EGK	114	BX	S114EGK	123	BX	T523AGP
94	AL	S94EGK	105	AL	S105EGK	115	BX	S115EGK	124	BX	T124KGP
95	AL	S95EGK	106	AL	S106EGK	116	BX	S116EGK	125	BX	T125KGP
96	AL	S96EGK	107	BX	S107EGK	117	BX	S117EGK	126	BX	T126KGP
97	AL	S97EGK	108	BX	S108EGK	118	BX	T118KGP	127	BX	T127KGP
98	AL	S98EGK	109	BX	S109EGK	119	BX	T119KGP	128	BX	T128KGP
99	AL	S955JGX	110	BX	S110EGK						

LDP129-133

Dennis Dart SLF 8.8m			Plaxton Pointer MPD			N29F		2001		

129	AF	Y829TGH	131	AF	Y831TGH	132	AF	Y832TGH	133	AF	Y833TGH
130	AF	Y803TGH									

Almost 300 Darts with Pointer bodywork have been delivered to the London arm of the Go-Ahead Group since 1996. Initially the Pointer body was built by Plaxton's and transferred to the Falkirk line under TransBus management. The current product is the Alexander-Dennis model. New in 2001, LDP193, SN51UAF, is a 10.1m bus allocated to Merton and is seen at Mitcham while operating on route 355 in June 2006. *Mark Lyons*

LDP134-141

Dennis Dart SLF 10.7m			Plaxton Pointer 2			N35D		2001		
134	AL	Y834TGH	136	AL	Y836TGH	138	AL	Y838TGH	140	AL	Y840TGH
135	AL	Y835TGH	137	AL	Y837TGH	139	AL	Y839TGH	141	AL	Y841TGH

LDP142-152

Dennis Dart SLF 8.8m			Plaxton Pointer MPD			N30F		2001		
142	NX	Y842TGH	145	NX	Y845TGH	148	NX	Y848TGH	151	A	Y851TGH
143	NX	Y843TGH	146	NX	Y846TGH	149	A	Y849TGH	152	A	Y852TGH
144	NX	Y844TGH	147	NX	Y847TGH	150	A	Y805TGH			

LDP153-190

Dennis Dart SLF 9.3m			Plaxton Pointer 2			N29F		2001		
153	Q	Y853TGH	163	Q	Y863TGH	172	PM	Y972TGH	182	Q	Y982TGH
154	Q	Y854TGH	164	Q	Y864TGH	173	PM	Y973TGH	183	Q	Y983TGH
155	Q	Y705TGH	165	Q	Y865TGH	174	PM	Y974TGH	184	Q	Y984TGH
156	Q	Y856TGH	166	Q	Y866TGH	175	PM	Y975TGH	185	Q	Y985TGH
157	Q	Y857TGH	167	PM	Y967TGH	176	PM	Y976TGH	186	Q	Y986TGH
158	Q	Y858TGH	168	PM	Y968TGH	178	PM	Y978TGH	187	Q	Y987TGH
159	Q	Y859TGH	169	PM	Y969TGH	179	PM	Y979TGH	188	Q	Y988TGH
160	Q	Y806TGH	170	PM	Y907TGH	180	PM	Y908TGH	189	Q	Y989TGH
161	Q	Y861TGH	171	PM	Y971TGH	181	PM	Y981TGH	190	Q	Y909TGH
162	Q	Y862TGH									

LDP191-237

Dennis Dart SLF 10.1m			Plaxton Pointer 2			N31D		2002-03		
191	AL	SN51UAD	203	AL	SN51UAS	215	SW	SK52MOF	227	AF	SK52MME
192	AL	SN51UAE	204	AL	SN51UAT	216	AL	SK52MOU	228	AF	SK52MMF
193	AL	SN51UAF	205	AL	SN51UAU	217	AL	SK52MOV	229	AF	SK52MMJ
194	AL	SN51UAG	206	AL	SN51UAV	218	SW	SK52MPE	230	AF	SK52MMO
195	AL	SN51UAH	207	AL	SN51UAW	219	SW	SK52MPF	231	AF	SK52MKX
196	AL	SN51UAJ	208	AL	SN51UAX	220	SW	SK52MPO	232	AF	SK52MKZ
197	AL	SN51UAK	209	AL	SN51UAY	221	SW	SK52MLU	233	AF	SK52MRO
198	AL	SN51UAL	210	AL	SN51UAZ	222	AF	SK52MLV	234	AF	SK52MRU
199	AL	SN51UAM	211	SW	SK52MMU	223	AF	SK52MLX	235	AF	SK52MRV
200	AL	SN51UAO	212	SW	SK52MMV	224	AF	SK52MLY	236	AF	SK52MRX
201	A	SN51UAP	213	SW	SK52MMX	225	AF	SK52MLZ	237	AF	SK52MRY
202	A	SN51UAR	214	SW	SK52MOA	226	AF	SK52MMA			

By 2003 the Darts had gained TransBus International names, as seen on LDP251, SN53KKH. By 2005 the TransBus operation had fallen into administration, but the factories continued assembling vehicles under the Administrator, Deloitte. A new company, called Alexander Dennis Limited (ADL) was then formed by a group of Scottish business people to purchase the bus facilities from the administrators who also chose a lozenge-shaped name badge. *Mark Lyons*

LDP238-262

TransBus Dart 10.1m   TransBus Pointer   N30D   2003

238	SW	SN53ETT	245	SW	SN53EVB	251	AL	SN53KKH	257	AL	SN53KKR
239	SW	SN53ETU	246	SW	SN53EVC	252	AL	SN53KKJ	258	AL	SN53KKT
240	SW	SN53ETV	247	SW	SN53EVD	253	AL	SN53KKL	259	AL	SN53KKU
241	SW	SN53ETX	248	SW	SN53EVE	254	AL	SN53KKM	260	AL	SN53KKV
242	SW	SN53ETY	249	AL	SN53KKF	255	AL	SN53KKO	261	AL	SN53KKW
243	SW	SN53ETZ	250	AL	SN53KKG	256	AL	SN53KKP	262	AL	SN53KKX
244	SW	SN53EVA									

LDP263-273

ADL Dart 8.8m   ADL Pointer   N29F   2005-06

263	SW	LX05EYP	266	SW	LX05EYT	269	SW	LX05EYW	272	SW	LX05EYA
264	SW	LX05EYR	267	SW	LX05EYU	270	SW	LX05EYY	273	NX	LX06EYT
265	SW	LX05EYS	268	SW	LX05EYV	271	SW	LX05EXZ			

LDP274-280

ADL Dart 10.1m   ADL Pointer   N28D   2006

274	NX	LX05EYU	276	NX	LX05EYW	278	NX	LX05FBE	280	NX	LX05FAF
275	NX	LX05EYV	277	NX	LX05FBD	279	NX	LX05FFA			

LDP281-291

ADL Dart 8.8m   ADL Pointer   N23F   2006

281	NX	LX06FAJ	284	NX	LX06FAO	287	SW	LX06FBB	290	SW	LX06EZV
282	NX	LX06FAK	285	NX	LX06FAU	288	SW	LX06FBC	291	SW	LX06EZW
283	NX	LX06FAM	286	NX	LX06FBA	289	SW	LX06EZU			

LDP292-294

ADL Dart 10.1m   ADL Pointer   N28F   2006

292	AF	LX06EZZ	293	AF	LX06EZJ	294	AF	LX06EZK

Go-Ahead London's first batch of thirty-one articulated buses was used to replace Leyland Nationals on Red Arrow services. Pictured on Waterloo Bridge while heading for Waterloo rail station is MAL16, BX02YYW.
Mark Lyons

MAL1-61

			Mercedes-Benz O530G			Mercedes-Benz Citaro	AN49T	2002-04			

1	RA	BX02YZC	17	RA	BX02YZA	32	NX	BN52GWC	47	NX	BD52LNC
2	RA	BX02YZG	18	RA	BX02YZB	33	NX	BN52GWD	48	NX	BD52LNE
3	RA	BX02YZH	19	RA	BX02YZC	34	NX	BN52GWE	49	NX	BD52LNF
4	RA	BX02YZJ	20	RA	BX02YZD	35	NX	BN52GVU	50	NX	BD52LNG
5	RA	BX02YZK	21	RA	BX02YYJ	36	NX	BX04NBD	51	NX	BU04EZK
6	RA	BX02YZL	22	RA	BX02YYK	37	NX	BD52LNO	52	NX	BD52LMO
7	RA	BX02YZM	23	RA	BX02YYL	38	NX	BD52LNP	53	NX	BL52ODK
8	RA	BX02YZN	24	RA	BX02YYM	39	NX	BD52LNR	54	NX	BL52ODM
9	RA	BX02YZO	25	RA	BX02YYN	40	NX	BD52LNT	55	NX	BL52ODN
10	RA	BX02YZP	26	RA	BX02YYO	41	NX	BD52LNU	56	NX	BL52ODP
11	RA	BX02YYS	27	RA	BX02YYP	42	NX	BD52LMU	57	NX	BL52ODR
12	RA	BX02YYT	28	RA	BX02YYR	43	NX	BD52LMV	58	NX	BU04UTM
13	RA	BX02YYU	29	RA	BX02YZR	44	NX	BD52LMX	59	NX	BL52ODT
14	RA	BX02YYV	30	RA	BX02YZS	45	NX	BD52LMY	60	NX	BL52ODU
15	RA	BX02YYZ	31	RA	BX02YZT	46	NX	BD52LNA	61	NX	BL52ODV
16	RA	BX02YYW									

MAL62-94

			Mercedes-Benz O530G			Mercedes-Benz Citaro	AN49T	2004			

62	Q	BX54EFC	71	Q	BX54UCV	79	Q	BX54UDJ	87	Q	BX54UDU
63	Q	BX54EFD	72	Q	BX54UCW	80	Q	BX54UDK	88	Q	BX54UDV
64	Q	BX54UCM	73	Q	BX54UCZ	81	Q	BX54UDL	89	Q	BX54UDW
65	Q	BX54UCN	74	Q	BX54UDB	82	Q	BX54UDM	90	Q	BX54UDY
66	Q	BX54UCO	75	Q	BX54UDD	83	Q	BX54UDN	91	Q	BX54UDZ
67	Q	BX54UCP	76	Q	BX54UDE	84	Q	BX54UDO	92	Q	BX54UEA
68	Q	BX54UCR	77	Q	BX54UDG	85	Q	BX54UDP	93	Q	BX54UEB
69	Q	BX54UCT	78	Q	BX54UDH	86	Q	BX54UDT	94	Q	BX54EFB
70	Q	BX54UCU									

The London Bus Handbook

In 1999, a batch of seventeen East Lancs Myllennium-bodied DAF SB220s was acquired for services to coincide with the opening of The Dome at Greenwich. These vehicles carried Select index marks of GMT(Greenwich Mean Time) to commemorate the occasion. Some seven years later, MD13, V13GMT, from Bexleyheath depot, is seen at North Greenwich on route 486. It continues to carry its representation of The Dome. *Richard Godfrey*

MD1-17

DAF SB220 12m   East Lancs Myllennium   N33D   1999   MD8-10 use LPG fuel.

1	BX	V1GMT	6	BX	V6GMT	10	BX	V10GMT	14	BX	V14GMT
2	BX	V2GMT	7	BX	V7GMT	11	BX	V11GMT	15	BX	V15GMT
3	BX	V3GMT	8	BX	V8GMT	12	BX	V12GMT	16	BX	V16GMT
4	BX	V4GMT	9	BX	V9GMT	13	BX	V13GMT	17	BX	V17GMT
5	BX	V5GMT									

NV104	u	P904RYO	Volvo Olympian YN2RV18Z4	Northern Counties Palatine	B47/27D	1997
NV107	u	P907RYO	Volvo Olympian YN2RV18Z4	Northern Counties Palatine	B47/27D	1997

NV161-187

Volvo Olympian   Northern Counties Palatine II   *Seating varies 1997-98 *165,70/1/6 are CO47/24D

161	u	R361LGH	168	A	R368LGH	176	A	R376LGH	182	NX	R382LGH
162	SW	R362LGH	170	SW	R370LGH	177	Q	R377LGH	183	A	R383LGH
163	SW	R363LGH	171	AL	R371LGH	178	AL	R378LGH	184	A	VLT284
164	u	R364LGH	173	NX	R373LGH	179	A	VLT179	185	A	R385LGH
165	NX	R365LGH	174	AL	R374LGH	180	u	R380LGH	186	A	R386LGH
166	Q	R166LGH	175	A	R375LGH	181	PM	R381LGH	187	A	R387LGH
167	A	R367LGH									

PDL1-27

Dennis Trident 9.9m   Plaxton President   N41/23D   2000-02

1	SW	X601EGK	8	SW	X608EGK	15	SW	PJ02PZN	22	SW	PJ02PZV
2	SW	X602EGK	9	SW	X609EGK	16	SW	PJ02PZO	23	SW	PJ02PZW
3	SW	X603EGK	10	SW	X701EGK	17	SW	PJ02PZP	24	SW	PJ02PZX
4	SW	X604EGK	11	SW	X611EGK	18	SW	PJ02PZR	25	SW	PJ02PZY
5	SW	X605EGK	12	SW	X612EGK	19	SW	PJ02PZS	26	SW	PJ02PZZ
6	SW	X606EGK	13	SW	X613EGK	20	SW	PJ02PZT	27	SW	PJ02RHF
7	SW	X607EGK	14	SW	PJ02PZM	21	SW	PJ02PZU			

PDL28-50

TransBus Trident 9.9m   TransBus President   N41/23D   2003

28	SW	PN03ULK	34	SW	PN03ULT	40	SW	PN03ULZ	46	SW	PN03UMF
29	SW	PN03ULL	35	SW	PN03ULU	41	SW	PN03UMA	47	SW	PN03UMG
30	SW	PN03ULM	36	SW	PN03ULV	42	SW	PN03UMB	48	SW	PN03UMH
31	SW	PN03ULP	37	SW	PN03ULW	43	SW	PN03UMC	49	SW	PN03UMJ
32	SW	PN03ULR	38	SW	PN03ULX	44	SW	PN03UMD	50	SW	PN03UMK
33	SW	PN03ULS	39	SW	PN03ULY	45	SW	PN03UME			

PVL1-38   Volvo B7TL 10m   Plaxton President   N41/21D   2000

No		Reg	No		Reg	No		Reg	No		Reg
1	BX	V301LGC	11	BX	V311LGC	21	BX	V921KGF	30	BX	V330LGC
2	BX	V302LGC	12	BX	V312LGC	22	BX	V322LGC	31	BX	V331LGC
3	BX	V303LGC	13	BX	V313LGC	23	BX	V392KGF	32	BX	V332LGC
4	BX	V304LGC	14	BX	V314LGC	24	BX	V324LGC	33	BX	V233LGC
5	BX	V305LGC	15	BX	V315LGC	25	BX	V325LGC	34	BX	V334LGC
6	BX	V306LGC	16	BX	V816KGF	26	BX	V226LGC	35	BX	V335LGC
7	BX	V307LGC	17	BX	V317LGC	27	BX	V327LGC	36	BX	V336LGC
8	BX	V308LGC	18	BX	V218LGC	28	BX	V228LGC	37	BX	V337LGC
9	BX	V209LGC	19	BX	V319LGC	29	BX	V329LGC	38	BX	V338LGC
10	BX	V310LGC	20	BX	V220LGC						

PVL39-143   Volvo B7TL 10m   Plaxton President   *N41/21D   2000   *58 is N41/19D

No		Reg	No		Reg	No		Reg	No		Reg
39	BX	W439WGH	66	SW	W466WGH	92	AL	W492WGH	118	AL	W518WGH
40	BX	W840WGH	67	AL	W467WGH	93	AL	W493WGH	119	AL	W519WGH
41	BX	W441WGH	68	AL	W468WGH	94	AL	W494WGH	120	BX	W402WGH
42	BX	W442WGH	69	AL	W469WGH	95	AL	W495WGH	121	AL	W521WGH
43	BX	W443WGH	70	AL	W578DGU	96	AL	W496WGH	122	AL	W522WGH
44	BX	W544WGH	71	PM	W471WGH	97	AL	W497WGH	123	AL	W523WGH
45	BX	W445WGH	72	PM	W472WGH	98	AL	W498WGH	124	AL	W524WGH
46	BX	W446WGH	73	PM	W473WGH	99	AL	W399WGH	125	AL	W425WGH
47	BX	W447WGH	74	AL	W474WGH	100	AL	W997WGH	126	AL	W526WGH
48	BX	W448WGH	75	NX	W475WGH	101	AL	W501WGH	127	AL	W527WGH
49	BX	W449WGH	76	AL	W476WGH	102	AL	W502WGH	128	AL	W428WGH
50	BX	W499WGH	77	AL	W477WGH	103	AL	W503WGH	129	AL	W529WGH
51	BX	W451WGH	78	SW	W478WGH	104	AL	W504WGH	130	AL	W403WGH
52	BX	W452WGH	79	NX	W479WGH	105	AL	W905WGH	131	AL	W531WGH
53	BX	W453WGH	80	A	W408WGH	106	AL	W506WGH	132	AL	W532WGH
54	BX	W454WGH	81	AL	W481WGH	107	AL	W507WGH	133	AL	W533WGH
55	BX	W998WGH	82	BX	W482WGH	108	AL	W508WGH	134	AL	W534WGH
56	AL	W956WGH	83	BX	W483WGH	109	AL	W509WGH	135	AL	W435WGH
57	AL	W457WGH	84	AL	W484WGH	110	AL	W401WGH	136	AL	W536WGH
58	AL	W458WGH	85	AL	W485WGH	111	AL	W511WGH	137	AL	W537WGH
59	Q	W459WGH	86	AL	W486WGH	112	AL	W512WGH	138	AL	W538WGH
60	BX	W996WGH	87	AL	W487WGH	113	AL	W513WGH	139	AL	W539WGH
61	AL	W461WGH	88	NX	W488WGH	114	AL	W514WGH	140	AL	W404WGH
62	SW	W462WGH	89	NX	W489WGH	115	AL	W415WGH	141	AL	W541WGH
63	AL	W463WGH	90	NX	W409WGH	116	AL	W516WGH	142	AL	W542WGH
64	SW	W464WGH	91	NX	W491WGH	117	AL	W517WGH	143	AL	W543WGH
65	PM	W465WGH									

PVL144-207   Volvo B7TL 10m   Plaxton President   N41/23D   2000

No		Reg	No		Reg	No		Reg	No		Reg
144	AL	X544EGK	160	PM	X616EGK	176	Q	X576EGK	192	A	X592EGK
145	AL	X745EGK	161	PM	X561EGK	177	NX	X577EGK	193	A	X593EGK
146	AL	X546EGK	162	PM	X562EGK	178	Q	X578EGK	194	A	X594EGK
147	AL	X547EGK	163	PM	X563EGK	179	A	X579EGK	195	u	X595EGK
148	AL	X548EGK	164	PM	X564EGK	180	A	X508EGK	196	u	X596EGK
149	AL	X549EGK	165	PM	X656EGK	181	A	X581EGK	197	u	X597EGK
150	AL	X599EGK	166	Q	X566EGK	182	A	X582EGK	198	u	X598EGK
151	AL	X551EGK	167	Q	X567EGK	183	A	X583EGK	199	u	X699EGK
152	AL	X552EGK	168	Q	X568EGK	184	A	X584EGK	200	u	X502EGK
153	AL	X553EGK	169	NX	X569EGK	185	A	X585EGK	201	u	X501EGK
154	AL	X554EGK	170	NX	X707EGK	186	A	X586EGK	202	u	X702EGK
155	AL	X615EGK	171	NX	X571EGK	187	A	X587EGK	203	u	X503EGK
156	NX	X556EGK	172	NX	X572EGK	188	A	X588EGK	204	u	X504EGK
157	NX	X557EGK	173	NX	X573EGK	189	A	X589EGK	205	u	X705EGK
158	NX	X558EGK	174	NX	X574EGK	190	A	X509EGK	206	A	X506EGK
159	NX	X559EGK	175	NX	X575EGK	191	A	X591EGK	207	A	X507EGK

Now five years old, PVLs within the Go-Ahead London fleet have started to undergo refurbishment. The first examples treated were those at Bexleyheath depot followed by Merton's. Freshly repainted and fitted with new glazing and additional opening upper-deck windows, PVL58, W458WGH, is seen in Mitcham. *Colin Lloyd*

PVL208-272

				Volvo B7TL	10m			Plaxton President			N41/23D	2000-02	private hire fleet

208	NX	Y808TGH	225	NX	Y825TGH	241	NX	Y741TGH	257	BX	PL51LDY
209	NX	Y809TGH	226	NX	Y826TGH	242	NX	Y742TGH	258	BX	PL51LDZ
210	NX	Y801TGH	227	NX	Y827TGH	243	NX	Y743TGH	259	BX	PL51LEF
211	NX	Y811TGH	228	NX	Y828TGH	244	NX	Y744TGH	260	BX	PN02XBH
212	NX	Y812TGH	229	NX	Y729TGH	245	NX	Y745TGH	261	BX	PN02XBJ
213	NX	Y813TGH	230	NX	Y703TGH	246	NX	Y746TGH	262	PM	PN02XBK
214	NX	Y814TGH	231	NX	Y731TGH	247	NX	Y747TGH	263	NX	PN02XBL
215	NX	Y815TGH	232	NX	Y732TGH	248	NX	Y748TGH	264	NX	PN02XBM
216	NX	Y816TGH	233	NX	Y733TGH	249	NX	Y749TGH	265	NX	PN02XBO
217	NX	Y817TGH	234	NX	Y734TGH	250	BX	PL51LDJ	266	NX	PN02XBP
218	NX	Y818TGH	235	NX	Y735TGH	251	AL	PL51LDK	267	BX	PN02XBR
219	NX	Y819TGH	236	NX	Y736TGH	252	AL	PL51LDN	268	BX	PN02XBS
220	NX	Y802TGH	237	NX	Y737TGH	253	AL	PL51LDO	269	BX	PN02XBT
221	NX	Y821TGH	238	NX	Y738TGH	254	BX	PL51LDU	270	BX	PN02XBU
222	NX	Y822TGH	239	NX	Y739TGH	255	BX	PL51LDV	271	BX	PN02XBV
223	NX	Y823TGH	240	NX	Y704TGH	256	BX	PL51LDX	272	BX	PN02XBW
224	NX	Y824TGH									

PVL273-354   Volvo B7TL   10m   Plaxton President   N41/23D   2002-03

273	BX	PJ02RAU	294	Q	PJ02RDZ	315	NX	PJ52LVS	336	PM	PJ52LWR
274	BX	PJ02RAX	295	Q	PJ02REU	316	NX	PJ52LVT	337	PM	PJ52LWS
275	BX	PJ02RBF	296	Q	PJ02RFE	317	NX	PJ52LVU	338	PM	PJ52LWT
276	PM	PJ02RBO	297	Q	PJ02RFF	318	NX	PJ52LVV	339	PM	PJ52LWU
277	SW	PJ02RBU	298	Q	PJ02RFK	319	NX	PJ52LVW	340	PM	PJ52LWV
278	SW	PJ02RBV	299	Q	PJ02RFL	320	NX	PJ52LVX	341	PM	PJ52LWW
279	SW	PJ02RBX	300	Q	PJ02RFN	321	NX	PJ52LVY	342	PM	PJ52LWX
280	SW	PJ02RBY	301	Q	PJ02RFO	322	NX	PJ52LVZ	343	NX	PF52WPT
281	Q	PJ02RBZ	302	Q	PJ02RFX	323	NX	PJ52LWA	344	NX	PF52WPU
282	Q	PJ02RCF	303	Q	PJ02RFY	324	NX	PJ52LWC	345	NX	PF52WPV
283	Q	PJ02RCO	304	Q	PJ02RFZ	325	NX	PJ52LWD	346	NX	PF52WPW
284	Q	PJ02RCU	305	Q	PJ02RGO	326	Q	PJ52LWE	347	NX	PF52WPX
285	Q	PJ02RCV	306	Q	PJ02RGU	327	Q	PJ52LWF	348	NX	PF52WPY
286	Q	PJ02RCX	307	Q	PJ02RGV	328	Q	PJ52LWG	349	NX	PF52WPZ
287	Q	PJ02RCY	308	Q	PJ02TVN	329	Q	PJ52LWH	350	NX	PF52WRA
288	Q	PJ02RCZ	309	Q	PJ02TVO	330	Q	PJ52LWK	351	NX	PF52WRC
289	Q	PJ02RDO	310	Q	PJ02TVP	331	NX	PJ52LWL	352	NX	PF52WRD
290	Q	PJ02RDU	311	Q	PJ02TVT	332	PM	PJ52LWM	353	NX	PF52WRE
291	Q	PJ02RDV	312	Q	PJ02TVU	333	PM	PJ52LWN	354	NX	PF52WRG
292	Q	PJ02RDX	313	NX	PJ52LVP	334	PM	PJ52LWO			
293	Q	PJ02RDY	314	NX	PJ52LVR	335	PM	PJ52LWP			

PVL355-389   Volvo B7TL   10m   TransBus President   N41/23D   2003

355	NX	PL03AGZ	364	BX	PJ53SOU	373	AL	PJ53NKK	382	AL	PJ53NKW
356	Q	PJ53NJZ	365	BX	PJ53SPU	374	AL	PJ53NKL	383	AL	PJ53NKX
357	Q	PJ53NKA	366	BX	PJ53SPV	375	AL	PJ53NKM	384	AL	PJ53NKZ
358	Q	PJ53NKC	367	BX	PJ53SPX	376	AL	PJ53NKN	385	AL	PJ53NLA
359	Q	PJ53NKD	368	BX	PJ53SPZ	377	AL	PJ53NKO	386	AL	PJ53NLC
360	Q	PJ53NKE	369	BX	PJ53SRO	378	AL	PJ53NKP	387	AL	PJ53NLD
361	Q	PJ53NKF	370	BX	PJ53SRU	379	AL	PJ53NKR	388	AL	PJ53NLE
362	BX	PJ53SOF	371	AL	PJ53NKG	380	AL	PJ53NKS	389	AL	PJ53NLF
363	BX	PJ53SOH	372	AL	PJ53NKH	381	AL	PJ53NKT			

PVL390-419   Volvo B7TL   10m   ADL President   N41/23D   2004-05

390	NX	LX54HAA	398	NX	LX54GZK	406	NX	LX54GYV	413	NX	LX54GZE
391	NX	LX54HAE	399	NX	LX54GZL	407	NX	LX54GYW	414	NX	LX54GZF
392	NX	LX54HAO	400	NX	LX54GZM	408	NX	LX54GYY	415	NX	LX54GZU
393	NX	LX54HAU	401	NX	LX54GZN	409	NX	LX54GZA	416	NX	LX54GZV
394	NX	LX54HBA	402	NX	LX54GZO	410	NX	LX54GZB	417	NX	LX54GZW
395	NX	LX54HBB	403	NX	LX54GZP	411	NX	LX54GZC	418	NX	LX54GZY
396	NX	LX54GZG	404	NX	LX54GZR	412	NX	LX54GZD	419	NX	LX54GZZ
397	NX	LX54GZH	405	NX	LX54GZT						

RM9	Q	VLT9	AEC Routemaster R2RH	Park Royal	B36/28R	1959	

RML887-2520   AEC Routemaster R2RH1   Park Royal   B40/32R   1961-67   *2516 is DRM and B40/32RD

887	AF	202UXJ	2318	AF	CUV318C	2516	Q	WLT516	2520	AF	JJD520D
2305	AF	CUV305C	2472	AF	JJD472D						

RML2604-2736   AEC Routemaster R2RH1   Park Royal   B40/32R   1967-68

2604	Q	NML604E	2618	AF	NML618E	2644	AF	NML644E	2693	AF	SMK693F
2605	AF	NML605E	2626	AF	NML626E	2654	w	NML654E	2725	Q	SMK725F
2606	AF	NML606E	2631	AF	NML631E	2669	w	SMK669F	2732	AF	SMK732F
2612	AF	NML612E	2637	AF	NML637E	2673	AF	SMK673F	2736	u	SMK736F
2615	AF	NML615E	2640	AF	NML640E	2680	AF	SMK680F			

VWL1	BX	LF51CYC	Volvo B7L 12m	Wrightbus Eclipse	N31D	2002	

WHY1-6   VDL Bus SB120   Wrightbus Cadet 2   N26D   2005-06

1	u	LX06ECN	3	u	LX55EAE	5	u	LX55EAJ	6	u	LX55EAG
2	u	LX55EAC	4	u	LX55EAF						

Between 2002 and 2005 two hundred and seventy-three Volvo B7TLs with Wrightbus Eclipse Gemini bodywork were supplied for use at Camberwell, Putney and Stockwell depots. Although initially used on specific routes, most are now fully integrated within each depot. One of almost two hundred at Stockwell, WVL143, LX53AYT, is seen passing Wandsworth Bridge station on route 87. *Richard Godfrey*

WVL1-121 Volvo B7TL 10.1m Wrightbus Eclipse Gemini 4.2m N41/23D 2002-03

1	SW	LG02KGP	32	AF	LF52ZRO	62	AF	LF52ZTG	92	SW	LF52ZND
2	SW	LG02KGU	33	AF	LF52ZRP	63	AF	LF52ZTH	93	SW	LF52ZNE
3	SW	LG02KGV	34	AF	LF52ZRR	64	AF	LF52ZTJ	94	SW	LF52ZNG
4	SW	LG02KGX	35	AF	LF52ZRT	65	AF	LF52ZTK	95	SW	LF52ZNH
5	SW	LG02KGY	36	AF	LF52ZRU	66	AF	LF52ZTL	96	SW	LF52ZNJ
6	SW	LG02KGZ	37	AF	LF52ZRV	67	AF	LF52ZTM	97	SW	LF52ZNK
7	SW	LG02KHA	38	AF	LF52ZRX	68	AF	LF52ZTN	98	SW	LF52ZNL
8	SW	LG02KHE	39	AF	LF52ZRY	69	AF	LF52ZTO	99	SW	LF52ZNM
9	SW	LG02KHF	40	AF	LF52ZRZ	70	AF	LF52ZTP	100	SW	LF52ZNN
10	SW	LG02KHH	41	AF	LF52ZSD	71	AF	LF52ZTR	101	SW	LF52ZNO
11	SW	LG02KHJ	42	AF	LF52ZPZ	72	SW	LF52ZPB	102	SW	LF52ZLZ
12	SW	LG02KHK	43	AF	LF52ZRA	73	SW	LF52ZPC	103	SW	LF52ZMO
13	SW	LG02KHL	44	AF	LF52ZRC	74	SW	LF52ZPD	104	SW	LF52ZMU
14	AF	LG02KHM	45	AF	LF52ZRD	75	SW	LF52ZPE	105	SW	LX03EXV
15	AF	LG02KHO	46	AF	LF52ZRE	76	SW	LF52ZPG	106	SW	LX03EXW
16	AF	LG02KHP	47	AF	LF52ZRG	77	SW	LF52ZPH	107	SW	LX03EXZ
17	AF	LG02KHR	48	AF	LF52ZRJ	78	SW	LF52ZPJ	108	SW	LX03EXU
18	AF	LG02KHT	49	AF	LF52ZRK	79	SW	LF52ZPK	109	SW	LX03EDR
19	AF	LG02KHU	50	AF	LF52ZRL	80	SW	LF52ZPL	110	SW	LX03EDU
20	AF	LG02KHV	51	AF	LF52ZRN	81	SW	LF52ZPM	111	SW	LX03EDV
21	AF	LG02KHW	52	AF	LF52ZPN	82	SW	LF52ZNP	112	SW	LX03EEA
22	AF	LG02KHX	53	AF	LF52ZPO	83	SW	LF52ZNR	113	SW	LX03EEB
23	AF	LG02KHY	54	AF	LF52ZPP	84	SW	LF52ZNS	114	SW	LX03EEF
24	AF	LG02KHZ	55	AF	LF52ZPR	85	SW	LF52ZNT	115	SW	LX03EEG
25	AF	LG02KJA	56	AF	LF52ZPS	86	SW	LF52ZNU	116	SW	LX03EEH
26	AF	LG02KJE	57	AF	LF52ZPU	87	SW	LF52ZNV	117	SW	LX03EEJ
27	AF	LG02KJF	58	AF	LF52ZPV	88	SW	LF52ZNW	118	SW	LX03EEM
28	AF	LF52ZSO	59	AF	LF52ZPW	89	SW	LF52ZNX	119	SW	LX03ECV
29	AF	LF52ZSP	60	AF	LF52ZPX	90	SW	LF52ZNY	120	SW	LX03ECW
30	AF	LF52ZSR	61	AF	LF52ZPY	91	SW	LF52ZNZ	121	SW	LX03ECY
31	AF	LF52ZST									

WVL122-159   Volvo B7TL 10.1m   Wrightbus Eclipse Gemini 4.2m N41/23D 2003-04

122	SW	LX53AZP	132	SW	LX53AZD	142	SW	LX53AYP	151	SW	LX53BJU
123	SW	LX53AZR	133	SW	LX53AZF	143	SW	LX53AYT	152	SW	LX53BEY
124	SW	LX53AZT	134	SW	LX53AZG	144	SW	LX53AYU	153	SW	LX53BGE
125	SW	LX53AZU	135	SW	LX53AZJ	145	SW	LX53AYV	154	SW	LX53BFK
126	SW	LX53AZV	136	SW	LX53AZL	146	SW	LX53AYW	155	SW	LX53BDY
127	SW	LX53AZW	137	SW	LX53AZN	147	SW	LX53AYY	156	SW	LX53BBZ
128	SW	LX53AZZ	138	SW	LX53AZO	148	SW	LX53AYZ	157	SW	LX53BAA
129	SW	LX53AZA	139	SW	LX53AYM	149	SW	LX53BJK	158	SW	LX53BDO
130	SW	LX53AZB	140	SW	LX53AYN	150	SW	LX53BJO	159	SW	LX53BAO
131	SW	LX53AZC	141	SW	LX53AYO						

WVL160-211   Volvo B7TL 10.1m   Wrightbus Eclipse Gemini 4.2m N41/23D 2005

160	SW	LX05FBY	173	AF	LX05FBN	186	AF	LX05FAU	199	AF	LX05EZR
161	SW	LX05FBZ	174	AF	LX05FBO	187	AF	LX05FBA	200	AF	LX05EZS
162	SW	LX05FCA	175	AF	LX05FBU	188	AF	LX05FBB	201	AF	LX05EZT
163	SW	LX05FCC	176	AF	LX05EZJ	189	AF	LX05FBC	202	AF	LX05EZU
164	SW	LX05FCD	177	AF	LX05EYM	190	AF	LX05EZV	203	AF	LX05EYZ
	SW	LX05FCE	178	AF	LX05EYO	191	AF	LX05EZW	204	AF	LX05EZA
	SW	LX05FCF	179	AF	LX05FBV	192	AF	LX05EZZ	205	AF	LX05EZB
	SW	LX05FBD	180	AF	LX05FAA	193	AF	LX05EZK	206	AF	LX05EZC
	AF	LX05FBE	181	AF	LX05FAF	194	AF	LX05EZL	207	AF	LX05EZD
	SW	LX05FBF	182	AF	LX05FAJ	195	AF	LX05EZM	208	AF	LX05EZE
	AF	LX05FBJ	183	AF	LX05FAK	196	AF	LX05EZN	209	AF	LX05EZF
	AF	LX05FBK	184	AF	LX05FAM	197	AF	LX05EZO	210	AF	LX05EZG
	AF	LX05FBL	185	AF	LX05FAO	198	AF	LX05EZP	211	AF	LX05EZH

212-273   Volvo B7TL 10.1m   Wrightbus Eclipse Gemini 4.2m N41/21D 2006

212	Q	LX06DXS	228	Q	LX06DZL	244	Q	LX06EAG	259	Q	LX06EBK
213	Q	LX06DXT	229	Q	LX06DZM	245	Q	LX06EAJ	260	Q	LX06EBL
214	Q	LX06DXU	230	Q	LX06DZN	246	Q	LX06EAK	261	Q	LX06EBM
215	Q	LX06DXV	231	Q	LX06DZO	247	Q	LX06EAL	262	Q	LX06EBN
216	Q	LX06DXW	232	Q	LX06DZP	248	Q	LX06EAM	263	Q	LX06EBO
217	Q	LX06DXY	233	Q	LX06DZR	249	Q	LX06EAO	264	Q	LX06EBP
218	Q	LX06DZA	234	Q	LX06DZS	250	Q	LX06EAP	265	Q	LX06EBU
219	Q	LX06DZB	235	Q	LX06DZT	251	Q	LX06EAW	266	Q	LX06EBW
220	Q	LX06DZC	236	Q	LX06DZU	252	Q	LX06EAY	267	Q	LX06EBZ
221	Q	LX06DZD	237	Q	LX06DZV	253	Q	LX06EBA	268	Q	LX06ECA
222	Q	LX06DZE	238	Q	LX06DZW	254	Q	LX06EBC	269	Q	LX06ECC
223	Q	LX06DZF	239	Q	LX06DZY	255	Q	LX06EBD	270	Q	LX06ECD
224	Q	LX06DZG	240	Q	LX06DZZ	256	Q	LX06EBE	271	Q	LX06ECE
225	Q	LX06DZH	241	Q	LX06EAA	257	Q	LX06EBG	272	Q	LX06ECF
226	Q	LX06DZJ	242	Q	LX06EAC	258	Q	LX06EBJ	273	Q	LX06ECJ
227	Q	LX06DZK	243	Q	LX06EAF						

Ancillary vehicles:

LDP75	PLt	R475LGH	Dennis Dart SLF 10m	Plaxton Pointer	TV	1997

NV109-128   Volvo Olympian YN2RV18Z4   Northern Counties Palatine   TV   1997

109	SWt	P909RYO	112	PLt	P912RYO	116	PLt	P916RYO	127	NXt	P927RYO
110	Qt	P910RYO	113	PLt	P913RYO	117	Qt	P917RYO	128	BXt	P928RYO
111	Qt	P911RYO	114	PLt	P914RYO	124	Qt	P924RYO			

NV131-152   Volvo Olympian   Northern Counties Palatine   TV   1998

131	MWt	R331LGH	137	PLt	R337LGH	143	MWt	R343LGH	147	MWt	R347LGH
132	MWt	R332LGH	138	MWt	R338LGH	144	PLt	R344LGH	148	At	R548LGH
133	PLt	R433LGH	141	NXt	R341LGH	145	PLt	545CLT	152	PLt	R552LGH
134	Qt	R334LGH	142	PLt	R342LGH						

Previous registrations:

166CLT	R366LGH	R476LGH	R476LGH, 176CLT
197CLT	R387LGH	R548LGH	R548LGH, WLT548
202UXJ	WLT887	R552LGH	R552LGH, 352CLT
LF52ZPX	LF52ZPX, VLT60	S638JGP	WLT990
P508RYM	P508RYM, 188CLT	S954JGX	WLT311
P509RYM	P509RYM, WLT379	S955JGX	WLT599
PL51LDY	PL51LDY, 257CLT	V146LGC	V146LGC, 46CLT
R345LGH	R345LGH, 545CLT	V332LGC	V332LGC, WLT532
R366LGH	R366LGH, 166CLT	VLT179	R379LGH
R370LGH	R370LGH, WLT470	VLT284	R384LGH
R377LGH	R377LGH, VLT277	W425WGH	W425WGH, WLT625
R472LGH	R472LGH, WLT872	W578DGU	170CLT
R474LGH	R474RGH, 174CLT	WLT516	CUV283C

Depots and allocations:

Bexleyheath (Erith Road) - BX - London Central

Dart	DML1	DML2	DML3	DML4	DML5	DML6	DML8	DML10	
	DML11	DML12	DML14	DML15	DML17	DML18	DML19	DML20	
	DMS6	DMS7	DMS8	DMS9	LDP4	LDP5	LDP6	LDP7	
	LDP16	LDP57	LDP77	LDP107	LDP108	LDP109	LDP110	LDP111	
	LDP112	LDP113	LDP114	LDP115	LDP116	LDP117	LDP118	LDP119	
	LDP120	LDP121	LDP122	LDP123	LDP124	LDP125	LDP126	LDP127	
	LDP128								
DAF SB220	MD1	MD2	MD3	MD4	MD5	MD6	MD7	MD8	
	MD9	MD10	MD11	MD12	MD13	MD14	MD15	MD16	
	MD17								
Volvo B7L	VWL1								
Olympian	NV72	NV128	NV135	NV139					
Volvo B7TL	PVL1	PVL2	PVL3	PVL4	PVL5	PVL6	PVL7	PVL8	
	PVL9	PVL10	PVL11	PVL12	PVL13	PVL14	PVL15	PVL16	
	PVL17	PVL18	PVL19	PVL20	PVL21	PVL22	PVL23	PVL24	
	PVL25	PVL26	PVL27	PVL28	PVL29	PVL30	PVL31	PVL32	
	PVL33	PVL34	PVL35	PVL36	PVL37	PVL38	PVL39	PVL40	
	PVL41	PVL42	PVL43	PVL44	PVL45	PVL46	PVL47	PVL48	
	PVL49	PVL50	PVL51	PVL52	PVL53	PVL54	PVL55	PVL60	
	PVL82	PVL83	PVL120	PVL171	PVL226	PVL254	PVL255		
	PVL257	PVL258	PVL259	PVL260	PVL261	PVL267	PVL268	PVL269	
	PVL270	PVL271	PVL272	PVL273	PVL274	PVL275	PVL362	PVL363	
	PVL364	PVL365	PVL366	PVL367	PVL368	PVL369	PVL370		

Representing the articulated buses with the Go-Ahead Group in London, is MAL93, BX54UEB, one of the latest batch is seen on route 12 which had been converted from Routemaster to Mercedes-Benz Citaro operation in 2002. Allocated to Camberwell Garage it is seen in Dulwich in June 2006. *Richard Godfrey*

Camberwell (Warner Road) - Q - London Central

Dart	LDP3	LDP64	LDP65	LDP67	LDP68	LDP70	LDP71	LDP72
	LDP73	LDP79	LDP81	LDP82	LDP83	LDP84	LDP86	LDP87
	LDP88	LDP153	LDP154	LDP155	LDP156	LDP157	LDP158	LDP159
	LDP160	LDP161	LDP162	LDP163	LDP164	LDP165	LDP166	LDP182
	LDP183	LDP184	LDP185	LDP186	LDP187	LDP188	LDP189	LDP190
Citaro	MAL62	MAL63	MAL64	MAL65	MAL66	MAL67	MAL68	MAL69
	MAL70	MAL71	MAL72	MAL73	MAL74	MAL75	MAL76	MAL77
	MAL78	MAL79	MAL80	MAL81	MAL82	MAL83	MAL84	MAL85
	MAL86	MAL87	MAL88	MAL89	MAL90	MAL91	MAL92	MAL93
	MAL94							
Routemaster	RML2516	RML2520						
Volvo B7TL	AVL1	AVL2	AVL3	AVL4	AVL5	AVL6	AVL7	AVL8
	AVL9	AVL10	AVL11	AVL12	AVL13	AVL14	AVL16	AVL18
	AVL20	AVL21	PVL59	PVL281	PVL282	PVL283	PVL284	PVL285
	PVL286	PVL287	PVL288	PVL289	PVL290	PVL291	PVL292	PVL293
	PVL294	PVL295	PVL296	PVL297	PVL298	PVL299	PVL300	PVL301
	PVL302	PVL303	PVL304	PVL305	PVL306	PVL307	PVL308	PVL309
	PVL310	PVL311	PVL312	PVL326	PVL327	PVL328	PVL329	PVL330
	PVL356	PVL357	PVL358	PVL359	PVL360	PVL361	WVL212	WVL213
	WVL214	WVL215	WVL216	WVL217	WVL218	WVL219	WVL220	WVL221
	WVL222	WVL223	WVL224	WVL225	WVL226	WVL227	WVL228	WVL229
	WVL230	WVL231	WVL232	WVL233	WVL234	WVL235	WVL236	WVL237
	WVL238	WVL239	WVL240	WVL241	WVL242	WVL243	WVL244	WVL245
	WVL246	WVL247	WVL248	WVL249	WVL250	WVL251	WVL252	WVL253
	WVL254	WVL255	WVL256	WVL257	WVL258	WVL259	WVL260	WVL261
	WVL262	WVL263	WVL264	WVL265	WVL266	WVL267	WVL268	WVL269
	WVL270	WVL271	WVL272	WVL273				
Training vehicles	NV110	NV111	NV114	NV117	NV124	NV126	NV134	NV166

*Buses in mauve are allocated to private hire duties

Merton (High Street) - AL - London General

Dart	LDP54	LDP55	LDP56	LDP59	LDP60	LDP61	LDP62	LDP85
	LDP78	LDP89	LDP90	LDP91	LDP92	LDP93	LDP94	LDP95
	LDP96	LDP97	LDP98	LDP99	LDP101	LDP102	LDP103	LDP104
	LDP105	LDP106	LDP134	LDP135	LDP136	LDP137	LDP138	LDP139
	LDP140	LDP141	LDP191	LDP192	LDP193	LDP194	LDP195	LDP196
	LDP197	LDP198	LDP199	LDP200	LDP201	LDP202	LDP203	LDP204
	LDP205	LDP206	LDP207	LDP208	LDP209	LDP210	LDP216	LDP217
	LDP249	LDP250	LDP251	LDP252	LDP253	LDP254	LDP255	LDP256
	LDP257	LDP258	LDP259	LDP260	LDP261	LDP262		
Routemaster	RML2604							
Olympian	NV171	NV174	NV178					
Volvo B7TL	PVL56	PVL57	PVL58	PVL63	PVL66	PVL67	PVL68	PVL69
	PVL70	PVL74	PVL76	PVL77	PVL78	PVL81	PVL84	PVL85
	PVL86	PVL87	PVL92	PLV93	PVL95	PVL96	PVL97	PVL98
	PVL99	PVL100	PVL101	PVL102	PVL103	PVL104	PVL105	PVL106
	PVL107	PVL108	PVL109	PVL110	PVL111	PVL112	PVL113	PVL114
	PVL115	PVL116	PVL117	PVL118	PVL119	PVL121	PVL122	PVL123
	PVL124	PVL125	PVL126	PVL127	PVL128	PVL129	PVL130	PVL131
	PVL132	PVL133	PVL134	PVL135	PVL136	PVL137	PVL138	PVL139
	PVL140	PVL141	PVL142	PVL143	PVL144	PVL145	PVL146	PVL147
	PVL148	PVL149	PVL150	PVL151	PVL152	PVL153	PVL154	PVL155
	PVL195	PVL206	PVL207	PVL251	PVL253	PVL371	PVL372	PVL373
	PVL374	PVL375	PVL376	PVL377	PVL378	PVL379	PVL380	PVL381
	PVL382	PVL383	PVL384	PVL385	PVL386	PVL387	PVL388	PVL389

The London Bus Handbook

New Cross (New Cross Road) - NX - London Central

Dart	LDP69	LDP76	LDP142	LDP143	LDP144	LDP145	LDP146	LDP147
	LDP148	LDP273	LDP274	LDP275	LDP276	LDP277	LDP278	LDP279
	LDP280	LDP281	LDP282	LDP283	LDP284	LDP285	LDP286	
Citaro Artic	MAL32	MAL33	MAL34	MAL35	MAL36	MAL37	MAL38	MAL39
	MAL40	MAL41	MAL42	MAL43	MAL44	MAL45	MAL46	MAL47
	MAL48	MAL49	MAL50	MAL51	MAL52	MAL53	MAL54	MAL55
	MAL56	MAL57	MAL58	MAL59	MAL60	MAL61		
Routemaster	RM9	RML2472						
Olympian	NV165	NV173	NV182					
Volvo B7TL	PVL65	PVL71	PVL72	PVL73	PVL78	PVL88	PVL89	PVL90
	PVL91	PVL94	PVL156	PVL157	PVL158	PVL159	PVL166	PVL167
	PVL168	PVL169	PVL170	PVL172	PVL173	PVL174	PVL175	PVL176
	PVL177	PVL208	PVL209	PVL210	PVL211	PVL212	PVL213	PVL214
	PVL215	PVL216	PVL217	PVL218	PVL219	PVL220	PVL221	PVL222
	PVL223	PVL224	PVL225	PVL226	PVL227	PVL228	PVL229	PVL230
	PVL231	PVL232	PVL233	PVL234	PVL235	PVL236	PVL237	PVL238
	PVL239	PVL240	PVL241	PVL242	PVL243	PVL244	PVL245	PVL246
	PVL247	PVL248	PVL249	PVL264	PVL313	PVL314	PVL315	PVL316
	PVL317	PVL318	PVL319	PVL320	PVL321	PVL322	PVL323	PVL324
	PVL325	PVL331	PVL343	PVL344	PVL345	PVL346	PVL347	PVL348
	PVL349	PVL350	PVL351	PVL352	PVL353	PVL354	PVL355	PVL390
	PVL391	PVL392	PVL393	PVL394	PVL395	PVL396	PVL397	PVL398
	PVL399	PVL400	PVL401	PVL402	PVL403	PVL404	PVL405	PVL406
	PVL407	PVL408	PVL409	PVL410	PVL411	PVL412	PVL413	PVL414
	PVL415	PVL416	PVL417	PVL418	PVL419			

Trainers	NV127	NV141

Peckham (Blackpool Road) - PM - London Central

Dart	LDP167	LDP168	LDP169	LDP170	LDP171	LDP172	LDP173	LDP174
	LDP175	LDP176	LDP177	LDP178	LDP179	LDP180	LDP181	
Olympian	NV181							
Volvo B7TL	AVL19	AVL22	AVL23	AVL24	AVL25	AVL26	AVL27	AVL28
	AVL29	AVL30	AVL31	AVL32	AVL33	AVL34	AVL35	AVL36
	AVL37	AVL38	AVL39	AVL40	AVL41	AVL42	AVL43	AVL44
	AVL45	AVL46	PVL160	PVL161	PVL162	PVL163	PVL164	PVL165
	PVL262	PVL332	PVL333	PVL334	PVL335	PVL336	PVL337	PVL338
	PVL339	PVL340	PVL341	PVL342				
Trident 2	E16	E17	E18	E19	E20	E21	E22	E23
	E24	E25	E26	E27	E28	E29	E30	E31
	E32	E33	E34	E35	E36	E37		

*Buses in mauve are allocated to private hire duties

Putney (Chelverton Road) - AF - London General

Dart	LDP129	LDP130	LDP131	LDP132	LDP133	LDP222	LDP223	LDP224
	LDP225	LDP226	LDP227	LDP228	LDP229	LDP230	LDP231	LDP232
	LDP233	LDP234	LDP235	LDP236	LDP237	LDP292	LDP293	LDP294
Routemaster	RML887							
Volvo B7TL	WVL14	WVL15	WVL16	WVL17	WVL18	WVL19	WVL20	WVL21
	WVL22	WVL23	WVL24	WVL25	WVL26	WVL27	WVL28	WVL29
	WVL30	WVL31	WVL32	WVL33	WVL34	WVL35	WVL36	WVL37
	WVL38	WVL39	WVL40	WVL41	WVL42	WVL43	WVL44	WVL45
	WVL46	WVL47	WVL48	WVL49	WVL50	WVL51	WVL52	WVL53
	WVL54	WVL55	WVL56	WVL57	WVL58	WVL59	WVL60	WVL61
	WVL62	WVL63	WVL64	WVL65	WVL66	WVL67	WVL68	WVL69
	WVL70	WVL71	WVL168	WVL169	WVL171	WVL172	WVL173	WVL174
	WVL175	WVL176	WVL177	WVL178	WVL179	WVL180	WVL181	WVL182
	WVL183	WVL184	WVL185	WVL186	WVL187	WVL188	WVL189	WVL190
	WVL191	WVL192	WVL193	WVL194	WVL195	WVL196	WVL197	WVL198
	WVL199	WVL200	WVL201	WVL202	WVL203	WVL204	WVL205	WVL206
	WVL207	WVL208	WVL209	WVL210	WVL211			

Stockwell (Binfield Road) - SW - London General

Dart	LDP2	LDP211	LDP212	LDP213	LDP214	LDP215	LDP218	LDP219
	LDP220	LDP221	LDP238	LDP239	LDP240	LDP241	LDP242	LDP243
	LDP244	LDP245	LDP246	LDP247	LDP248	LDP263	LDP264	LDP265
	LDP266	LDP267	LDP268	LDP269	LDP270	LDP271	LDP272	LDP287
	LDP288	LDP289	LDP290	LDP291				
Routemaster	RML2305	RML2318						
Olympian	NV162	NV170						
Trident	PDL1	PDL3	PDL4	PDL5	PDL8	PDL9	PDL11	PDL12
	PDL13	PDL14	PDL15	PDL16	PDL17	PDL18	PDL19	PDL20
	PDL21	PDL22	PDL23	PDL24	PDL25	PDL26	PDL27	PDL28
	PDL29	PDL30	PDL31	PDL32	PDL33	PDL34	PDL35	PDL36
	PDL37	PDL38	PDL39	PDL40	PDL41	PDL42	PDL43	PDL44
	PDL45	PDL46	PDL47	PDL48	PDL49	PDL50		
Trident 2	E1	E2	E3	E4	E5	E6	E7	E8
	E9	E10	E11	E12	E13	E14	E15	E38
	E39							
Volvo B7TL	PVL62	PVL64	PVL263	PVL276	PVL277	PVL278	PVL279	PVL280
	WVL1	WVL2	WVL3	WVL4	WVL5	WVL6	WVL7	WVL8
	WVL9	WVL10	WVL11	WVL12	WVL13	WVL72	WVL73	WVL74
	WVL75	WVL76	WVL77	WVL78	WVL79	WVL80	WVL81	WVL82
	WVL83	WVL84	WVL85	WVL86	WVL87	WVL88	WVL89	WVL90
	WVL91	WVL92	WVL93	WVL94	WVL95	WVL96	WVL97	WVL98
	WVL99	WVL100	WVL101	WVL102	WVL103	WVL104	WVL105	WVL106
	WVL107	WVL108	WVL109	WVL110	WVL111	WVL112	WVL113	WVL114
	WVL115	WVL116	WVL117	WVL118	WVL119	WVL120	WVL121	WVL122
	WVL123	WVL124	WVL125	WVL126	WVL127	WVL128	WVL129	WVL130
	WVL131	WVL132	WVL133	WVL134	WVL135	WVL136	WVL137	WVL138
	WVL139	WVL140	WVL141	WVL142	WVL143	WVL144	WVL145	WVL146
	WVL147	WVL148	WVL149	WVL150	WVL151	WVL152	WVL153	WVL154
	WVL155	WVL156	WVL157	WVL158	WVL159	WVL160	WVL161	WVL162
	WVL163	WVL164	WVL165	WVL166	WVL167	WVL169		
Trainer	NV109							

Sutton (Bushey Road) - A - London General

Dart	LDP1	LDP8	LDP9	LDP14	LDP37	LDP40	LDP41	LDP42
	LDP43	LDP44	LDP45	LDP46	LDP47	LDP48	LDP49	LDP51
	LDP52	LDP53	LDP74	LDP149	LDP150	LDP151	LDP152	
Olympian	NV167	NV168	NV175	NV176	NV179	NV183	NV184	NV185
	NV186	NV187						
Volvo B7TL	EVL1	EVL2	EVL3	EVL4	EVL5	EVL6	EVL7	EVL8
	EVL9	EVL10	EVL11	EVL12	EVL13	EVL14	EVL15	EVL16
	EVL17	EVL18	EVL19	EVL20	EVL21	EVL22	EVL23	EVL24
	EVL25	EVL26	EVL27	EVL28	EVL29	EVL30	EVL31	EVL32
	EVL33	EVL34	EVL35	EVL36	EVL37	EVL38	EVL39	EVL40
	EVL41	EVL42	EVL43	EVL44	EVL45	EVL46	EVL47	EVL48
	EVL49	EVL50	EVL51	EVL52	PVL61	PVL80	PVL179	PVL180
	PVL181	PVL182	PVL183	PVL184	PVL185	PVL186	PVL187	PVL188
	PVL189	PVL190	PVL191	PVL192	PVL193	PVL194	PVL252	PVL265
	PVL266							
Trainer	NV148							

Representing the 2002 intake of a batch of fourteen Tridents is PDL17, PJ02PZP. These vehicles were last for this fleet badged as Dennis products although, the company was already under TransBus ownership. Pictured in Parliament Square while operating route 88, this Stockwell allocated route was formerly numbered 77A and was the last TfL route to have a suffix letter. *Richard Godfrey*

Waterloo (Cornwall Street) - RA - Red Arrow

Citaro Artic	MAL1	MAL2	MAL3	MAL4	MAL5	MAL6	MAL7	MAL8
	MAL9	MAL10	MAL11	MAL12	MAL13	MAL14	MAL15	MAL16
	MAL17	MAL18	MAL19	MAL20	MAL21	MAL22	MAL23	MAL24
	MAL25	MAL26	MAL27	MAL28	MAL29	MAL30	MAL31	

Wimbledon (Plough Lane) - PL - London General

Trainers	NV112	NV113	NV116	NV131	NV132	NV133	NV137	NV138
	NV142	NV143	NV144	NV145	NV147	NV152		

Several training buses are allocated to Driving Instructors rather than depots.

Unallocated/stored - u

Dart	PDL2	PDL6	PDL7	PDL10	LDP15	LDP58	LDP66	LDP75
SB120	WHY1	WHY2	WHY3	WHY4	WHY5	WHY6		

On loan:

Go-Ahead Oxford	LDP32	LDP39						
Go-Ahead South Coast	LDP36							
Go-Ahead Birmingham	NV104	NV107	NV161	NV163	NV180			
East Thames Buses	LDP34	LDP63	PVL196	PVL197	PVL198	PVL199	PVL200	PVL201
	PVL202	PVL203	PVL204	PVL205				

GO-AHEAD METROBUS

Metrobus Ltd, Wheatstone Close, Crawley, RH10 1DQ

117	CY	N417MPN	Dennis Lance 11m		Optare Sigma	B47F	1996	Brighton & Hove, 2003
118	CY	N418MPN	Dennis Lance 11m		Optare Sigma	B47F	1996	Brighton & Hove, 2003
158	CY	L58UNS	Volvo B10B		Alexander Strider	B51F	1993	Whitelaw, Stonehouse, 2002
159	CY	L59UNS	Volvo B10B		Alexander Strider	B51F	1993	Whitelaw, Stonehouse, 2002

201-219
TransBus Dart 10.7m — TransBus Pointer — N36D — 2003

201	CY	SN03WKU	206	CY	SN03WLH	211	C	SN03WLZ	216	ON	SN03WMP
202	CY	SN03WKY	207	CY	SN03WLL	212	C	SN03WMC	217	ON	SN03WMT
203	CY	SN03WLA	208	CY	SN03WLP	213	C	SN03WMF	218	ON	SN03WMV
204	CY	SN03WLE	209	C	SN03WLU	214	C	SN03WMG	219	ON	SN03WMY
205	CY	SN03WLF	210	C	SN03WLX	215	ON	SN03WMK			

220-223
TransBus Dart 10.5m — Caetano Nimbus — N32D — 2004 — Tellings-Golden Miller, 2005

220	ON	KX04HRD	221	ON	KX04HRE	222	ON	KX04HRF	223	ON	KX04HRG

224-227
Dennis Dart SLF 10m — Plaxton Pointer — N36F — 1996 — London General, 2002

224	CY	P724RYL	225	CY	P725RYL	226	CY	P726RYL	227	CY	P727RYL

Metrobus has now started to displace the East Lancs-bodied Dennis Tridents supplied new in 1999. All surviving Tridents are operating outside the TfL area and thus retain the blue and yellow livery as seen on 419, LV51YCE, when pictured on route 261 in High Street, Bromley. *Mark Lyons*

Recent arrivals with Metrobus consist of a dozen ADL Darts with East Lancs Myllennium bodies. Interestingly, these are fitted with the latest front-end design from the new Esteem range. Number 265, PN06UYV, is seen loading in Dingwall Road, East Croydon. *Laurie Rufus*

228-236

			ADL Dart 8.8m			East Lancs Esteem		N24F	2006		
228	ON	PO56JEU	231	ON	JO56JFF	233	ON	PO56JFJ	235	ON	JF56JFN
229	ON	PO56JFA	232	ON	JO56JFG	234	ON	PO56JFK	236	ON	JF56JFU
230	ON	PO56JFE									

241-245

			Dennis Dart SLF 10m			Plaxton Pointer		N35F*	1998	*241 is N32F	
241	CY	R741BMY	243	CY	R743BMY	244	CY	R744BMY	245	CY	R745BMY
242	CY	R742BMY									

246	CY	R746FGX	Dennis Dart SLF 10m	Plaxton Pointer	N35F	1998
247	CY	R747FGX	Dennis Dart SLF 10m	Plaxton Pointer	N35F	1998

251-256

			ADL Dart 8.8m			ADL Mini Pointer		N29F	2004		
251	ON	SN54GPV	253	ON	SN54GPY	255	ON	SN54GRF	256	ON	SN54GRK
252	ON	SN54GPX	254	ON	SN54GPZ						

257-268

			ADL Dart 8.8m			East Lancs Myllennium*		N24F	2006	*Esteem fronts are fitted	
257	ON	PN06UYL	260	C	PN06UYP	263	C	PN06UYT	266	C	PN06UYW
258	ON	PN06UYM	261	C	PN06UYR	264	C	PN06UYU	267	C	PN06UYX
259	ON	PN06UYO	262	C	PN06UYS	265	C	PN06UYV	268	C	PN06UYY

271-289

			TransBus Dart 8.8m			TransBus Pointer		N29F	2003		
271	C	SN03YBA	276	C	SN03YBK	281	ON	SN03YBY	286	ON	SN03YCK
272	C	SN03YBB	277	C	SN03YBR	282	ON	SN03YBZ	287	ON	SN03YCL
273	C	SN03YBC	278	ON	SN03YBS	283	ON	SN03YCD	288	ON	SN03YCM
274	C	SN03YBG	279	ON	SN03YBT	284	ON	SN03YCE	289	ON	SN03YCT
275	C	SN03YBH	280	ON	SN03YBX	285	ON	SN03YCF			

Over ninety East Lancs-bodied Scania OmniDekkas now form the majority of the Metrobus double-deck fleet. Route 161, which plies between North Greenwich station and Chislehurst, received a batch of these to replace early Tridents in 2006. The type is represented by 908, YN55PZL. *Laurie Rufus*

291-299

			Dennis Dart SLF 8.8m			Plaxton Pointer MPD		N29F	2000	

291	CY	W791VMV	294	CY	W794VMV	296	CY	W796VMV	298	CY	W798VMV
292	CY	W792VMV	295	CY	W795VMV	297	CY	W797VMV	299	CY	W799VMV
293	CY	W793VMV

301-308

			Dennis Dart SLF 10m			Plaxton Pointer 2		N33F	1997	Limebourne, 1999

| 301 | CY | P301HDP | 303 | CY | P303HDP | 305 | CY | P305HDP | 307 | CY | P307HDP |
| 302 | CY | P302HDP | 304 | CY | P304HDP | 306 | CY | P306HDP | 308 | CY | P308HDP |

309	CY	T309SMV	Dennis Dart SLF 10.2m	Alexander ALX200	N32F	1999
310	CY	T310SMV	Dennis Dart SLF 10.2m	Alexander ALX200	N32F	1999
311	CY	T311SMV	Dennis Dart SLF 10.2m	Alexander ALX200	N32F	1999

312-319

			Dennis Dart SLF 8.8m			Plaxton Pointer MPD		N29F	1999-2000	

| 312 | ON | T312SMV | 314 | CY | T314SMV | 316 | C | T316SMV | 319 | C | W319VGX |
| 313 | ON | T313SMV | 315 | C | T315SMV | 317 | C | W317VGX |

| 320 | CY | LX03OJP | TransBus Dart SLF 10.7m | TransBus Pointer | N37F | 2003 |
| 321 | CY | LX03OJN | TransBus Dart SLF 10.7m | TransBus Pointer | N37F | 2003 |

322-338

			Dennis Dart SLF 10.7m			Plaxton Pointer 2		N31D	1999-2000	

322	C	V322KMY	326	C	V326KMY	330	C	V330KMY	335	ON	W335VGX
323	C	V323KMY	327	C	V327KMY	331	C	V331KMY	336	ON	W336VGX
324	C	V324KMY	328	C	V328KMY	332	ON	W332VGX	337	ON	W337VGX
325	C	V325KMY	329	C	V329KMY	334	ON	W334VGX	338	ON	W338VGX

339-344

			Dennis Dart SLF 8.8m			Plaxton Pointer MPD		N29F	2000	

| 339 | C | W339VGX | 342 | ON | W342VGX | 343 | ON | W343VGX | 344 | CY | X344YGU |
| 341 | ON | W341VGX |

348-358

			Dennis Dart SLF 8.8m			Plaxton Pointer MPD		N21F*	2001	*356-8 are N27F
348	ON	Y348HMY	352	ON	Y352HMY	354	ON	Y354HMY	357	ON	Y357HMY
349	ON	Y349HMY	353	ON	Y353HMY	356	ON	Y356HMY	358	ON	Y358HMY
351	ON	Y351HMY								

359-376

			Dennis Dart SLF 11m			Caetano Nimbus		N38F	2001
359	CY	Y359HMY	364	CY	Y364HMY	368	CY	Y368HMY	373	CY	Y373HMY
361	CY	Y361HMY	365	CY	Y365HMY	369	CY	Y369HMY	374	CY	Y374HMY
362	CY	Y362HMY	366	CY	Y366HMY	371	CY	Y371HMY	376	CY	Y376HMY
363	CY	Y363HMY	367	CY	Y367HMY	372	CY	Y372HMY		

377	CY	Y377HMY	Dennis Dart SLF 10m	Caetano Nimbus	N34F	2001
378	CY	Y378HMY	Dennis Dart SLF 10m	Caetano Nimbus	N34F	2001
379	CY	Y379HMY	Dennis Dart SLF 10m	Caetano Nimbus	N34F	2001

381-393

			Dennis Dart SLF 8.8m			Plaxton Pointer MPD		N27F	2001
381	ON	Y381HKE	384	ON	Y384HKE	387	ON	Y387HKE	391	ON	Y391HKE
382	ON	Y382HKE	385	ON	Y385HKE	388	ON	Y388HKE	392	ON	Y392HKE
383	ON	Y383HKE	386	ON	Y386HKE	389	ON	Y389HKE	393	ON	Y393HKE

398	ON	BU04UTN	Mercedes-Benz Sprinter 411cdi	Koch	N16F	2004	Tellings-Golden Miller, 2005
399	ON	BU04UTP	Mercedes-Benz Sprinter 411cdi	Koch	N16F	2004	Tellings-Golden Miller, 2005

417-428

			Dennis Trident 9.9m			East Lancs Lolyne 4.4m		N45/23D	2001-02
417	ON	LV51YCC	420	ON	LV51YCF	423	ON	LV51YCJ	426	ON	LV51YCM
418	ON	LV51YCD	421	ON	LV51YCG	424	ON	LV51YCK	427	ON	LV51YCN
419	ON	LV51YCE	422	ON	LV51YCH	425	ON	LV51YCL	428	ON	LV51YCO

431-447

			Scania N94UD OmniDekka 10.6m East Lancs 4.4m					N45/29D	2003
431	C	YV03PZW	436	C	YV03PZF	440	C	YV03PZK	444	C	YV03RCZ
432	C	YV03PZX	437	C	YV03PZG	441	C	YV03PZL	445	C	YV03RAU
433	C	YV03PZY	438	C	YV03PZH	442	C	YV03PZM	446	C	YV03RAX
434	C	YV03PZZ	439	C	YV03PZJ	443	C	YV03RCY	447	C	YV03RBF
435	C	YV03PZE								

451-471

			Scania N94UD OmniDekka 10.6m East Lancs 4.4m					N45/29D	2003
451	C	YU52XVK	457	C	YU52XVR	462	C	YN03DFK	467	ON	YN03DFX
452	C	YU52XVL	458	C	YN03DFD	463	C	YN03DFL	468	C	YN03DFY
453	C	YU52XVM	459	C	YN03DFE	464	C	YN03DFP	469	ON	YV03RBU
454	C	YU52XVN	460	C	YN03DFG	465	C	YN03DFU	470	ON	YV03RBX
455	C	YN03DFA	461	C	YN03DFJ	466	C	YN03DFV	471	ON	YV03RBY
456	C	YN03DFC								

472-497

			Scania N94UD OmniDekka 10.6m East Lancs 4.4m					N45/29D	2003-05
472	ON	YN53RYA	479	ON	YN53RYM	486	ON	YN53RYY	492	ON	YN53RZE
473	ON	YN53RYB	480	ON	YN53RYP	487	ON	YN53RYZ	493	ON	YN53RZF
474	ON	YN53RYC	481	ON	YN53RYR	488	ON	YN53RZA	494	ON	YN54AJU
475	ON	YN53RYD	482	ON	YN53RYT	489	ON	YN53RZB	495	ON	YN54AJV
476	ON	YN53RYF	483	ON	YN53RYV	490	ON	YN53RZC	496	ON	YN54AJX
477	ON	YN53RYH	484	ON	YN53RYW	491	C	YN53RZD	497	ON	YN54AJY
478	ON	YN53RYK	485	ON	YN53RYX					

513	CY	YP52CTO	Scania OmniCity CN94UB 12m	Scania	N42F	2002

514-530

			Scania OmniCity CN94UB 12m			Scania		N37D	2003
514	ON	YN53RXF	519	ON	YN53RXL	523	ON	YN53RXR	527	ON	YN53RXW
515	ON	YN53RXG	520	ON	YN53RXM	524	ON	YN53RXT	528	ON	YN53RXX
516	ON	YN53RXH	521	ON	YN53RXO	525	ON	YN53RXU	529	ON	YN53RXY
517	ON	YN53RXJ	522	ON	YN53RXP	526	ON	YN53RXV	530	ON	YN53RXZ
518	ON	YN53RXK								

531-545
Scania OmniCity CN94UB 12m — Scania — N37D* — 2003-05 — *541-5 are N36F

531	CY	YN03UWU	535	CY	YN03WPR	539	CY	YN03WRL	543	C	YN05HFG
532	CY	YN03UWY	536	CY	YN03WRF	540	CY	YN03WRP	544	C	YN05HFH
533	CY	YN03UPM	537	CY	YN03WRG	541	C	YN05HFE	545	C	YN05HFJ
534	CY	YN03WPP	538	CY	YN03WRJ	542	C	YN05HFF			

546-558
Scania OmniCity CN94UB 12m — Scania — N37D* — 2005 — *552-558 are N34D

546	CY	YN05HCA	550	CY	YN05HCF	553	CY	YN55PWK	556	CY	YN55PWU
547	CY	YN05HCC	551	CY	YN05HCG	554	CY	YN55PWL	557	CY	YN55PWV
548	CY	YN05HCD	552	CY	YN55PWJ	555	CY	YN55PWO	558	CY	YN55PWX
549	CY	YN05HCE									

601-623
Scania OmniTown N94UB 10.6m — East Lancs Myllennium* — N29D — 2006 — *Esteem fronts are fitted

601	ON	YM55SWU	607	ON	YM55SXA	613	ON	YN06JXT	619	ON	YM55SXO
602	ON	YM55SWV	608	ON	YM55SXB	614	ON	YM55SXH	620	ON	YM55SXP
603	ON	YN06JXR	609	ON	YM55SXC	615	ON	YN06JXU	621	ON	YM55SXR
604	ON	YM55SWX	610	ON	YM55SXD	616	ON	YN06JXV	622	ON	YN06JXY
605	ON	YM55SWY	611	ON	YM55SXE	617	ON	YN06JXW	623	ON	YN06JXZ
606	ON	YN06JXS	612	ON	YM55SXF	618	ON	YN06JXX			

721	u	M721CGO	Dennis Dart 9.8m	Plaxton Pointer	B35F	1995	
726	u	N726KGF	Dennis Dart 9.8m	Plaxton Pointer	B35F	1995	
757	u	P895PWW	Dennis Dart 9.8m	Plaxton Pointer	B40F	1997	
758	u	R58GNW	Dennis Dart 9.8m	Plaxton Pointer	B40F	1997	Ambermile, Honley, 1998

817-829
Volvo Olympian YN2RV18Z4 — Northern Counties Palatine — B47/29F — 1996

817	CY	P817SGP	821	CY	P821SGP	824	CY	P824SGP	828	CY	P828SGP
818	CY	P818SGP	822	CY	P822SGP	825	CY	P825SGP	829	CY	P829SGP
819	CY	P819SGP	823	CY	P823SGP	826	CY	P826SGP			

830-845
Volvo Olympian — East Lancs Pyoneer — B47/25D — 1997

830	CY	R830MFR	834	CY	R834MFR	838	CY	R838MFR	843	CY	R843MFR
831	CY	R831MFR	835	CY	R835MFR	839	CY	R839MFR	844	CY	R844MFR
832	CY	R832MFR	836	CY	R836MFR	841	CY	R841MFR	845	CY	R845MFR
833	CY	R833MFR	837	CY	R837MFR	842	CY	R842MFR			

901-927
Scania N94UD OmniDekka 10.6m — East Lancs 4.4m — N45/26D — 2006

901	ON	YN55PZC	908	ON	YN55PZL	915	ON	YN55PZW	922	C	YN06JYG
902	ON	YN55PZD	909	ON	YN55PZM	916	ON	YN55PZX	923	C	YN06JYH
903	ON	YN55PZE	910	ON	YN55PZO	917	C	YN06JYB	924	C	YN06JYJ
904	ON	YN55PZF	911	ON	YN55PZP	918	C	YN06JYC	925	C	YN06JYK
905	ON	YN55PZG	912	ON	YN55PZR	919	C	YN06JYD	926	C	YN06JYL
906	ON	YN55PZH	913	ON	YN55PZU	920	C	YN06JYE	927	C	YN06JYO
907	ON	YN55PZJ	914	ON	YN55PZV	921	C	YN06JYF			

928-946
Scania N94UD OmniDekka 10.6m — East Lancs 4.4m — N45/26D — 2006

928	CY	YN56FDA	933	ON	YM56FDG	938	-	YM56FDO	943	-	YM56FDY
929	CY	YM56FDC	934	ON	YM56FDJ	939	-	YM56FDP	944	-	YM56FDZ
930	ON	YM56FDD	935	-	YM56FDK	940	-	YM56FDU	945	-	YM56FEF
931	ON	YM56FDE	936	-	YM56FDL	941	-	YM56FDV	946	-	YM56FEG
932	ON	YM56FDF	937	-	YM56FDM	942	-	YM56FDX			

Special Event vehicle:

RML2317	CY	CUV317C	AEC Routemaster R2RH1	Park Royal	B40/32R	1965	London Central, 2004

Ancillary vehicles:

7762	LR	M502VJO	Dennis Dart 9.8m	Marshall C37	TV	1995	Oxford Citybus, 2004
7763	LR	M511VJO	Dennis Dart 9.8m	Marshall C37	TV	1995	Oxford Citybus, 2004
7764	LR	M516VJO	Dennis Dart 9.8m	Marshall C37	TV	1995	Oxford Citybus, 2004
7765	LR	M520VJO	Dennis Dart 9.8m	Marshall C37	TV	1995	Oxford Citybus, 2004
7766	CY	M506VJO	Dennis Dart 9.8m	Marshall C37	TV	1995	Oxford Citybus, 2004
7767	CY	M507VJO	Dennis Dart 9.8m	Marshall C37	TV	1995	Oxford Citybus, 2004
7768	CY	M508VJO	Dennis Dart 9.8m	Marshall C37	TV	1995	Oxford Citybus, 2004
7769	CY	M518VJO	Dennis Dart 9.8m	Marshall C37	TV	1995	Oxford Citybus, 2004

Created in 1977 as an orbital Green Line route linking Heathrow Airport with North Kent through numerous south London suburbs, route 726 has seen gradual retrenchment from Gravesend to its present terminus in Croydon. Now known as route X26, this limited stop service uses five single-doored Scania OmniCity including 544, YN05HFH. *Laurie Rufus*

8001-8015

			Ford Transit		Ford		Crew	2003	
8001	ON	GV53RHU	8005	ON	GV53RJO	8010	C	GV53MDX	8013	C	GP53CLV
8002	ON	GV53RHY	8006	ON	GV53RJX	8011	C	GP53CPY	8014	CY	GP53RBX
8003	ON	GV53RHZ	8007	C	GV53RJY	8012	C	GP53COJ	8015	CY	AM03AGU
8004	ON	GV53RJJ	8009	C	GV53RKF					

8017	C	RO06TUU	Mercedes-Benz Vito 111cdi	Mercedes-Benz	Crew	2005

Depots and allocations:

Crawley (Wheatstone Close) - CY

Dart	201	202	203	204	205	206	207	208
	224	225	226	227	241	242	243	244
	245	246	247	291	292	293	294	295
	296	297	298	299	301	302	303	304
	305	306	307	308	309	310	311	314
	320	321	344	359	361	362	363	364
	365	366	367	368	369	370	371	372
	373	374	375	376	377	378	379	757
	758							
Lance	117	118						
Volvo B10B	158	159						
OmniCity	513	531	532	533	534	535	536	537
	538	539	540	546	547	548	549	550
	551	552	553	554	555	556	557	558
Routemaster	RM2317							
Olympian	817	818	819	820	821	822	823	824
	825	826	827	828	829	830	831	832
	833	834	835	836	837	838	839	841
	842	843	844	845				
OmniDekka	928	929						
Ancillary	7766	7767	7768	7769	8014	8015		

Croydon (Beddington Lane) - C

Dart	209	210	211	212	213	214	260	261
	262	263	264	265	266	267	268	271
	272	273	274	275	276	277	315	316
	317	318	319	322	323	324	325	326
	327	328	328	330	331	339		
OmniCity	541	542	543	544	545			
OmniDekka	431	432	433	434	435	436	437	438
	439	440	441	442	443	444	445	446
	447	451	452	453	454	455	456	457
	458	459	460	461	462	463	464	465
	466	468	491	917	918	919	920	921
	922	923	924	925	926	927		
Ancillary	8007	8009	8010	8011	8012	8013	8017	

Orpington (Farnborough Hill, Green Street Green) - ON

Mercedes-Benz	398	399						
Dart SLF	215	216	217	218	219	220	221	222
	223	228	229	230	231	232	233	234
	235	236	251	252	253	254	255	256
	257	258	259	278	279	280	281	282
	283	284	285	286	287	288	289	312
	313	332	334	335	336	337	338	341
	342	343	348	349	351	352	353	354
	356	357	358	381	382	383	384	385
	386	387	388	389	391	392	393	721
	726							
OmniCity	514	515	516	517	518	519	520	521
	522	523	524	525	526	527	528	529
	530							
OmniTown	601	602	603	604	605	606	607	608
	609	610	611	612	613	614	615	616
	617	618	619	620	621	622	623	
Trident	417	418	419	420	421	422	423	424
	425	426	427	428				
Scania OmniDekka	467	469	470	471	472	473	474	475
	476	477	478	479	480	481	482	483
	484	485	486	487	488	489	490	492
	493	494	495	496	497	901	902	903
	904	905	906	907	908	909	910	911
	912	913	914	915	916	930	931	932
	933	934						
Ancillary	8001	8002	8003	8004	8005	8006		

Orpington (Lagoon Road, St Mary Cray) - LR

Ancillary	7762	7763	7764	7765		Dart	723

The C37 was one of the final step-floor designs to emerge from the Marshall factory before the onset of the low-floor revolution. Metrobus 7764, M516VJO, originated in Oxford. It was displaying its eye-catching livery at Eltham station in this unusual view.
Laurie Rufus

HAMILTON

D L Bennett, 589-591 Uxbridge Road, Hayes, UB4 8HP

AG02AWP	Ayats Bravo Plus A3E/BR1	Ayats	C57/18DT	2002	Sun Fun, Earith, 2002
AK52LYV	Ayats Atlantis A2E/AT35V923	Ayats	C53FT	2002	
FJ05HYN	TransBus R410	Caetano Enigma	C49FT	2005	
FJ05HYO	TransBus R410	Caetano Enigma	C49FT	2005	
FJ05HYP	Volvo B12B	Caetano Enigma	C49FT	2005	
FJ55BXM	Volvo B12B	Caetano Enigma	C53F	2005	
FJ06GGV	Volvo B12B	Caetano Enigma	C49FT	2006	
FJ06GGX	Volvo B12B	Caetano Enigma	C49FT	2006	
FJ06GGY	Volvo B12B	Caetano Enigma	C49FT	2006	
FJ06GGZ	Volvo B12B	Caetano Enigma	C49FT	2006	

Depot: Pronto Yard, Uxbridge Road, Uxbridge

Pictured while operating a National Express service in Cambridge is Hamilton's FJ05HYN, now the oldest of the Caetano Enigma coaches operated. The underframe for this coach is the less common TransBus R410.
Keith Grimes

ISLEWORTH

Isleworth Coaches Ltd, 14/15 Phoenix Distribution Park, Phoenix Way, Heston, TW5 9NB

W667SJF	Iveco EuroRider 391E.12.35	Beulas Ei Mundo	C49FT	2000	Cavalier, Brentford, 2005
X806NJB	Volvo B10M-62	Plaxton Excalibur	C49FT	2001	Bus Eireann, 2005
AB52BUS	Irisbus EuroRider 391E.12.35	Beulas Ei Mundo	C53F	2002	
DB52BUS	Irisbus EuroRider 391E.12.35	Beulas Ei Mundo	C51FT	2002	
AB03BUS	Irisbus EuroRider 397E.12.35	Beulas Ei Mundo	C53FT	2003	
AB04BUS	Irisbus EuroRider 397E.12.35	Beulas Ei Mundo	C51FT	2004	
WA54EDC	Mercedes-Benz Vario 0815	Sitcar Beluga	C30F	2004	Mule Travel, Hanwell, 2005
AB05BUS	Irisbus EuroRider 397E.12.35	Beulas Ei Mundo	C51FT	2005	
YN05AUP	Irisbus EuroMidi CC80	Indcar Maxim 2	C29F	2005	Mule Travel, Hanwell, 2006
AB55BUS	Volvo B7R	Sunsundegei Sideral	C57F	2005	
AB06BUS	Irisbus EuroRider 397E.12.35	Beulas Aura	C53F	2006	
YN06PEO	Mercedes-Benz Vario 0814	Plaxton Cheetah	C29F	2006	

Previous registration:
X806NJB   01D8063

Web: www.isleworthcoaches.co.uk
Named vehicles: W667SLF Micky Pearce; X806NJB Cassandra; AB52BUS Del Boy; DB52BUS Rodney; AB03BUS Boycie; AB04BUS Trigger; AB05BUS Grandad; YN05AUP Denzil; AB55BUS Slater; AB06BUS Uncle Albert

The expanded fleet of Isleworth Coaches typifies the investment made by many London area coach companies. DB52BUS is one of five Iveco EuroRiders with Beulas El Mundo bodywork now in the fleet, this example arriving in 2002. It is seen in Tooley Street, which lies between London Bridge and Tower Bridge on the south side of the River Thames. The coach shows the standard livery worn by the majority of the vehicles in this fleet. *Colin Lloyd*

M C H

MCH (Minibuses) Ltd, 51 Wallingford Road, Uxbridge, UB8 2RW

W889UJB	Mercedes-Benz Sprinter 208	Olympus	M8	2000
MCH999	Mercedes-Benz Sprinter 614	Olympus	C24F	2000
MCH252	Mercedes-Benz Sprinter 211cdi	Olympus	M8	2001
Y992OCT	Mercedes-Benz Vario O814	Autobus Nouvelle 2	C33F	2001
MCH85	Mercedes-Benz Sprinter 614	Autobus	C24F	2001
MCH384	Mercedes-Benz Sprinter 413cdi	Olympus	M16	2001
MU51VZT	Mercedes-Benz Sprinter 208cdi	Olympus	M8	2001
YR02UNW	Neoplan Starliner N516 SHD	Neoplan	C48FT	2002
MCH98	Mercedes-Benz Sprinter 413cdi	Olympus	M16	2002
MCH456	Mercedes-Benz Sprinter 411cdi	Concept	M16	2002
6MCH	Neoplan Skyliner N122/3	Neoplan	C40/14CT	2002
MCH96	Mercedes-Benz Sprinter 413cdi	Olympus	M16	2003
YN03AXP	Neoplan Euroliner N316 SHD	Neoplan	C53F	2003
MCH815	Mercedes-Benz Sprinter 413cdi	Olympus	M16	2003
MCH298	Mercedes-Benz Sprinter 313cdi	Olympus	M16	2003
MCH994	Mercedes-Benz Sprinter 313cdi	Olympus	M16	2003
MCH709	Mercedes-Benz Vario O814	Autobus Nouvelle 2	C29F	2004
YX04DLZ	Mercedes-Benz Vario O814	Autobus Nouvelle 2	C29F	2004
YX54BHU	Mercedes-Benz Vario O814	Autobus Nouvelle 2	C29F	2004
YN54WFD	Mercedes-Benz Atego 1223L	Unvi/Esker Touring	C39F	2004
7MCH	Neoplan Skyliner N122/3	Neoplan	C40/12CT	2004
AE05EFF	BMC 1100FE	BMC	B60F	2005
AE05EFG	BMC 1100FE	BMC	B60F	2005
BX05UUY	Mercedes-Benz Touro 1836RL	Mercedes-Benz	C49FT	2005
MCH957	Mercedes-Benz Sprinter 413cdi	Mercedes-Benz	M16	2005
MCH547	Mercedes-Benz Sprinter 413cdi	Mercedes-Benz	M16	2005

The Mercedes-Benz Atego chassis is more associated with vans than buses. Here a body from Esker Touring is used by MCH to provide a thirty-nine seat coach. It was photographed in Uxbridge. *Colin Lloyd*

Typical of the MCH Minibuses is Mercedes-Benz Sprinter 413cdi.One of many in the fleet to carry a MCH index number, MCH815 is seen passing through Trafalgar Square. *Colin Lloyd*

MCH51	Mercedes-Benz Sprinter 616cdi	Ferqui/Optare Soroco Plus	C19F	2005
YX05DJY	Mercedes-Benz Vario 0814	Autobus Nouvelle 2	C33F	2005
YN05UVG	Mercedes-Benz Atego 1223L	Unvi/Esker Touring	C41F	2005
YN05RXT	Mercedes-Benz Sprinter 616cdi	Unvi/Esker Riada 616	C22F	2005
YN55WPJ	Mercedes-Benz Sprinter 616cdi	Unvi/Esker Riada 616	C22F	2005
MX55VJU	Mercedes-Benz Sprinter 311cdi	Olympus	M12	2005
KE55DCV	Mercedes-Benz Sprinter 416cdi	Olympus	M16	2005
9MCH	Neoplan Starliner N516SHD	Neoplan	C48FT	2005
YX55ADO	Mercedes-Benz Vario 0814	Autobus Nouvelle 2	C29F	2005
YX55ADV	Mercedes-Benz Vario 0814	Autobus Nouvelle 2	C29F	2005
YN06CFK	Mercedes-Benz Vario 0814	Autobus Nouvelle 2	C29F	2006
YN06JFO	Mercedes-Benz Vario 0814	Autobus Nouvelle 2	C29F	2006
BX06UNF	Mercedes-Benz Touro 1836RL	Mercedes-Benz	C49FT	2006
YX06AWM	Mercedes-Benz Sprinter 616cdi	Ferqui/Optare Soroco Plus	C19F	2005
YX06DOJ	Mercedes-Benz Sprinter 416cdi	Olympus	M16	2005
YX06DOU	Mercedes-Benz Sprinter 416cdi	Olympus	M16	2005

Previous registrations:

6MCH	YR52ZKM		MCH384	MF51OAG
7MCH	YN54JPO		MCH456	YR52OCS
9MCH	YN05BXJ		MCH547	HF05AEW
MCH51	YX05AVR		MCH709	YX04FXC
MCH85	Y993OCT		MCH815	MX53PVT
MCH96	MW03GVE		MCH957	HF05AEV
MCH98	MK52UGY		MCH994	MX53ZND
MCH252	Y184KAN		MCH998	W594WCA
MCH298	MX53PUK			

Web: www.mch-coaches.co.uk:

METROLINE

Metroline - Armchair

Metroline Travel Ltd, 66-68 College Road, Harrow, HA1 1BE

Part of the Comfort DelGro Group

AV1	HD	P481MBY	Volvo Olympian YN2RV18Z4		Alexander RH		B43/25D	1996	
AV2	HD	P482MBY	Volvo Olympian YN2RV18Z4		Alexander RH		B43/25D	1996	
AV3	HD	P483MBY	Volvo Olympian YN2RV18Z4		Alexander RH		B43/25D	1996	

AV23-38

Volvo Olympian   Alexander RH   B43/25D   1998

23	PV	S233RLH	27	PV	S127RLE	31	PB	S131RLE	35	PB	S135RLE
24	PV	S124RLE	28	PB	S128RLE	32	HD	S132RLE	36	HD	S136RLE
25	PV	S125RLE	29	PB	S129RLE	33	PB	S133RLE	37	EW	S137RLE
26	PV	S126RLE	30	PB	S130RLE	34	PB	S134RLE	38	PB	S138RLE

DP12-43

Dennis Dart SLF 10.1m   Plaxton Pointer 2   N31D   2000   Centra, Heathrow, 2006

12	PA	W112WGT	18	PA	W118WGT	26	PA	W126WGT	33	PA	W133WGT
14	PA	W114WGT	19	PA	WI19WGT	27	PA	W127WGT	34	PA	W134WGT
16	PA	W116WGT	22	PA	W122WGT	32	PA	W132WGT	43	PA	W143WGT
17	PA	W117WGT	24	PA	W124WGT						

DML533-535

Dennis Dart SLF 10.2m   Marshall Capital   N31F   1999

533	PA	T63KLD	534	PA	T64KLD	535	PB	T65KLD

DA140-152

Dennis Dart SLF 10.2m   Alexander ALX200   N27D   1999

140	AH	T140AUA	144	AH	T144AUA	147	AH	T147AUA	150	AH	T150AUA
141	AH	T141AUA	145	AH	T145AUA	148	AH	T148AUA	151	AH	T151AUA
142	AH	T142AUA	146	AH	T146AUA	149	AH	T149AUA	152	AH	T152AUA
143	AH	T143AUA									

Metroline was the first operator to receive a batch of new Alexander Enviro400 bodied Dennis Trident 2s when twenty-eight were delivered to Holloway depot during 2005-2006. These were soon put to work on route 24 linking Hampstead with Pimlico and passing through Camden Town, Trafalgar Square and Victoria. TE689, LK55KKZ, was caught in Wilton Road, Victoria soon after entering service. *Mark Lyons*

Operated by Metroline from the former Armchair base in Brentford are thirteen DA class Alexander ALX200-bodied Darts purchased in 1999. Originally in orange and white livery, all of this batch are now in compliant TfL red. DA141, T141AUA, leaves Hammersmith bus station bound for the former bus garage site at Mortlake. *Colin Lloyd*

DLD22-53

| | | | | Dennis Dart SLF 10.1m | | Plaxton Pointer 2 | | N30D* | 1997 | *24, 50/1 are N31D |

22	NW	R122RLY	30	NW	R130RLY	38	NW	R138RLY	46	NW	R146RLY
23	NW	R123RLY	31	NW	R131RLY	39	NW	R139RLY	47	NW	R147RLY
24	NW	R124RLY	32	NW	R132RLY	40	NW	R140RLY	48	PV	R148RLY
25	NW	R125RLY	33	NW	R133RLY	41	NW	R141RLY	49	NW	R149RLY
26	PV	R126RLY	34	NW	R134RLY	42	PV	R142RLY	50	PV	R150RLY
27	NW	R127RLY	35	NW	R135RLY	43	NW	R143RLY	51	AC	R151RLY
28	NW	R128RLY	36	NW	R136RLY	44	NW	R144RLY	52	AC	R152RLY
29	NW	R129RLY	37	NW	R137RLY	45	NW	R145RLY	53	AC	R153RLY

DLD54-74

| | | | | Dennis Dart SLF 10.1m | | Plaxton Pointer 2 | | N30D* | 1998 | *74 is N31D |

54	NW	R154VLA	60	AH	R160VLA	65	AH	R165VLA	70	AH	R170VLA
55	NW	R155VLA	61	AH	R161VLA	66	AH	R166VLA	71	AH	R171VLA
56	NW	R156VLA	62	AH	R162VLA	67	AH	R167VLA	72	AH	R172VLA
57	NW	R157VLA	63	AH	R163VLA	68	AH	R168VLA	73	W	R173VLA
58	NW	R158VLA	64	AH	R164VLA	69	AH	R169VLA	74	AH	R174VLA
59	NW	R159VLA									

DLD86-100

| | | | | Dennis Dart SLF 10.1m | | Plaxton Pointer 2 | | N25F | 1998 | |

86	AC	S286JLP	90	AC	S290JLP	94	AC	S294JLP	98	AC	S298JLP
87	AC	S287JLP	91	AC	S291JLP	95	AC	S295JLP	99	AC	S299JLP
88	AC	S288JLP	92	AC	S292JLP	96	AC	S296JLP	100	AC	S301JLP
89	AC	S289JLP	93	AC	S293JLP	97	AC	S297JLP			

| DLS101 | PB | P101OLX | Dennis Dart SLF 9.2m | | Plaxton Pointer | | N32F | 1997 |
| DLS102 | PB | P102OLX | Dennis Dart SLF 9.2m | | Plaxton Pointer | | N32F | 1997 |

DLD108-132

| | | | | Dennis Dart SLF 10.1m | | Plaxton Pointer 2 | | N31D | 1999 | |

108	W	T48KLD	115	W	T35KLD	121	KX	V134GBY	127	KX	V127GBY
109	W	T49KLD	116	W	T56KLD	122	KX	V122GBY	128	KX	V128GBY
110	W	T39KLD	117	AH	T47KLD	123	KX	V133GBY	129	KX	V129GBY
111	W	T51KLD	118	KX	V118GBY	124	KX	V124GBY	130	KX	V130GBY
112	W	T52KLD	119	KX	V119GBY	125	KX	V125GBY	131	KX	V131GBY
113	W	T53KLD	120	KX	V120GBY	126	KX	V126GBY	132	KX	V132GBY
114	W	T54KLD									

The London Bus Handbook

Metroline has one of the largest fleets of Darts in London with well over three hundred examples in stock. The models range from the 8.8m Mini Pointer Dart through to a 10.7m example (class DLF) which is used by Thorpe's. Representing a standard dual-doored 10.1m model is DLD40, R140RLY, seen here on route 251, approaching its terminus at Arnos Grove. *Richard Godfrey*

DLD133-149

		Dennis Dart SLF 10.1m			Plaxton Pointer 2		N31D	2000		
133	KX	W133ULR	138	EW	W138ULR	142	EW	W142ULR	146	EW	W146ULR
134	KX	W134ULR	139	EW	W139ULR	143	EW	W143ULR	147	EW	W147ULR
135	KX	W151ULR	140	EW	W152ULR	144	EW	W144ULR	148	EW	W148ULR
136	KX	W136ULR	141	EW	W141ULR	145	EW	W153ULR	149	KX	W149ULR
137	EW	W137ULR								

DLM150	HT	X667LLX	Dennis Dart SLF 8.8m	Plaxton Pointer MPD	N26F	2000
DLM151	HT	X668LLX	Dennis Dart SLF 8.8m	Plaxton Pointer MPD	N26F	2000

DLM152-160

		Dennis Dart SLF 8.8m			Plaxton Pointer MPD		N29F	2001		
152	HT	Y252NLK	155	HT	Y251NLK	157	HT	Y257NLK	159	HT	Y259NLK
153	HT	Y253NLK	156	HT	Y256NLK	158	HT	Y258NLK	160	HT	Y151NLK
154	HT	Y254NLK								

DLD161-197

		Dennis Dart SLF 10.1m			Plaxton Pointer 2		N30D	2001		
161	KX	Y661NLO	171	KX	Y671NLO	180	PV	Y158NLK	189	PV	Y249NLK
162	KX	Y662NLO	172	KX	Y672NLO	181	NW	Y659NLO	190	PV	Y154NLK
163	KX	Y663NLO	173	KX	Y673NLO	182	PV	Y652NLO	191	PV	Y261NLK
164	KX	Y664NLO	174	KX	Y674NLO	183	NW	Y653NLO	192	PV	Y262NLK
165	KX	Y665NLO	175	KX	Y675NLO	184	NW	Y654NLO	193	PV	Y263NLK
166	KX	Y161NLK	176	KX	Y153NLK	185	PV	Y658NLO	194	PV	Y264NLK
167	KX	Y667NLO	177	KX	Y237NLK	186	PV	Y656NLO	195	PV	Y265NLK
168	KX	Y668NLO	178	KX	Y238NLK	187	PV	Y657NLO	196	PV	Y159NLK
169	KX	Y669NLO	179	PV	Y239NLK	188	PV	Y248NLK	197	PV	Y157NLK
170	KX	Y152NLK								

DLD198-207

		Dennis Dart SLF 10.1m			Plaxton Pointer 2		N30D	2002		
198	NW	LN51KXD	201	NW	LN51KXG	204	NW	LN51KXK	206	NW	LN51KXM
199	NW	LN51KXE	202	NW	LN51KXH	205	NW	LN51KXL	207	NW	LN51KXO
200	NW	LN51KXF	203	NW	LN51KXJ					

In 2006, Metroline commenced a repaint programme that introduced a light blue skirt rather than the usual dark blue one. This arrangement also included the former Thorpe buses as seen here by DLF37, S537JLM, pictured in Golders Green in July 2006. These Darts retain their Thorpe's identity rather than carrying Metroline fleet-names and logos. *Colin Lloyd*

DSD208-217

			Dennis Dart SLF 9.3m			Plaxton Pointer 2		N27D	2002		
208	NW	LR02BDV	211	NW	LR02BDZ	214	NW	LR02BEU	216	NW	LR02BFA
209	NW	LR02BDX	212	NW	LR02BEJ	215	NW	LR02BEY	217	NW	LR02BFE
210	NW	LR02BDY	213	NW	LR02BEO						

DLF9	PB	R309NGM	Dennis Dart SLF 10.1m			Plaxton Pointer		N33F	1997		Frank Thorpe, 2004

DLF29-40

			Dennis Dart SLF 10.1m			Plaxton Pointer 2		N29D	1998		Frank Thorpe, 2004
29	PA	S529JLM	32	PA	S532JLM	35	PA	S535JLM	38	PA	S538JLM
30	PA	S530JLM	33	PA	S533JLM	36	PA	S536JLM	39	PA	S539JLM
31	PA	S531JLM	34	PA	S534JLM	37	PA	S537JLM	40	PA	S540JLM

DLF41	u	P41MLE	Dennis Dart SLF 9.2m			Plaxton Pointer		N27D	1996		Frank Thorpe, 2004

DLF63-79

			Dennis Dart SLF 10.1m			Plaxton Pointer 2		N29D	2000		Frank Thorpe, 2004
63	PA	W963TRP	67	PA	W967TRP	72	PA	W972TRP	76	PA	W976TRP
64	PA	W964TRP	68	PA	W968TRP	73	PA	W973TRP	77	PA	W977TRP
65	PA	W965TRP	69	PA	W969TRP	74	PA	W974TRP	79	PA	X179BNH
66	PA	W966TRP	71	PA	W971TRP	75	PA	W975TRP			

DLF80-110

			Dennis Dart SLF 10.1m			Plaxton Pointer 2		N30D	2002		Frank Thorpe, 2004
80	PA	KM02HDJ	88	PA	KU52YKR	96	PA	KU52YKC	104	PB	KU52YKZ
81	PA	KM02HDK	89	PA	KU52YKS	97	PA	KU52YKD	105	PB	KU52YLA
82	PA	KU52YLG	90	PA	KU52YKT	98	PA	KU52YKE	106	PB	KU52YLB
83	PA	KU52YLH	91	PA	KU52YKV	99	PA	KU52YKF	107	PB	KU52YLC
84	PA	KU52YKL	92	PA	KU52YKX	100	PA	KU52YKG	108	PB	KU52YLD
85	PA	KU52YKN	93	PA	KU52YKY	101	PA	KU52YKH	109	PB	KU52YLE
86	PA	KU52YKO	94	PA	KU52YKA	102	PA	KU52YKJ	110	PB	KU52YLF
87	PA	KU52YKP	95	PA	KU52YKB	103	PA	KU52YKK			

Metroline midi-buses are dominated by the Dennis Dart, most of which have the Pointer bodywork. In addition, around eighty have the Marshall Capital body in either 9.3 metre or 10.2 metre lengths. Seen at Golders Green in September 2005 is DML533, T63KLD, one of only three examples of this body in the Metroline fleet which were supplied in 1999. *Richard Godfrey*

MLF122 PA	AJ02ZRY	Dennis Dart SLF 10.2m	Marshall Capital	N28D	2002	Frank Thorpe, 2004	
DLF123 PA	KX53SDV	TransBus Dart 10.2m	TransBus Pointer	N30D	2003	Frank Thorpe, 2004	
DLF124 PA	KX53SDU	TransBus Dart 10.2m	TransBus Pointer	N30D	2003	Frank Thorpe, 2004	
DLF125 PA	Y641AVV	Dennis Dart SLF 10.7m	Plaxton Pointer	N36D	2001	Frank Thorpe, 2004	

DML1-18
Dennis Dart SLF 10.2m · Marshall Capital · N28D · 1998

1	PA	R681MEW	6	PA	R686MEW	11	PA	R691MEW	15	NW	R695MEW
2	PA	R682MEW	7	PA	R687MEW	12	PA	R692MEW	16	NW	R696MEW
3	PA	R683MEW	8	PA	R688MEW	13	PA	R693MEW	17	NW	R697MEW
4	PA	R684MEW	9	PA	R689MEW	14	PA	R694MEW	18	NW	R698MEW
5	PA	R685MEW	10	PA	R690MEW						

DML33-47
Dennis Dart SLF 10.2m · Marshall Capital · N28D · 1998

33	W	R863MCE	37	W	R867MCE	41	W	R871MCE	45	W	R875MCE
34	W	R864MCE	38	W	R868MCE	42	W	R872MCE	46	W	R876MCE
35	W	R865MCE	39	W	R869MCE	43	W	R873MCE	47	W	R877MCE
36	W	R866MCE	40	W	R870MCE	44	W	R874MCE			

DMS1-29
Dennis Dart SLF 9.3m · Marshall Capital · N32F · 1998

1	PB	R701MEW	9	PB	R709MEW	16	PB	S516KFL	23	PB	S523KFL
2	PB	R702MEW	10	PB	R710MEW	17	PB	S517KFL	24	PB	S524KFL
3	PB	R703MEW	11	PB	R711MEW	18	PB	S518KFL	25	PB	S525KFL
4	PB	R704MEW	12	PB	R699MEW	19	PB	S519KFL	26	PB	S526KFL
5	PB	R705MEW	13	PB	S513KFL	20	PB	S520KFL	27	PB	S527KFL
6	PB	R706MEW	14	PB	S514KFL	21	PB	S521KFL	28	PB	S528KFL
7	PB	R707MEW	15	PB	S515KFL	22	PB	S522KFL	29	PB	S529KFL
8	PB	R708MEW									

With the advent of low-floor double-deck operation in London, Metroline took into stock the Dennis Trident chassis. The first batch comprised sixty-five with Plaxton President bodies, while the second batch was bodied by Alexander using its ALX400 product. One of the latter is TA95, T195CLO, seen here at Brent Cross shopping centre on a sunny day in January 2006. Route 182 operates with a Monday-Friday pvr of twenty-two buses with workings based at Harrow Weald depot. *Richard Godfrey*

DT1-22

		Dennis Trident 9.9m			Alexander ALX400			N43/20D	2003						
1	AH	KN52NCD	7	AH	KN52NDG	13	AH	KN52NDV	18	AH	KN52NEJ				
2	AH	KN52NCE	8	AH	KN52NDJ	14	AH	KN52NDX	19	AH	KN52NEO				
3	AH	KN52NDC	9	AH	KN52NDK	15	AH	KN52NDY	20	AH	KN52NEU				
4	AH	KN52NDD	10	AH	KN52NDL	16	AH	KN52NDZ	21	AH	KN52NEY				
5	AH	KN52NDE	11	AH	KN52NDO	17	AH	KN52NEF	22	AH	KN52NFA				
6	AH	KN52NDF	12	AH	KN52NDU										

OSL1	PA	YJ51JWY	Optare Solo M850		Optare		N17F	2001	Frank Thorpe, 2004
OSL2	PA	YJ51JWZ	Optare Solo M850		Optare		N17F	2001	Frank Thorpe, 2004

TP1-65

		Dennis Trident 9.9m			Plaxton President 4.4m		N41/21D*	1999	*2-31 are N45/22D

1	HT	T101KLD	18	HT	T118KLD	34	HT	T134CLO	50	HT	V750HBY
2	HT	WLT826	19	HT	T119KLD	35	HT	T135CLO	51	HT	V751HBY
3	HT	T103KLD	20	HT	T120KLD	36	HT	T136CLO	52	HT	V752HBY
4	HT	T104KLD	21	HT	T71KLD	37	HT	T137CLO	53	HT	V753HBY
5	HT	T105KLD	22	HT	T122KLD	38	HT	T138CLO	54	HT	V754HBY
6	HT	T106KLD	23	HT	T73KLD	39	HT	T139CLO	55	HT	V755HBY
7	HT	T107KLD	24	HT	T124KLD	40	HT	T140CLO	56	HT	V756HBY
8	HT	T108KLD	25	HT	T125KLD	41	HT	T141CLO	57	HT	V757HBY
9	HT	T109KLD	26	HT	T126KLD	42	HT	T142CLO	58	HT	V758HBY
10	HT	T110KLD	27	HT	T127KLD	43	HT	T143CLO	59	HT	V759HBY
11	HT	T81KLD	28	HT	T128KLD	44	HT	T144CLO	60	HT	V760HBY
12	HT	T112KLD	29	HT	T129KLD	45	HT	T145CLO	61	HT	V761HBY
13	HT	T113KLD	30	HT	T97KLD	46	HT	T146CLO	62	HT	V762HBY
14	HT	T114KLD	31	HT	T98KLD	47	HT	V307GLB	63	HT	V763HBY
15	HT	T115KLD	32	HT	T132CLO	48	HT	T148CLO	64	HT	V764HBY
16	HT	T116KLD	33	HT	T133CLO	49	HT	V749HBY	65	HT	V765HBY
17	HT	T117KLD									

Oxford Street is the location of this view of freshly repainted TA105, T205CLO, operating on route 139 out of Cricklewood depot. This route is normally the domain of the TP class, although here is one of the occasions when an Alexander-bodied Trident undertakes a duty. *Mark Lyons*

TA66-117

Dennis Trident 9.9m   Alexander ALX400 4.4m   N45/19D   1999

66	W	T61KLD	79	W	T79KLD	92	HD	T192CLO	105	W	T205CLO
67	W	T67KLD	80	W	T89KLD	93	HD	T193CLO	106	W	T206CLO
68	W	T68KLD	81	HD	T38KLD	94	HD	T194CLO	107	W	T207CLO
69	W	T69KLD	82	HD	T182CLO	95	HD	T195CLO	108	W	V308GLB
70	W	T37KLD	83	HD	T183CLO	96	HD	T196CLO	109	W	V309GLB
71	W	T41KLD	84	HD	T184CLO	97	HD	T197CLO	110	W	V310GLB
72	W	T72KLD	85	HD	T185CLO	98	HD	T198CLO	111	W	V311GLB
73	W	T43KLD	86	HD	T186CLO	99	HD	T199CLO	112	W	V312GLB
74	W	T74KLD	87	HD	T187CLO	100	W	T218CLO	113	W	V313GLB
75	W	T75KLD	88	HD	T188CLO	101	W	T201CLO	114	W	V314GLB
76	W	T76KLD	89	HD	T189CLO	102	W	T202CLO	115	W	V315GLB
77	W	T87KLD	90	HD	T190CLO	103	W	V303GLB	116	W	V316GLB
78	W	T78KLD	91	HD	T191CLO	104	W	T204CLO	117	W	V317GLB

TAL118-134

Dennis Trident 10.5m   Alexander ALX400 4.4m   N45/24D   2000

118	W	X341HLL	123	W	X343HLL	127	W	X327HLL	131	W	X331HLL
119	W	X319HLL	124	W	X324HLL	128	W	X338HLL	132	W	X332HLL
120	W	X336HLL	125	W	X335HLL	129	W	X329HLL	133	W	X339HLL
121	W	X337HLL	126	W	X326HLL	130	W	X342HLL	134	W	X334HLL
122	W	X322HLL									

VPL135-161

Volvo B7TL 10.6m   Plaxton President 4.4m   N43/25D   2000-01

135	HT	X635LLX	142	HT	X642LLX	149	EW	X649LLX	156	EW	X656LLX
136	HT	X636LLX	143	EW	X643LLX	150	EW	X663LLX	157	EW	X657LLX
137	HT	X637LLX	144	EW	X644LLX	151	EW	X651LLX	158	EW	X658LLX
138	HT	X638LLX	145	EW	X645LLX	152	EW	X652LLX	159	EW	X659LLX
139	HT	X639LLX	146	EW	X646LLX	153	EW	X653LLX	160	EW	X662LLX
140	HT	X664LLX	147	EW	X647LLX	154	EW	X654LLX	161	EW	X661LLX
141	HT	X641LLX	148	EW	X648LLX	155	EW	X665LLX			

With a peak vehicle requirement of fifty-five buses for four double-deck routes, Edgware depot operates a fleet of sixty buses. All are the longer 10.6metre Volvo B7TL fitted with Plaxton President 4.4m high bodies. Seen in October 2005 at Swiss Cottage is VPL217, LK51XGM, on route 113 that links Oxford Circus with Edgware. *Richard Godfrey*

VPL162-236   Volvo B7TL 10.6m   Plaxton President 4.4m   N43/24D   2001

162	EW	Y162NLK	181	AC	Y181NLK	200	EW	Y149NLK	219	EW	LK51XGO
163	EW	Y163NLK	182	AC	Y182NLK	201	EW	Y201NLK	220	EW	LK51XGP
164	EW	Y164NLK	183	AC	Y183NLK	202	EW	Y202NLK	221	EW	LK51XGR
165	EW	Y165NLK	184	AC	Y184NLK	203	EW	Y203NLK	222	EW	LK51XGS
166	EW	Y166NLK	185	AC	Y185NLK	204	EW	Y204NLK	223	EW	LK51XGT
167	EW	Y167NLK	186	AC	Y186NLK	205	EW	LK51XGD	224	EW	LK51XGU
168	AC	Y168NLK	187	AC	Y187NLK	206	EW	Y246NLK	225	EW	LK51XGV
169	AC	Y169NLK	188	AC	Y188NLK	207	EW	Y207NLK	226	EW	LK51XGW
170	AC	Y196NLK	189	AC	Y189NLK	208	EW	Y208NLK	227	EW	LK51XGX
171	AC	Y171NLK	190	AC	Y198NLK	209	EW	Y209NLK	228	EW	LK51XGY
172	AC	Y172NLK	191	AC	Y191NLK	210	EW	Y143NLK	229	EW	LK51XGZ
173	AC	Y173NLK	192	AC	Y192NLK	211	EW	LK51XGE	230	EW	LK51XHA
174	AC	Y174NLK	193	AC	Y193NLK	212	EW	LK51XGF	231	EW	LK51XHB
175	AC	Y195NLK	194	AC	Y194NLK	213	EW	LK51XGG	232	EW	Y232NLK
176	AC	Y176NLK	195	AC	Y144NLK	214	EW	LK51XGH	233	EW	Y233NLK
177	AC	Y177NLK	196	AC	Y146NLK	215	EW	LK51XGJ	234	EW	Y234NLK
178	AC	Y178NLK	197	AC	Y147NLK	216	EW	LK51XGL	235	EW	Y235NLK
179	AC	Y179NLK	198	AC	Y148NLK	217	EW	LK51XGM	236	EW	Y236NLK
180	AC	Y197NLK	199	AC	Y199NLK	218	EW	LK51XGN			

TPL237-296   Dennis Trident 10.6m   Plaxton President 4.4m   N43/24D   2002

237	HT	LN51KXP	252	HT	LN51KYH	267	PB	LN51KZB	282	HT	LR02BBX
238	HT	LN51KXR	253	HT	LN51KYJ	268	PB	LN51KZC	283	HT	LR02BBZ
239	HT	LN51KXS	254	HT	LN51KYK	269	PB	LN51KZD	284	HT	LR02BCE
240	HT	LN51KXT	255	HT	LN51KYO	270	PB	LR02BAA	285	HT	LR02BCF
241	HT	LN51KXU	256	PB	LN51KYP	271	PB	LR02BAO	286	HT	LR02BCK
242	HT	LN51KXV	257	PB	LN51KYR	272	PB	LR02BAU	287	HT	LR02BCO
243	HT	LN51KXW	258	PB	LN51KYS	273	PB	LR02BAV	288	HT	LR02BCU
244	HT	LN51KXY	259	PB	LN51KYT	274	PB	LR02BBE	289	HT	LR02BCV
245	HT	LN51KXZ	260	PB	LN51KYU	275	PB	LR02BBF	290	HT	LR02BCX
246	HT	LN51KYA	261	PB	LN51KYV	276	PB	LR02BBJ	291	HT	LR02BCY
247	HT	LN51KYB	262	PB	LN51KYW	277	PB	LR02BBK	292	HT	LR02BCZ
248	HT	LN51KYC	263	PB	LN51KYX	278	PB	LR02BBN	293	HT	LR02BDE
249	HT	LN51KYE	264	PB	LN51KYY	279	PB	LR02BBO	294	HT	LR02BDF
250	HT	LN51KYF	265	PB	LN51KYZ	280	HT	LR02BBU	295	HT	LR02BDO
251	HT	LN51KYG	266	PB	LN51KZA	281	HT	LR02BBV	296	HT	LR02BDU

TP297-316

Dennis Trident 9.9m			Plaxton President 4.4m			N39/21D			2002		
297	PV	LR02BFF	302	PV	LT02ZZG	307	PV	LT02ZZM	312	PV	LT02ZZS
298	PV	LR02BFJ	303	PV	LT02ZZH	308	PV	LT02ZZN	313	PV	LT02ZZU
299	PV	LT02ZZD	304	PV	LT02ZZJ	309	PV	LT02ZZO	314	PV	LT02ZZV
300	PV	LT02ZZE	305	PV	LT02ZZK	310	PV	LT02ZZP	315	PV	LT02ZZW
301	PV	LT02ZZF	306	PV	LT02ZZL	311	PV	LT02ZZR	316	W	LT02ZZX

VP317-347

Volvo B7TL 10m			Plaxton President 4.4m			N39/21D			2002		
317	HD	LR52BLK	325	HD	LR52BMY	333	HD	LR52BNK	341	HT	LR52BNZ
318	HD	LR52BLN	326	HD	LR52BMZ	334	HD	LR52BNL	342	HT	LR52BOF
319	HD	LR52BLV	327	HD	LR52BNA	335	HD	LR52BNN	343	HT	LR52BOH
320	HD	LR52BLX	328	HD	LR52BNB	336	HD	LR52BNO	344	HT	LR52BOJ
321	HD	LR52BLZ	329	HD	LR52BND	337	HT	LR52BNU	345	HT	LR52BOU
322	HT	LR52BMO	330	HT	LR52BNE	338	HT	LR52BNV	346	HT	LR52BOV
323	HD	LR52BMU	331	HD	LR52BNF	339	HT	LR52BNX	347	HT	LR52BPE
324	HD	LR52BMV	332	HD	LR52BNJ	340	HT	LR52BNY			

TP348-428

TransBus Trident 9.9m			Transbus President 4.4m			N39/21D			2003		
348	HT	LR52KVM	369	W	LR52KWL	389	W	LR52KXH	409	PB	LK03CDA
349	HT	LR52KVO	370	W	LR52KWM	390	W	LR52KXJ	410	PB	LK03CDD
350	HT	LR52KVP	371	W	LR52KWN	391	W	LR52KXK	411	PB	LK03CGE
351	HT	LR52KVS	372	W	LR52KWO	392	W	LR52KXL	412	PV	LK03CDF
352	HT	LR52KVT	373	W	LR52KWP	393	W	LR52KXM	413	PV	LK03CDG
353	HT	LR52KVU	374	W	LR52KWS	394	W	LR52KXN	414	PV	LK03CDJ
354	HT	LR52KVV	375	W	LR52KWT	395	W	LR52KXO	415	PV	LK03CDL
355	HT	LR52KVW	376	W	LR52KWU	396	W	LR52KXP	416	PV	LK03CDM
356	HT	LR52KVX	377	W	LR52KWV	397	W	LR52KXS	417	PV	LK03CDN
357	HT	LR52KVY	378	W	LR52KWW	398	W	LR52KXT	418	PV	LK03CDP
358	PB	LR52KVZ	379	W	LR52KWX	399	W	LR52KXU	419	PV	LK03CDU
359	PB	LR52KWA	380	W	LR52KWY	400	W	LR52KXV	420	PV	LK03CDV
360	PB	LR52KWB	381	W	LR52KWZ	401	W	LR52KXW	421	PV	LK03CDX
361	PB	LR52KWC	382	W	LR52KXA	402	PB	LR52KXX	422	PV	LK03CDY
362	PB	LR52KWD	383	W	LR52KXB	403	PB	LK03CEJ	423	PV	LK03CDZ
363	W	LR52KWE	384	W	LR52KXC	404	PB	LK03CEN	424	PV	LK03CEN
364	W	LR52KWF	385	W	LR52KXD	405	PB	LK03CEU	425	PV	LK03CGF
365	W	LR52KWG	386	W	LR52KXE	406	PB	LK03CEV	426	PB	LK03CGG
366	W	LR52KWH	387	W	LR52KXF	407	PB	LK03CEX	427	PB	LK03CGU
367	W	LR52KWJ	388	W	LR52KXG	408	PB	LK03CEY	428	PB	LK03CGV
368	W	LR52KWK									

Representing the long Tridents with Plaxton bodies within the Metroline fleet is TPL263, LN51KYX, a vehicle based at Potters Bar. It was captured at Childs Hill in October 2005 while operating route 82. Divided between Holloway and Potters Bar depots, this batch of sixty buses was purchased in 2002.
Richard Godfrey

Illustrating the nearside of the President body is VP323, LR52BMU, seen here in Wembley on route 182.
Laurie Rufus

TP429-465
TransBus Trident 9.9m Transbus President 4.4m N39/21D 2003

429	PB	LK03GFU	439	PB	LK03GGV	448	PB	LK03GHH	457	PB	LK03GJG
430	PB	LK03GFV	440	PB	LK03GGX	449	PB	LK03GHJ	458	PB	LK03GJU
431	PB	LK03GFX	441	PB	LK03GGY	450	PB	LK03GHN	459	PB	LK03GJV
432	PB	LK03GFY	442	PB	LK03GGZ	451	PB	LK03GHU	460	PB	LK03GJX
433	PB	LK03GFZ	443	PB	LK03GHA	452	PB	LK03GHV	461	PB	LK03GJY
434	PB	LK03GGA	444	PB	LK03GHB	453	PB	LK03GHX	462	PB	LK03GJZ
435	PB	LK03GGF	445	PB	LK03GHD	454	PB	LK03GHY	463	PB	LK03GKA
436	PB	LK03GGJ	446	PB	LK03GHF	455	PB	LK03GHZ	464	PB	LK03GKC
437	PB	LK03GGP	447	PB	LK03GHG	456	PB	LK03GJF	465	PB	LK03GKD
438	PB	LK03GGU									

VP466-511
Volvo B7TL 10m TransBus President 4.4m N39/21D 2003

466	AC	LK03GKE	478	AC	LK03GLF	490	PV	LK03GMZ	501	HT	LK53LXU
467	HD	LK03GKF	479	AC	LK03GLJ	491	PV	LK03GNF	502	HT	LK53LXV
468	HD	LK03GKG	480	AC	LK03GLV	492	PV	LK03GNJ	503	HT	LK53LXW
469	HD	LK03GKJ	481	AC	LK03GLY	493	PV	LK03GNN	504	HT	LK53LXX
470	AC	LK03GKL	482	PV	LK03GLZ	494	PV	LK03GNP	505	HT	LK53LXY
471	AC	LK03GKN	483	PV	LK03GME	495	PV	LK53LXM	506	HT	LK53LXZ
472	AC	LK03GKP	484	PV	LK03GMF	496	PV	LK53LXN	507	HT	LK53LYA
473	AC	LK03GKU	485	PV	LK03GMG	497	HT	LK53LXO	508	HT	LK53LYC
474	AC	LK03GKV	486	PV	LK03GMU	498	HT	LK53LXP	509	HT	LK53LYD
475	AC	LK03GKX	487	PV	LK03GMV	499	HT	LK53LXR	510	HT	LK53LYF
476	AC	LK03GKY	488	PV	LK03GMX	500	HT	LK53LXT	511	HT	LK53LYG
477	AC	LK03GKZ	489	PV	LK03GMY						

The London Bus Handbook

In 2005, a further batch of twenty-two 9.9metre Tridents was delivered to Cricklewood depot for route 266. These vehicles were the last ALX400s for Metroline, as the next batch of double-deckers ordered formed the TE class being Trident 2s with Enviro400 bodies. Brent Cross shopping centre in January 2006 finds TA659, LK05GHH, showing the then new Alexander Dennis insignia below the windscreen. *Richard Godfrey*

VP512-580

Volvo B7TL 10m TransBus President 4.4m N39/21D 2004

512	AC	LK04CPY	530	AC	LK04CTZ	547	AC	LK04CVH	564	AC	LK04EKY
513	AC	LK04CPZ	531	AC	LK04CUA	548	AC	LK04CVJ	565	AC	LK04EKZ
514	AC	LK04CRF	532	AC	LK04CUC	549	AC	LK04CVL	566	AC	LK04ELC
515	AC	LK04CRJ	533	AC	LK04CUG	550	AC	LK04CVM	567	AC	LK04ELH
516	AC	LK04CRU	534	AC	LK04CUH	551	AC	LK04CVN	568	AC	LK04ELJ
517	AC	LK04CRV	535	AC	LK04CUJ	552	AC	LK04CVP	569	AC	LK04ELU
518	AC	LK04CRZ	536	AC	LK04CUU	553	AC	LK04CVR	570	AC	LK04ELV
519	AC	LK04CSF	537	AC	LK04CUW	554	AC	LK04CVS	571	AC	LK04ELW
520	AC	LK04CSU	538	AC	LK04CUX	555	AC	LK04CVT	572	AC	LK04ELX
521	AC	LK04CSV	539	AC	LK04CUY	556	AC	LK04CVU	573	AC	LK04EMF
522	AC	LK04CSX	540	AC	LK04CVA	557	AC	LK04CVV	574	AC	LK04EMJ
523	AC	LK04CSY	541	AC	LK04CVB	558	AC	LK04CVW	575	AC	LK04EMV
524	AC	LK04CSZ	542	AC	LK04CVC	559	AC	LK04CVX	576	AC	LK04EMX
525	AC	LK04CTE	543	AC	LK04CVD	560	AC	LK04EKU	577	AC	LK04ENE
526	AC	LK04CTF	544	AC	LK04CVE	561	AC	LK04EKV	578	AC	LK04ENF
527	AC	LK04CTU	545	AC	LK04CVF	562	AC	LK04EKW	579	AC	LK04ENH
528	AC	LK04CTV	546	AC	LK04CVG	563	AC	LK04EKX	580	AC	LK04ENJ
529	AC	LK04CTX									

VPL581-603

Volvo B7TL 10.6m TransBus President 4.4m N43/24D 2004

581	KX	LK04NLZ	587	KX	LK04NMU	593	KX	LK04NNB	599	KX	LK04NNH
582	KX	LK04NMA	588	KX	LK04NMV	594	KX	LK04NNC	600	KX	LK04NNJ
583	KX	LK04NME	589	KX	LK04NMX	595	KX	LK04NND	601	KX	LK04NNL
584	KX	LK04NMF	590	KX	LK04NMY	596	KX	LK04NNE	602	KX	LK04NNM
585	KX	LK04NMJ	591	KX	LK04NMZ	597	KX	LK04NNF	603	KX	LK04NNP
586	KX	LK04NMM	592	KX	LK04NNA	598	KX	LK04NNG			

VP604-628

Volvo B7TL 10m TransBus President 4.4m N39/21D 2004

604	HD	LK04UWJ	611	HD	LK04UWT	617	HD	LK04UWZ	623	HD	LK04UXF
605	HD	LK04UWL	612	HD	LK04UWU	618	HD	LK04UXA	624	HD	LK04UXG
606	HD	LK04UWM	613	HD	LK04UWV	619	HD	LK04UXB	625	HD	LK04UXH
607	HD	LK04UWN	614	HD	LK04UWW	620	HD	LK04UXC	626	HD	LK54FWE
608	HD	LK04UWP	615	HD	LK04UWX	621	HD	LK04UXD	627	HD	LK54FWF
609	HD	LK04UWR	616	HD	LK04UWY	622	HD	LK04UXE	628	HD	LK54FWG
610	HD	LK04UWS									

Towards the end of 2005 and into early 2006, the Enviro400 made its debut on the streets of London when Metroline put twenty-eight examples to work on route 24. Seen in Trafalgar Square soon after entering service, TE666, LK55KJX, shows the now-usual use of gold-coloured advert frames prior to the adverts being fitted.
Colin Lloyd

VP629-637

| | | | | | | | | | | Volvo B7TL 10.6m | TransBus President 4.4m | N43/24D | 2005 |

629	HT	LK54FWH	632	HT	LK54FWM	634	HT	LK54FWO	636	HT	LK54FWR
630	HT	LK54FWJ	633	HT	LK54FWN	635	HT	LK54FWP	637	HT	LK54FWT
631	HT	LK54FWL									

TA638-659

| | | | | | | | | | | ADL Trident 9.9m | ADL ALX400 4.4m | N41/19D | 2005 |

638	W	LK05GFO	644	W	LK05GGE	650	W	LK05GGV	655	W	LK05GHB
639	W	LK05GFV	645	W	LK05GGF	651	W	LK05GGX	656	W	LK05GHD
640	W	LK05GFX	646	W	LK05GGJ	652	W	LK05GGY	657	W	LK05GHF
641	W	LK05GFY	647	W	LK05GGO	653	W	LK05GGZ	658	W	LK05GHG
642	W	LK05GFZ	648	W	LK05GGP	654	W	LK05GHA	659	W	LK05GHH
643	W	LK05GGA	649	W	LK05GGU						

NSM660-664

| | | | | | | | | | | Optare Solo M780 | Optare | N21F | 2005 |

| 660 | u | YK05CCD | 662 | u | YK05CCJ | 663 | u | YK05CCN | 664 | u | YK05CCO |
| 661 | u | YK05CCE | | | | | | | | | |

TE665-692

| | | | | | | | | | | ADL Trident 2 10.1m | ADL Enviro 400 4.4m | N41/26D | 2005-06 |

665	HT	LK55KJV	672	HT	LK55KKD	679	HT	LK55KKM	686	HT	LK55KKV
666	HT	LK55KJX	673	HT	LK55KKE	680	HT	LK55KKO	687	HT	LK06FLA
667	HT	LK55KJY	674	HT	LK55KKF	681	HT	LK55KKP	688	HT	LK55KKY
668	HT	LK55KJZ	675	HT	LK55KKG	682	HT	LK55KKR	689	HT	LK55KKZ
669	HT	LK55KKA	676	HT	LK55KKH	683	HT	LK55KKS	690	HT	LK55KLA
670	HT	LK55KKB	677	HT	LK55KKJ	684	HT	LK55KKT	691	HT	LK06FLB
671	HT	LK55KKC	678	HT	LK55KKL	685	HT	LK55KKU	692	HT	LK06FLC

DLD693-711

| | | | | | | | | | | ADL Dart 10.1m | ADL Pointer | N28D | 2006 |

693	HT	LK55KLE	698	HT	LK55KLO	703	HT	LK55KLX	708	HT	LK55KMG
694	HT	LK55KLF	699	HT	LK55KLP	704	HT	LK55KLZ	709	HT	LK55KMJ
695	HT	LK55KLJ	700	HT	LK55KLS	705	HT	LK55KMA	710	HT	LK55KMM
696	HT	LK55KLL	701	HT	LK55KLU	706	HT	LK55KME	711	HT	LK55KMO
697	HT	LK55KLM	702	HT	LK55KLV	707	HT	LK55KMF			

The London Bus Handbook

Originally bought new in 2001 by Armchair, DP1004, Y63LTF, is one of the batch of eight 10.1m Plaxton Pointers acquired with that business by Metroline in 2004. It has since lost its orange and white livery and now sports standard Metroline colours. August 2006 finds the bus on route 117 in Ashford en route to one of the south-westerly extremities of TfL routes, Staines. *Mark Lyons*

TE712-723

				ADL Trident 2 10.1m			ADL Enviro 400 4.4m		N41/26D	2006
712	HT	LK56FHE	715	HT	LK56FHH	718	HT	LK56FHN	721	HT	LK56FHR
713	HT	LK56FHF	716	HT	LK56FHJ	719	HT	LK56FHO	722	HT	LK56FHS
714	HT	LK56FHG	717	HT	LK56FHM	720	HT	LK56FHP	723	HT	LK56FHT

DP962	PB	Y962KRX	Dennis Dart SLF 8.8m	Plaxton Pointer 2	N29F	2001

DP1001-1016

Dennis Dart SLF 10.1m   Plaxton Pointer 2   N30D   2001-02

1001	AH	RX51FNP	1005	AH	RX51FNW	1009	AH	RL51DOA	1013	AH	RL51DNY
1002	AH	RX51FNS	1006	AH	RX51FNV	1010	AH	RL51DNX	1014	AH	RL51DNV
1003	AH	RX51FNT	1007	AH	RX51FNU	1011	AH	RL51DOJ	1015	AH	RL51DOU
1004	AH	Y63LTF	1008	AH	RX51FNY	1012	AH	RL51DOH	1016	AH	RL51DNU

DP1017-1048

Dennis Dart SLF 10.1m   Plaxton Pointer 2   N30D   2002

1017	AH	KP02PUF	1025	AH	KP02PVK	1033	AH	KU02YUB	1041	AH	KU02YUK
1018	AH	KP02PUH	1026	AH	KP02PVJ	1034	AH	KU02YUC	1042	AH	KM02HFK
1019	AH	KP02PUJ	1027	AH	KP02PVL	1035	AH	KU02YUD	1043	AH	KM02HFN
1020	AH	KP02PUO	1028	AH	KP02PVO	1036	AH	KP02PWU	1044	AH	KM02HFL
1021	AH	KP02PVD	1029	AH	KP02PVN	1037	AH	KP02PWV	1045	AH	KM02HFO
1022	AH	KP02PVE	1030	AH	KP02PVT	1038	AH	KP02PWO	1046	AH	KM02HGD
1023	AH	KP02PUK	1031	AH	KP02PVU	1039	AH	KU02YUE	1047	AH	KM02HGE
1024	AH	KP02PVF	1032	AH	KP02PWN	1040	AH	KU02YUJ	1048	AH	KM02HGF

DP1049	AH	KX54NJO	ADL Dart 10.1m	ADL Pointer	N30D	2004

Special event vehicles:

RM644	HT	WLT644	AEC Routemaster RH2H	Park Royal	O36/28RD	1961	London Transport
RML903	HT	WLT903	AEC Routemaster RH2H/1	Park Royal	B40/32R	1962	London Transport
RMC1513	HT	513CLT	AEC Routemaster RH2H	Park Royal	B32/25RD	1962	London Transport
M1	HT	THX101S	MCW Metrobus DR101/3	MCW	B43/28D	1978	London Transport

Low-floor buses, now the normal requirement throughout the TfL area, are supplied by all operators with very few exceptions, but some depots provide services outside the TfL domain. One depot to do so is Potters Bar which operates route 242 linking Waltham Cross with Potters Bar on a route serving suburban Hertfordshire. AV24, S124RLE, is seen just prior to its transfer to Perivale, entering Waltham Cross bus station. *Colin Lloyd*

Ancillary vehicles:

DP273	PV	P673MLE	Dennis Dart 9m	Plaxton Pointer	Staff	1997
DP274	HT	P674MLE	Dennis Dart 9m	Plaxton Pointer	Eng training	1997
DP275	PV	P673MLE	Dennis Dart 9m	Plaxton Pointer	Staff	1997
DP276	PA	P673MLE	Dennis Dart 9m	Plaxton Pointer	Staff	1997

EDR11-44
Dennis Dart 9.8m   Plaxton Pointer   TV   1996

11	EWt	P286MLD	**31**	EWt	P307MLD	**35**	EWt	P311MLD	**40**	EWt	P316MLD
13	HDt	P288MLD	**32**	EWt	P308MLD	**37**	EWt	P313MLD	**41**	ACt	P317MLD
14	HDt	P289MLD	**33**	EWt	P309MLD	**38**	EWt	P314MLD	**43**	ACt	P319MLD
27	ACt	P303MLD	**34**	EWt	P310MLD	**39**	EWt	P315MLD	**44**	HDt	P320MLD

M151	W	33LUG	MCW Metrobus DR101/3	MCW	Classroom 1979	London Transport

V201-210
Volvo Olympian YN2RV18Z4   Northern Counties Palatine II   TV   1993   MTL London, 1998

201	HTt	L201SKD	**204**	HTt	L204SKD	**207**	HTt	L207SKD	**209**	HTt	L209SKD
202	HTt	L202SKD	**205**	HTt	L205SKD	**208**	HTt	L208SKD	**210**	HTt	L210SKD
203	HTt	L203SKD	**206**	HTt	L206SKD						

V212-217
Volvo Olympian YN2RV18Z4   Northern Counties Palatine II   TV   1994   MTL London, 1998

212	HTt	L212TWM	**214**	HTt	L214TWM	**216**	HTt	L216TWM	**217**	HTt	L217TWM
213	HTt	L213TWM	**215**	HTt	L215TWM						

Previous registrations:

33LUG	BYX151V	WLT826	T102KLD

Depots and allocations:

Brentford (Commerce Road) - AH

Dart	DLD60	DLD61	DLD62	DLD63	DLD64	DLD65	DLD66	DLD74
	DLD117	DLD136	DA140	DA141	DA142	DA143	DA144	DA145
	DA146	DA147	DA148	DA149	DA150	DA151	DA152	DLD177
	DP1001	DP1002	DP1003	DP1004	DP1005	DP1006	DP1007	DP1008
	DP1009	DP1010	DP1011	DP1012	DP1013	DP1014	DP1015	DP1016
	DP1017	DP1018	DP1019	DP1020	DP1021	DP1022	DP1023	DP1024
	DP1025	DP1026	DP1027	DP1028	DP1029	DP1030	DP1031	DP1032
	DP1033	DP1034	DP1035	DP1036	DP1037	DP1038	DP1039	DP1040
	DP1041	DP1042	DP1043	DP1044	DP1045	DP1046	DP1047	DP1048
	DP1049							
Trident	DT1	DT2	DT3	DT4	DT5	DT6	DT7	DT8
	DT9	DT10	DT11	DT12	DT13	DT14	DT15	DT16
	DT17	DT18	DT19	DT20	DT21	DT22		

Cricklewood (Edgware Road) - W

Dart	DML33	DML34	DML35	DML36	DML37	DML38	DML39	DML40
	DML41	DML42	DML43	DML44	DML45	DML46	DML47	DLD53
	DLD108	DLD109	DLD110	DLD111	DLD112	DLD113	DLD114	DLD115
Trident	TA66	TA67	TA68	TA69	TA70	TA71	TA72	TA73
	TA74	TA75	TA76	TA77	TA78	TA79	TA80	TA100
	TA101	TA102	TA103	TA104	TA105	TA106	TA107	TA108
	TA109	TA110	TA111	TA112	TA113	TA114	TA115	TA116
	TA117	TAL118	TAL119	TAL120	TAL121	TAL122	TAL123	TAL124
	TAL125	TAL126	TAL127	TAL128	TAL129	TAL130	TAL131	TAL132
	TAL133	TAL134	TA316	TP363	TP364	TP365	TP366	TP367
	TP368	TP369	TP370	TP371	TP372	TP373	TP374	TP375
	TP376	TP377	TP378	TP379	TP380	TP381	TP382	TP383
	TP384	TP385	TP386	TP387	TP388	TP389	TP390	TP391
	TP392	TP393	TP394	TP395	TP396	TP397	TP398	TP399
	TP400	TP401	TA639	TA640	TA641	TA642	TA643	TA644
	TA645	TA646	TA647	TA648	TA649	TA650	TA651	TA652
	TA653	TA654	TA655	TA656	TA657	TA658	TA659	
Training	M151							

Edgware (Station Road) - EW

Dart	DLD116	DLD137	DLD138	DLD139	DLD140	DLD141	DLD142	DLD143
	DLD144	DLD145	DLD146	DLD147	DLD148			
Olympian	AV37							
Volvo B7TL	VPL143	VPL144	VPL145	VPL146	VPL147	VPL148	VPL149	VPL150
	VPL151	VPL152	VPL153	VPL154	VPL155	VPL156	VPL157	VPL158
	VPL159	VPL160	VPL161	VPL162	VPL163	VPL164	VPL165	VPL166
	VPL167	VPL200	VPL201	VPL202	VPL203	VPL204	VPL205	VPL206
	VPL207	VPL208	VPL209	VPL210	VPL211	VPL212	VPL213	VPL214
	VPL215	VPL216	VPL217	VPL218	VPL219	VPL220	VPL221	VPL222
	VPL223	VPL224	VPL225	VPL226	VPL227	VPL228	VPL229	VPL230
	VPL231	VPL232	VPL233	VPL234	VPL235	VPL236		
Training	EDR11	EDR31	EDR32	EDR32	EDR34	EDR35	EDR37	EDR38
	EDR39	EDR40						

Harrow Weald (High Road) - HD

Olympian	AV1	AV2	AV3	AV32	AV36			
Trident	TA81	TA82	TA83	TA84	TA85	TA86	TA87	TA88
	TA89	TA90	TA91	TA92	TA93	TA94	TA95	TA96
	TA97	TA98	TA99					
Volvo B7TL	VP317	VP318	VP319	VP320	VP321	VP323	VP324	VP325
	VLP326	VP327	VP328	VP329	VP331	VP332	VP333	VP334
	VLP335	VP336	VP467	VP468	VP469	VP604	VP605	VP606
	VP607	VP608	VP609	VP610	VP611	VP612	VP613	VP614
	VP615	VP616	VP617	VP618	VP619	VP620	VP621	VP622
	VP623	VP624	VP625	VP626	VP627	VP628		
Training	EDR13	EDR14	EDR44					

Holloway (Pemberton Gardens) - HT

Dart	DLM151	DLM152	DLM153	DLM154	DLM155	DLM156	DLM157	DLM158
	DLM159	DLM160	DLD693	DLD694	DLD695	DLD696	DLD697	DLD698
	DLD699	DLD700	DLD701	DLD702	DLD703	DLD704	DLD705	DLD706
	DLD707	DLD708	DLD709	DLD710	DLD711			
Routemaster	RM644	RML903	RMC1513					
Metrobus	M1							
Trident	TP1	TP2	TP3	TP4	TP5	TP6	TP7	TP8
	TP9	TP10	TP11	TP12	TP13	TP14	TP15	TP16
	TP17	TP18	TP19	TP20	TP21	TP22	TP23	TP24
	TP25	TP26	TP27	TP28	TP29	TP30	TP31	TP32
	TP33	TP34	TP35	TP36	TP37	TP38	TP39	TP40
	TP41	TP42	TP43	TP44	TP45	TP46	TP47	TP48
	TP49	TP50	TP51	TP52	TP53	TP54	TP55	TP56
	TP57	TP58	TP59	TP60	TP61	TP62	TP63	TP64
	TP65	TPL237	TPL238	TPL239	TPL240	TPL241	TPL242	TPL243
	TPL244	TPL245	TPL246	TPL247	TPL248	TPL249	TPL250	TPL251
	TPL252	TPL253	TPL254	TPL255	TP348	TP349	TP350	TP351
	TP352	TP353	TP354	TP355	TP356	TP357	TPL280	TPL281
	TPL282	TPL283	TPL284	TPL285	TPL286	TPL287	TPL288	TPL289
	TPL290	TPL291	TPL292	TPL293	TPL294	TPL295	TPL296	
Trident 2	TE665	TE666	TE667	TE668	TE669	TE670	TE671	TE672
	TE673	TE674	TE675	TE676	TE677	TE678	TE679	TE680
	TE681	TE682	TE683	TE684	TE685	TE686	TE687	TE688
	TE689	TE690	TE691	TE692	TE712	TE713	TE714	TE715
	TE716	TE717	TE718	TE719	TE720	TE721	TE722	TE723
Volvo B7TL	VPL135	VPL136	VPL137	VPL138	VPL139	VPL140	VPL141	VPL142
	VP322	VP330	VP337	VP338	VP339	VP340	VP341	VP342
	VP343	VP344	VP345	VP346	VP347	VP497	VP498	VP499
	VP500	VP501	VP502	VP503	VP504	VP505	VP506	VP507
	VP508	VP509	VP510	VP511	VPL629	VPL630	VPL631	VPL632
	VPL633	VPL634	VPL635	VPL636	VPL637			
Trainers	V201	V203	V204	V206	V207	V208	V209	V214
	V215	V216	V217					

King's Cross (York Way) - KX (Managed from Holloway)

Dart	DLD118	DLD119	DLD120	DLD121	DLD122	DLD123	DLD124	DLD125
	DLD126	DLD127	DLD128	DLD129	DLD130	DLD131	DLD132	DLD133
	DLD134	DLD135	DLD149	DLD161	DLD162	DLD163	DLD164	DLD165
	DLD166	DLD167	DLD168	DLD169	DLD170	DLD171	DLD172	DLD173
	DLD174	DLD175	DLD176					
Volvo B7TL	VPL581	VPL582	VPL583	VPL584	VPL585	VPL586	VPL587	VPL588
	VPL589	VPL590	VPL591	VPL592	VPL593	VPL594	VPL595	VPL596
	VPL597	VPL598	VPL599	VPL600	VPL601	VPL602	VPL603	
Ancillary	DP276							

North Wembley (East Lane) - NW

Dart							
DML6	DML7	DML8	DML9	DML10	DML11	DML12	DML13
DML14	DML15	DML16	DML17	DML18	DLD22	DLD23	DLD24
DLD25	DLD26	DLD27	DLD28	DLD29	DLD30	DLD31	DLD32
DLD33	DLD34	DLD35	DLD36	DLD37	DLD38	DLD39	DLD40
DLD41	DLD42	DLD43	DLD44	DLD45	DLD46	DLD47	DLD48
DLD49	DLD50	DLD54	DLD55	DLD56	DLD57	DLD58	DLD59
DLD67	DLD68	DLD69	DLD70	DLD71	DLD73	DLD185	DLD187
DLD188	DLD198	DLD199	DLD200	DLD201	DLD202	DLD203	DLD204
DLD205	DLD206	DLD207	DSD208	DSD209	DSD210	DSD211	DSD212
DSD213	DSD214	DSD215	DSD216	DSD217			

Coaches							
P845WUG	P846WUG						

Training							
MM255	MM259	MM265	MM266	MM267			

Perivale (Alperton Lane) - PV

Solo	NSM660	NSM661	NSM662	NSM663	NSM664			
Dart	DLM150	DLD178	DLD179	DLD180	DLD181	DLD182	DLD183	DLD184
	DLD186	DLD187	DLD188	DLD189	DLD190	DLD191	DLD192	DLD193
	DLD194	DLD195	DLD196	DLD197	EDR18			
Trident	TP297	TP298	TP299	TP300	TP301	TP302	TP303	TP304
	TP305	TP306	TP307	TP308	TP309	TP310	TP311	TP312
	TP313	TP314	TP315	TP412	TP413	TP414	TP415	
	TP416	TP417	TP418	TP419	TP420	TP421	TP422	TP423
	TP424	TP425						

Ancillary							
DP274							

Perivale (Horsenden Lane South) - PA - Thorpe

Solo	OSL1	OSL2						
Dart	DML1	DML2	DML3	DML4	DML5	DLF9	DLF29	DLF30
	DLF31	DLF32	DLF33	DLF34	DLF35	DLF36	DLF37	DLF38
	DLF39	DLF40	DLF41	DLF63	DLF64	DLF65	DLF66	DLF67
	DLF68	DLF68	DLF71	DLF72	DLF73	DLF74	DLF75	DLF76
	DLF77	DLF79	DLF80	DLF81	DLF83	DLF84	DLF85	DLF87
	DLF88	DLF89	DLF90	DLF91	DLF92	DLF93	DLF94	DLF95
	DLF96	DLF97	DLF98	DLF99	DLF100	DLF101	DLF102	DLF103
	DLF104	DLF105	DLF106	DLF107	DLF108	DLF109	DLF110	DLF122
	DLF123	DLF124	DLF125	DML519	DML520	DML521	DML522	DML523
	DML524	DML525	DML526	DML527	DML528	DML529	DML530	DML531
	DML532	DML533	DML534					

Potters Bar (High Street) - PB

Dart	DMS1	DMS2	DMS3	DMS4	DMS5	DMS6	DMS7	DMS8
	DMS9	DMS10	DMS11	DMS12	DMS13	DMS14	DMS15	DMS16
	DMS17	DMS18	DMS19	DMS20	DMS21	DMS22	DMS23	DMS24
	DMS25	DMS26	DMS28	DMS29	DLS101	DLS102	DML535	DP982
Olympian	AV23	AV24	AV25	AV26	AV27	AV28	AV29	AV30
	AV31	AV33	AV34	AV35	AV38			
Trident	TPL256	TPL257	TPL258	TPL259	TPL260	TPL261	TPL262	TPL263
	TPL264	TPL265	TPL266	TPL267	TPL268	TPL269	TPL270	TPL271
	TPL272	TPL273	TPL274	TPL275	TPL276	TPL277	TPL278	TPL279
	TP358	TP359	TP360	TP361	TP362	TP402	TP403	TP404
	TP405	TP406	TP407	TP408	TP409	TP410	TP411	TP426
	TP427	TP428	TP429	TP430	TP431	TP432	TP433	TP434
	TP435	TP436	TP437	TP438	TP439	TP440	TP441	TP442
	TP443	TP444	TP445	TP446	TP447	TP448	TP449	TP450
	TP451	TP452	TP453	TP454	TP455	TP456	TP457	TP458
	TP459	TP460	TP461	TP462	TP463	TP464	TP465	

Metroline use a TE class for their Alexander Dennis Trident 2s with Enviro 400 bodywork, Representing the initial batch is TE679, LK55KKM, seen operating route 24. Alexander Dennis are shortly to provide a further twelve of this type. *Laurie Rufus*

Willesden (High Road) - AC

Dart	DLD51	DLD52	DLD86	DLD87	DLD88	DLD89	DLD90	DLD91
	DLD92	DLD93	DLD94	DLD95	DLD96	DLD97	DLD98	DLD99
	DLD100							
Volvo B7TL	VPL168	VPL169	VPL170	VPL171	VPL172	VPL173	VPL174	VPL175
	VPL176	VPL177	VPL178	VPL179	VPL180	VPL181	VPL182	VPL183
	VPL184	VPL185	VPL186	VPL187	VPL188	VPL189	VPL190	VPL191
	VPL192	VPL193	VPL194	VPL195	VPL196	VPL197	VPL198	VPL199
	VP470	VP471	VP472	VP473	VP474	VP475	VP476	VP477
	VP478	VP479	VP480	VP481	VP482	VP512	VP513	VP514
	VP515	VP516	VP517	VP518	VP519	VP520	VP521	VP522
	VP523	VP524	VP525	VP526	VP527	VP528	VP529	VP530
	VP531	VP532	VP533	VP534	VP535	VP536	VP537	VP538
	VP539	VP540	VP541	VP542	VP543	VP544	VP545	VP546
	VP547	VP548	VP549	VP550	VP551	VP552	VP553	VP554
	VP555	VP556	VP557	VP558	VP559	VP560	VP561	VP562
	VP563	VP564	VP565	VP566	VP567	VP568	VP569	VP570
	VP571	VP572	VP573	VP574	VP575	VP576	VP577	VP578
	VP579	VP580						
Training	EDR27	EDR41	EDR43					

Unallocated and reserve - u

Volvo	V202	V205	V210

REDWING

Redwing - Reliance

Pullmanor Ltd, 10 Dylan Road, Herne Hill, London, SE24 0HL
Grangeville Ltd, 8 Norfolk Road, Gravesend, DA12 2PS

011	TW	FJ03ZZN	Irisbus EuroRider 397E.12.35	Beulas Stergo ε	C49FT	2003
012	TW	FJ03ZZP	Irisbus EuroRider 397E.12.35	Beulas Stergo ε	C49FT	2003
013	TW	FJ06ZMO	Volvo B12M	VDL Berkhof Axial 50	C51FT	2006
014	TW	FJ03ZZS	Irisbus EuroRider 397E.12.35	Beulas Stergo ε	C49FT	2003
015	TW	FJ06ZMV	Volvo B12B	VDL Berkhof Axial 50	C51FT	2006
016	TW	FJ03ZZU	Irisbus EuroRider 397E.12.35	Beulas Stergo ε	C49FT	2003
017	TW	FJ06ZLZ	Volvo B12M	VDL Berkhof Axial 50	C51FT	2006
018	TW	FJ06ZMU	Volvo B12B	VDL Berkhof Axial 50	C51FT	2006
019	TW	FJ03ZZX	Irisbus EuroRider 397E.12.35	Beulas Stergo ε	C49FT	2003
020	TW	FJ03ZZY	Irisbus EuroRider 397E.12.35	Beulas Stergo ε	C49FT	2003
201	RW	YN05ATO	Irisbus MidiRider 395E.9.27	Beulas Midi-Star ε	C35FT	2005
202	RW	BX55FYG	Mercedes-Benz 0510 Tourino	Mercedes-Benz	C34F	2005

211-215   Setra S315 GT-HD   Setra   C49FT   2005

211	RW	BX54EDL	213	RW	BX54EDP	214	RW	BX54EDR	215	RW	BX54EDU
212	RW	BX54EDO								

216	RW	BX06UMK	Mercedes-Benz Touro 1836RL	Mercedes-Benz	C49FT	2006
217	RW	BX06UML	Mercedes-Benz Touro 1836RL	Mercedes-Benz	C49FT	2006
221	EE	YN55KWR	Irisbus MidiRider 395E.12.35	Beulas Cygnus	C49FT	2005

223-226   Setra S315 GT-HD   Setra   C49FT   2004

223	RW	BU04EYR	224	RW	BU04EYS	225	GB	BU04EYT	226	GB	BU04EYX

230-235   Irisbus EuroRider 391E.12.35   Beulas Stergo ε   C49FT   2005

230	RW	YN54AAE	232	RW	YN54AAJ	234	RW	YN54AAU	235	RW	YN05ATU
231	RW	YN54AAF	233	RW	YN54AAK					

251-259   Mercedes-Benz 1836RL   Mercedes-Benz Touro   C53F   2006

251	CM	BX06UMC	253	RW	BX06UMB	256	RW	BX06UMF	258	RW	BX06UMH
252	CM	BX06UMD	254	RW	BX06UME	257	RW	BX06UMG	259	RW	BX06UMJ

The group based on the Redwing operation includes Reliance of Gravesend, and is now in the ownership of Addison Lee. The TWH name has now gone. One of several Beulas Stergo ε bodied Irisbus EuroRiders in the fleet is 235, YN05ATU seen here at London Bridge. *Dave Heath*

Several Mercedes-Benz Touro coaches operated by Redwing are used on top-line coaching duties. Amongst the latest arrivals is 259, BX06UMJ, which is seen in Artillery Row, Westminster. *Colin Lloyd*

281-294 — Irisbus EuroRider 391E.12.35 — Beulas Stergo ε — C53F — 2005

281	EE	YN05AUA	284	EE	YN05AUF	287	EE	YN05AUK	292	SS	YN05ATX
282	EE	YN05AUC	285	EE	YN05AUH	288	EE	YN05AUL	293	RW	YN05ATY
283	EE	YN05AUE	286	EE	YN05AUJ	291	RW	YN05AYV	294	RW	YN05ATZ

295-299 — Setra S315 GT-HD — Setra — C49FT — 2005

295	GB	BX05UVC	297	GB	BX05UVE	298	GB	BX05UVG	299	GB	BX05UVH
296	GB	BX05UVD							

227	RE	YU04XJH	Irisbus EuroRider 397E.12.31	Plaxton Paragon	C53F	2004
228	RE	YU04XJJ	Irisbus EuroRider 397E.12.31	Plaxton Paragon	C53F	2004

271-278 — Irisbus EuroRider 397E.12.35 — Beulas Stergo ε — C53F* — 2002-03 — *276/7 are C49FT

271	RE	FD03YOK	273	RE	LX03KRD	275	RE	FD03YOP	277	RE	FN52GUH
272	RE	FD03YOL	274	RE	FD03YON	276	RE	FN52GUG	278	RE	LX03KRE

279	RE	YN54AAO	Irisbus EuroRider 397E.12.35	Beulas Stergo ε	C53F	2005
280	RE	YN54AAV	Irisbus EuroRider 397E.12.35	Beulas Stergo ε	C53F	2005
289	RE	FD03YOJ	Irisbus EuroRider 397E.12.35	Beulas Stergo ε	C53F	2003
290	RE	FD03YOH	Irisbus EuroRider 397E.12.35	Beulas Stergo ε	C53F	2003
864	TW	YN55KWO	Irisbus EuroRider 397E.12.35	Beulas Stergo ε	C49FT	2005
865	TW	YN55KWP	Irisbus EuroRider 397E.12.35	Beulas Stergo ε	C49FT	2005
866	TW	YN55KWS	Irisbus EuroRider 397E.12.35	Beulas Stergo ε	C49FT	2005
867	TW	YN55KWT	Irisbus EuroRider 397E.12.35	Beulas Cygnus	C49FT	2005
868	TW	YN55KWU	Irisbus EuroRider 397E.12.35	Beulas Cygnus	C49FT	2005

Web: www.redwing-coaches.co.uk; www.reliance-travel.co.uk; www.ukcoachhire.com.

Allocation codes: RE - Reliance; RW - Redwing; EE - Evan Evans; GB - Globus; CM - Cosmos.

Liveries: Red and cream; red and grey (new Evan Evans): 221; red and cream (old Evan Evans): 281-8; white and red (Globus): 225/6, 295-9; white, red and yellow (Cosmos): 251/2; white: 276/7, FJ03ZZN/P/S/U/X/Y, YN55KWO/P/S/T/U, FJ06ZLZ, FJ06ZMO/U/V.

ROYALE EUROPEAN

J Kent, 8 North Feltham Industrial Estate, Falcon Way, Feltham, TW14 0XQ

A20YAL	Setra S315 GT-HD	Setra	C49FT	2002	Anderson, Castleford, 2006
RE03JAK	Setra S315 GT-HD	Setra	C49FT	2003	
RE53JAK	Scania K114EB4	Irizar Century	C49FT	2003	
RE54JAK	Setra S315 GT-HD	Setra	C49FT	2004	
YN05RXX	Mercedes-Benz Sprinter 616cdi	Clari/Esker Riada 616	C23F	2005	
RE56JAK	Volvo B12T	Van Hool T925 Astrobel	C61/18DT	2006	

Previous registrations

A20YAL	BD51YMJ		RE56JAK	WA56ENO
RE03JAK	BU03LYZ			

The latest arrival in the Royale European fleet, and probably the most expensive coach in London is RE56JAK, seen here in a rare picture of the vehicle with its initial index mark WA56END. The Van Hool T925 is the double-deck version of the T9 series, a length which would allow the fixing of a ski-box and yet still remain within the maximum vehicle length regulations. *Jef Johnson*

TELLINGS - GOLDEN MILLER

Tellings Golden Miller - Linkline

Tellings-Golden Miller Coaches Ltd, Ensign Close, Exeter Way, London Heathrow Airport, TW6 2PQ

Link Line Coaches Ltd, 1 Wrottesley Road, Harlesden, NW10 5XA

C89NNV	Volvo B10M-61	Caetano Stagecoach	B57F	1986	
P10TGM	Volvo B10M-62	Van Hool Alizée HE	C32FT	1997	
R957RCH	Volvo B9M	Plaxton Première 320	C43F	1997	Airlinks, Feltham, 2005
R958RCH	Volvo B9M	Plaxton Première 320	C43F	1997	Airlinks, Feltham, 2005
R959RCH	Volvo B9M	Plaxton Première 320	C43F	1997	Airlinks, Feltham, 2005
R177TKU	Volvo B10M-62	Plaxton Première 350	C49FT	1997	Link Line, Harlesden, 2003
R50TGM	Volvo B10M-62	Plaxton Première 320	C53F	1998	
T10TGM	Volvo B10M-62	Plaxton Première 320	C53F	1999	
T20TGM	Volvo B10M-62	Plaxton Première 320	C53F	1999	
W50BCL	Volvo B10M-62	Plaxton Première 350	C57F	2000	Burtons, Haverhill, 2003
W393OUF	Toyota Coaster BB50R	Caetano Optimo IV	C22F	2000	Airlinks, Feltham, 2005
W40TGM	Volvo B10M-62	Plaxton Paragon	C53F	2000	Burtons, Haverhill, 2003
W50TGM	Volvo B10M-62	Plaxton Paragon	C53F	2000	
W80TGM	Volvo B10M-62	Plaxton Première 320	C57F	2000	
W433UMX	Volvo B7R	Plaxton Prima	C53F	2000	Burtons, Haverhill, 2003
W627UMV	Volvo B7R	Plaxton Prima	C53F	2000	Burtons, Haverhill, 2003
X152ENJ	Mercedes-Benz Vario O814	Plaxton Cheetah	C24F	2001	Airlinks, Feltham, 2005
X153ENJ	Mercedes-Benz Vario O814	Plaxton Cheetah	C24F	2001	Airlinks, Feltham, 2005
X154ENJ	Mercedes-Benz Vario O814	Plaxton Cheetah	C24F	2001	Airlinks, Feltham, 2005
X157ENJ	Mercedes-Benz Vario O814	Plaxton Cheetah	C24F	2001	Airlinks, Feltham, 2005
X158ENJ	Mercedes-Benz Vario O814	Plaxton Cheetah	C24F	2001	Airlinks, Feltham, 2005
X159ENJ	Mercedes-Benz Vario O814	Plaxton Cheetah	C24F	2001	Airlinks, Feltham, 2005
X216HCD	Mercedes-Benz Vario O814	Plaxton Cheetah	C24F	2001	Airlinks, Feltham, 2005
X217HCD	Mercedes-Benz Vario O814	Plaxton Cheetah	C24F	2001	Airlinks, Feltham, 2005
X218HCD	Mercedes-Benz Vario O814	Plaxton Cheetah	C24F	2001	Airlinks, Feltham, 2005
X219HCD	Mercedes-Benz Vario O814	Plaxton Cheetah	C24F	2001	Airlinks, Feltham, 2005
X221HCD	Mercedes-Benz Vario O814	Plaxton Cheetah	C24F	2001	Airlinks, Feltham, 2005
X223HCD	Mercedes-Benz Vario O814	Plaxton Cheetah	C24F	2001	Airlinks, Feltham, 2005

Many coaches in Tellings-Golden Miller's fleet carry cherished or select index marks. One of these is MM03TGM, a Volvo B12B fitted with a Caetano Enigma body. It was seen in Trafalgar Square.
Colin Lloyd

To cater for smaller groups, coach operators use mini or midi-sized vehicles, such as the coach-built Caetano Optimo which is mounted on a Toyota Coaster chassis. Tellings-Golden Miller currently has two of these vehicles with the elder, W393OUF, seen here circumnavigating Inner Ring East at Heathrow Airport in June 2006. *Colin Lloyd*

Y501TGJ	Volvo B10M-62	Plaxton Panther	C53F	2001
Y504TGJ	Volvo B10M-62	Plaxton Paragon	C53F	2001
Y506TGJ	Volvo B10M-62	Plaxton Panther	C53F	2001
Y507TGJ	Volvo B10M-62	Plaxton Panther	C53F	2001
Y10TGM	Irisbus EuroRider 391E.12.35	Beulas Stergo ε	C49FT	2001
Y15TGM	Irisbus EuroRider 391E.12.35	Beulas Stergo ε	C49FT	2001
Y20TGM	Volvo B10M-62	Plaxton Panther	C53F	2001
Y30TGM	Volvo B10M-62	Plaxton Panther	C53F	2001
YN51WGY	Volvo B10M-62	Plaxton Panther	C53F	2001
YN51WGZ	Volvo B10M-62	Plaxton Panther	C53F	2001
KP51UEV	Volvo B10M-62	Plaxton Panther	C49FT	2001
KP51UEW	Volvo B10M-62	Plaxton Panther	C49FT	2001
KP51UEX	Volvo B10M-62	Plaxton Panther	C49FT	2001
KP51UEY	Volvo B10M-62	Plaxton Panther	C49FT	2001
KP51UEZ	Volvo B10M-62	Plaxton Panther	C49FT	2001
KP51SYF	Volvo B10M-62	Plaxton Première 350	C51FT	2002
3401MW	Toyota Coaster BB50R	Caetano Optimo V	C22F	2002
5141MW	Setra S315 GT-HD	Setra	C49FT	2002
5579MW	Volvo B10M-62	Caetano Enigma	C46FT	2002
5877MW	Volvo B10M-62	Caetano Enigma	C48FT	2002
6764MW	Setra S315 GT-HD	Setra	C49FT	2002
KU02YUF	Volvo B10M-62	Plaxton Paragon	C49FT	2002
KU02YUG	Volvo B10M-62	Plaxton Paragon	C49FT	2002
3262MW	Volvo B7R	Plaxton Profile	C53F	2003
6963MW	Volvo B7R	Plaxton Profile	C53F	2003
LB52UYK	Volvo B12M	Plaxton Panther	C49FT	2003
GB03TGM	Setra S415 HD	Setra	C49FT	2003
UK03TGM	Volvo B12B	Caetano Enigma	C48FT	2004
MM03TGM	Volvo B12B	Caetano Enigma	C48FT	2004
GB04TGM	Volvo B12M	Caetano Enigma	C48FT	2004
UK04TGM	Volvo B12B	Caetano Enigma	C53F	2004
KX04HSJ	Volvo B12B	TransBus Paragon	C49FT	2004
YN54WWF	Volvo B12B	TransBus Panther	C49FT	2004
YN54WWG	Volvo B12B	TransBus Panther	C49FT	2004
GS05TGM	Volvo B12B	Van Hool T9 Alicron	C32FT	2005

The Tellings group also contains Burtons, Classic and Link Line. Representing the latter is rear-engined Volvo B12B, GB03LLC, which carries Caetano Enigma bodywork. *Colin Lloyd*

YN55WSU	Volvo B12B	Plaxton Panther	C49FT	2005
YN55WSV	Volvo B12B	Plaxton Panther	C49FT	2005
YN55WSW	Volvo B12B	Plaxton Panther	C49FT	2005
YN06CJV	Scania K340 EB4	VDL Berkhof Axial 50	C55FT	2006
YN06CJX	Scania K340 EB4	VDL Berkhof Axial 50	C55FT	2006
YN06CJY	Scania K114 EB4	Irizar Century Style	C53F	2006
YN06CJZ	Scania K114 EB4	Irizar Century Style	C53F	2006
YN06PFD	Volvo B12M	Plaxton Panther	C50FT	2006
YN06PFE	Volvo B12M	Plaxton Panther	C50FT	2006
YN06PFF	Volvo B12M	Plaxton Panther	C50FT	2006
YN06PFG	Volvo B12M	Plaxton Panther	C50FT	2006
KC06EVN	Mercedes-Benz Vito 111cdi	Mercedes-Benz	M7	2006
KC06EVP	Mercedes-Benz Vito 111cdi	Mercedes-Benz	M7	2006

Link Line fleet

R763DUB	Mercedes-Benz Vario O814	Plaxton Beaver 2	B27F	1997	Burtons, Haverhill, 2006
R174VBM	Mercedes-Benz Vario O814	Plaxton Beaver 2	B27F	1997	Burtons, Haverhill, 2006
S131NRB	Mercedes-Benz Vario O814	Plaxton Beaver 2	B33F	1998	City of Nottingham, 2006
T571FFC	Mercedes-Benz 308	Mercedes-Benz	M12	1999	
T576FFC	Mercedes-Benz 308	Mercedes-Benz	M12	1999	Mudi-Bond, Cassington, 2002
W30BCL	Irisbus EuroMidi CC80E	Indcar Maxim	C29F	2000	
W442CWX	Optare Solo M920	Optare	N30F	2000	Metrobus, 2006
Y292PDN	Optare Solo M920	Optare	N31F	2001	
RL51ZKR	Dennis Dart SLF 9m	Caetano Nimbus	N29F	2002	
RL51ZKS	Dennis Dart SLF 9m	Caetano Nimbus	N29F	2002	
CE52UWW	Optare Solo M920	Optare	N29F	2002	Bebbs, Llantwit Fardre, 2006
EO52OZT	LDV Convoy	Crystals	M16	2002	
RN52EYH	Dennis Dart SLF 9m	Caetano Nimbus	N29F	2003	
RN52EYJ	Dennis Dart SLF 9m	Caetano Nimbus	N29F	2003	
GB03LLC	Volvo B12B	Caetano Enigma	C48FT	2003	
UK03LLC	Volvo B12B	Caetano Enigma	C48FT	2003	
GB04LLC	Volvo B7R	TransBus Prima	C53F	2004	
HX04HUH	Dennis Dart SLF 9m	Caetano Nimbus	N29F	2004	
HX04HUK	Dennis Dart SLF 9m	Caetano Nimbus	N29F	2004	

Previous registrations:

W30BCL	W654SJF		W627UMV	W40BCL
W433UMX	W30BCL			

Liveries: white, blue and yellow; blue and gold (Gold Service): P10TGM, GB03TGM, GS05TGM; white, blue and orange (Gulliver's Travel Agency): YN51WGY/Z; National Express: KP51SYF, KP51UEV/W/X/Y/Z, KU02YUF/G, LB52UYK, KX04HSJ, YN54WWF/G, YN55WSU/V/W; white, maroon and gold (Link Line coaches); white (Link Line buses).
Web: www.tellingsgoldenmiller.co.uk; www.linkline-coaches.co.uk

TRAMLINK

Tramlink

Tram Operations Ltd, Macmillan House, Paddington Station, London, W2 1TY

2530-2553		Bombardier 30.1m		Bombardier Flexity Swift LF		AB70T		1998-99	
2530	2533	2536	2539	2542	2544	2546	2548	2550	2552
2531	2534	2537	2540	2543	2545	2547	2549	2551	2553
2532	2535	2538	2541						

Depot: Therapia Lane, Croydon

First operates the Croydon Tramlink service with Bombardier Transportation carrying out fleet maintenance. The trams are in a red and white scheme reflecting the original London Transport livery. The operation is managed by First in a consortium looking after the whole system, which runs between Croydon, Wimbledon, Elmers End and Beckenham. Fleet numbers were chosen to continue from where London Transport's trams ended. Bombardier-built 2530 is heading for Wimbledon on the reserved track which dominates the system away from Croydon centre. *Bill Potter*

TRANSDEV

Transdev London

London United Busways Ltd, Busways House, Wellington Road, Twickenham, TW2 5NX

Single-deck buses

DP1-11

Dennis Dart SLF   10.7m   Plaxton Pointer   N36F   1998

1	TV	S301MKH	4	V	S304MKH	7	V	S307MKH	10	HH	S310MKH
2	V	S302MKH	5	TV	S305MKH	8	V	S308MKH	11	TV	S311MKH
3	V	S303MKH	6	V	S306MKH	9	V	S309MKH			

DP12-22

Dennis Dart SLF   10.7m   Plaxton Pointer 2   N31D*   1999   *19-22 are N27D

12	HH	T412KAG	15	HH	T415KAG	18	HH	T418KAG	21	HH	T421KAG
13	HH	T413KAG	16	HH	T416KAG	19	HH	T419KAG	22	HH	T422KAG
14	HH	T414KAG	17	HH	T417KAG	20	HH	T420KAG			

DP23-33

Dennis Dart SLF   10.7m   Plaxton Pointer 2   N34D   1999

23	HH	T423KAG	26	HH	T426KAG	29	HH	T429KAG	32	AV	T432KAG
24	HH	T424KAG	27	AV	T427KAG	30	V	T430KAG	33	AV	T433KAG
25	HH	T425KAG	28	AV	T428KAG	31	AV	T431KAG			

DP34-99

Dennis Dart SLF   10.7m   Plaxton Pointer 2   N31D   1999

34	AV	T334PRH	51	AV	T351PRH	68	AV	T368PRH	84	HH	V784FKH
35	AV	T335PRH	52	AV	T352PRH	69	AV	T369PRH	85	HH	V785FKH
36	AV	T336PRH	53	AV	T353PRH	70	AV	T370PRH	86	HH	V886FKH
37	AV	T337PRH	54	AV	T354PRH	71	AV	T371PRH	87	V	V787FKH
38	AV	T338PRH	55	AV	T455PRH	72	AV	T372PRH	88	HH	V788FKH
39	AV	T339PRH	56	AV	T356PRH	73	AV	T373PRH	89	V	V789FKH
40	AV	T340PRH	57	AV	T357PRH	74	AV	T374PRH	90	AV	V790FKH
41	AV	T341PRH	58	AV	T358PRH	75	AV	T375PRH	91	HH	V791FKH
42	AV	T342PRH	59	AV	T359PRH	76	AV	T976SRH	92	S	V792FKH
43	AV	T343PRH	60	AV	T360PRH	77	AV	T977SRH	93	TV	V793FKH
44	AV	T344PRH	61	AV	T361PRH	78	S	T978SRH	94	HH	V794FKH
45	AV	T345PRH	62	AV	T362PRH	79	S	T979SRH	95	V	V795FKH
46	AV	T346PRH	63	AV	T363PRH	80	HH	T980SRH	96	S	V796FKH
47	AV	T347PRH	64	AV	T364PRH	81	AV	V781FKH	97	HH	V797FKH
48	AV	T348PRH	65	AV	T365PRH	82	S	V782FKH	98	HH	V798FKH
49	AV	T349PRH	66	AV	T366PRH	83	HH	V783FKH	99	V	V799FKH
50	AV	T350PRH	67	AV	T367PRH						

Hayes Station Bridge in June 2006 finds DP28, T428KAG, heading towards its home. Prior to gaining full repaints most Transdev buses carried dual logos, with London United, as shown in this view. *Colin Lloyd*

The picturesque surroundings of Richmond Bridge provide an attractive backdrop to Hounslow-based Dennis Dart, DP502, X602OKH. Several different shades have been tried for the grey skirting on these buses, but that shown here appears to be the most common. *Mark Lyons*

DPS1-16

Dennis Dart SLF		10.1m			Plaxton Pointer 2			N27D		1999				
1	S	V801KAG	5	u	V805KAG	9	S	V809KAG	13	S	V813KAG			
2	S	V802KAG	6	S	V806KAG	10	S	V810KAG	14	S	V814KAG			
3	S	V803KAG	7	S	V807KAG	11	S	V811KAG	15	S	V815KAG			
4	u	V904KAG	8	S	V808KAG	12	S	V812KAG	16	S	V816KAG			

SDP503-557

Dennis Dart SLF 10.1m   Plaxton Pointer 2   N31D   1999   Blazefield Holdings, 2002

503	SO	T503JPP	515	SO	V515JBH	525	SO	V525JBH	535	SO	V535JBH
504	SO	T504JPP	516	SO	V516JBH	526	SO	V526JBH	536	SO	V536JBH
506	SO	V506JBH	517	SO	V517JBH	527	SO	V527JBH	537	SO	V537JBH
507	SO	V507JBH	518	V	V518JBH	528	SO	V528JBH	538	SO	V538JBH
508	SO	V508JBH	519	SO	V519JBH	529	SO	V529JBH	539	V	V539JBH
509	SO	V509JBH	520	SO	V520JBH	530	SO	V530JBH	551	SO	V551JBH
510	SO	V510JBH	521	SO	V521JBH	531	SO	V531JBH	552	SO	V552JBH
511	SO	V511JBH	522	SO	V522JBH	532	SO	V532JBH	553	SO	V553JBH
512	SO	V512JBH	523	SO	V523JBH	533	SO	V533JBH	556	SO	V556JBH
513	SO	V513JBH	524	SO	V524JBH	534	SO	V534JBH	557	SO	V557JBH
514	SO	V514JBH									

DPF558-562

Dennis Dart SLF 9.3m   Plaxton Pointer 2   N29F   1999   Blazefield Holdings, 2002

558	SO	V558JBH	560	SO	V560JBH	561	SO	V561JBH	562	SO	V562JBH
559	SO	V559JBH									

DP500-509

Dennis Dart SLF 10.7m   Plaxton Pointer 2   N31D   2000

500	AV	X611OKH	503	AV	X603OKH	506	AV	X606OKH	508	AV	X608OKH
501	AV	X601OKH	504	AV	X604OKH	507	AV	X607OKH	509	AV	X609OKH
502	AV	X602OKH	505	AV	X605OKH						

Hounslow Heath depot operates route 285 using specially branded 10.1m Dennis Darts. Linking Heathrow Airport with Kingston, DPS562, SN51SZZ, is seen on the Bath Road in March 2006 showing off its livery to good effect. *Mark Lyons*

DPS511-533
Dennis Dart SLF 10.1m   Plaxton Pointer 2   N27D   2000

511	HH	X511UAT	**517**	HH	X517UAT	**523**	HH	X523UAT	**529**	HH	X529UAT
512	HH	X512UAT	**518**	HH	X518UAT	**524**	HH	X524UAT	**531**	HH	X531UAT
513	HH	X513UAT	**519**	HH	X519UAT	**526**	HH	X526UAT	**532**	HH	X532UAT
514	HH	X514UAT	**521**	HH	X521UAT	**527**	HH	X527UAT	**533**	HH	X533UAT
516	HH	X516UAT	**522**	HH	X522UAT						

DPS534-557
Dennis Dart SLF 10.1m   Plaxton Pointer 2   N30D   2001

534	TV	Y534XAG	**541**	TV	Y541XAG	**547**	TV	Y547XAG	**553**	TV	Y553XAG
536	TV	Y536XAG	**542**	TV	Y542XAG	**548**	TV	Y548XAG	**554**	TV	Y554XAG
537	TV	Y537XAG	**543**	TV	Y543XAG	**549**	TV	Y549XAG	**556**	TV	Y556XAG
538	TV	Y538XAG	**544**	TV	Y544XAG	**551**	TV	Y551XAG	**557**	TV	Y557XAG
539	TV	Y539XAG	**546**	TV	Y546XAG	**552**	TV	Y552XAG			

DPS558-578
Dennis Dart SLF 10.1m   Alexander ALX200   N29D   2001

558	HH	SN51SZV	**564**	HH	SN51SXY	**569**	HH	SN51SXO	**574**	HH	SN51SZK
559	HH	SN51SZW	**565**	HH	SN51SXZ	**570**	HH	SN51SXC	**575**	HH	SN51SZL
560	HH	SN51SZX	**566**	HH	SN51SXK	**571**	HH	SN51SZF	**576**	HH	SN51SZO
561	HH	SN51SZY	**567**	V	SN51SXL	**572**	HH	SN51SZG	**577**	HH	SN51SZP
562	HH	SN51SZZ	**568**	HH	SN51SXM	**573**	HH	SN51SZJ	**578**	HH	SN51SZR
563	HH	SN51SXX									

DPS579-602
Dennis Dart SLF 10.1m   Alexander ALX200   N30D   2001

579	HH	SN51TAU	**585**	FW	SN51TCX	**591**	TV	SN51TBU	**597**	TV	SN51TDO
580	FW	SN51TBY	**586**	FW	SN51TDX	**592**	TV	SN51TCK	**598**	TV	SN51TEO
581	FW	SN51TCV	**587**	TV	SN51TBO	**593**	TV	SN51TCZ	**599**	TV	SN51TBX
582	FW	SN51TDV	**588**	TV	SN51TCJ	**594**	TV	SN51TEJ	**600**	TV	SN51TCU
583	FW	SN51TAV	**589**	TV	SN51TCY	**595**	TV	SN51TBV	**601**	TV	SN51TDU
584	FW	SN51TBZ	**590**	TV	SN51TDZ	**596**	TV	SN51TCO	**602**	TV	SN51TEU

DPK625, SN06JPX, is one of a pair of Alexander-Dennis Mini Pointers that joined Transdev in 2006. *Mark Lyons*

DPK603-615

		Dennis Dart SLF 8.8m			Plaxton Pointer MPD		N29F	2001	

603	TV	SN51SXP	607	TV	SN51SXU	610	TV	SN51SXD	613	TV	SN51SXG
604	TV	SN51SXR	608	TV	SN51SXV	611	TV	SN51SXE	614	TV	SN51SXH
605	TV	SN51SXS	609	TV	SN51SXW	612	TV	SN51SXF	615	TV	SN51SXJ
606	TV	SN51SXT									

DPK616-623

		Dennis Dart SLF 8.8m			Plaxton Pointer MPD		N29F	2002	

616	TV	LG02FEX	618	V	LG02FFB	620	TV	LG02FFD	622	V	LG02FFH
617	TV	LG02FFA	619	V	LG02FFC	621	V	LG02FFE	623	V	LG02FFJ

DPK624	TV	SN06JPV	ADL Dart 8.8m	ADL Mini Pointer	N23F	2006
DPK625	TV	SN06JPX	ADL Dart 8.8m	ADL Mini Pointer	N23F	2006

DPS624-680

		Dennis Dart SLF 10.1m			Plaxton Pointer 2		N30D	2002	

624	V	SK02XGT	639	V	SK02XHP	653	TV	LG02FFX	667	V	LG02FGU
625	V	SK02XGU	640	V	SK02XHR	654	TV	LG02FFY	668	FW	LG02FGV
626	V	SK02XGV	641	TV	LG02FFK	655	TV	LG02FFZ	669	FW	LG02FGX
627	V	SK02XGW	642	TV	LG02FFL	656	TV	LG02FGA	670	FW	LG02FGZ
628	V	SK02XGX	643	TV	LG02FFM	657	TV	LG02FGC	671	FW	LG02FHA
629	V	SK02XHD	644	TV	LG02FFN	658	TV	LG02FGD	672	FW	LG02FHB
630	V	SK02XHE	645	TV	LG02FFO	659	TV	LG02FGE	673	FW	LG02FHC
631	V	SK02XHF	646	TV	LG02FFP	660	V	LG02FGF	674	FW	LG02FHD
632	V	SK02XHG	647	TV	LG02FFR	661	u	LG02FGJ	675	FW	LG02FHE
633	V	SK02XHH	648	TV	LG02FFS	662	V	LG02FGK	676	FW	LG02FHF
634	V	SK02XHJ	649	TV	LG02FFT	663	u	LG02FGM	677	FW	LG02FHH
635	V	SK02XHL	650	TV	LG02FFU	664	AV	LG02FGN	678	FW	LG02FHJ
636	V	SK02XHM	651	TV	LG02FFV	665	u	LG02FGO	679	FW	LG02FHK
637	V	SK02XHN	652	TV	LG02FFW	666	V	LG02FGP	680	FW	LG02FHL
638	V	SK02XHO									

DPS681-694

		Dennis Dart SLF 10.1m			Plaxton Pointer 2		N30D	2004	

681	AV	SN03LDY	685	AV	SN03LEV	689	FW	SN03LFE	692	FW	SN03LFH
682	AV	SN03LDZ	686	FW	SN03LFA	690	FW	SN03LFF	693	FW	SN03LFJ
683	AV	SN03LEF	687	FW	SN03LFB	691	FW	SN03LFG	694	AV	SN03LFK
684	AV	SN03LEJ	688	FW	SN03LFD						

Following conversion from Routemaster operation to 'pay as you board', new Scania OmniDekkas with 10.6m bodies entered service on route 13 from Edgware depot. These premises remain unique as they are divided, within their confines, and are used by both Metroline and Transdev. Seen turning into Regent Street from Oxford Circus in August 2006 is SLE35, YN55NKD. *Mark Lyons*

Double-deck buses

SLE1-20

Scania OmniDekka N94UD — East Lancs — N49/27D — 2004-05

1	BT	YN54OAA	6	BT	YN54OAH	11	FW	YN55NHE	16	FW	YN55NHK
2	BT	YN54OAB	7	FW	YN55NHA	12	FW	YN55NHF	17	FW	YN55NHL
3	BT	YN54OAC	8	FW	YN55NHB	13	FW	YN55NHG	18	FW	YN55NHM
4	BT	YN54OAE	9	FW	YN55NHC	14	FW	YN55NHH	19	FW	YN55NHO
5	BT	YN54OAG	10	FW	YN55NHD	15	FW	YN55NHJ	20	FW	YN55NHP

SLE21-64

Scania OmniDekka N94UD — East Lancs — N45/27D — 2005 — *43-64 are N45/26D

21	BT	YN55NHT	32	BT	YN55NJV	43	V	YN55NKM	54	V	YN55NLC
22	BT	YN55NHU	33	BT	YN55NKA	44	V	YN55NKO	55	V	YN55NLD
23	BT	YN55NHV	34	BT	YN55NKC	45	V	YN55NKP	56	V	YN55NLE
24	BT	YN55NHX	35	BT	YN55NKD	46	V	YN55NKR	57	V	YN55NLG
25	BT	YN55NHY	36	BT	YN55NKE	47	V	YN55NKS	58	V	YN55NLJ
26	BT	YN55NHZ	37	BT	YN55NKF	48	V	YN55NKT	59	V	YN55NLK
27	BT	YN55NJE	38	BT	YN55NKG	49	V	YN55NKU	60	V	YN55NLL
28	BT	YN55NJF	39	BT	YN55NKH	50	V	YN55NKW	61	V	YN55NLM
29	BT	YN55NJJ	40	BT	YN55NKJ	51	V	YN55NKX	62	V	YN55NLO
30	BT	YN55NJK	41	BT	YN55NKK	52	V	YN55NKZ	63	V	YN55NLP
31	BT	YN55NJU	42	BT	YN55NKL	53	V	YN55NLA	64	V	YN55NLR

SP1-15

Scania OmniDekka CN94UD — Scania — N41/23D — 2006

1	S	YN56FCA	5	S	YN56FCF	9	-	-	13	-	-
2	S	YN56FCC	6	S	YN56FCG	10	-	-	14	-	-
3	S	YN56FCD	7	S	YN56FCJ	11	-	-	15	-	-
4	S	YN56FCE	8	-	-	12	-	-			

Route 94 is one of the busiest that Transdev operates and requires a pvr of thirty-one buses. Operated from Shepherd's Bush, the 94 links Acton in the west with Piccadilly Circus. It also uses the very busy Notting Hill Gate and Bayswater Road corridor. Pictured on one of these workings at Oxford Circus is all-TransBus Trident TLA27, SN53KJF. *Mark Lyons*

TLA1-32

TransBus Trident 10.5m | TransBus ALX400 | N45/23D | 2003-04

1	S	SN53EUF	9	S	SN53EUR	17	S	SN53KHR	25	S	SN53KJA
2	S	SN53EUH	10	S	SN53EUT	18	S	SN53KHT	26	S	SN53KJE
3	S	SN53EUJ	11	S	SN53EUU	19	S	SN53KHU	27	S	SN53KJF
4	S	SN53EUK	12	S	SN53EUV	20	S	SN53KHV	28	S	SN53KJJ
5	S	SN53EUL	13	S	SN53EUW	21	S	SN53KHW	29	S	SN53KJK
6	S	SN53EUM	14	S	SN53EUX	22	S	SN53KHX	30	S	SN53KJO
7	S	SN53EUO	15	S	SN53EUY	23	S	SN53KHY	31	S	SN53KJU
8	S	SN53EUP	16	S	SN53EUZ	24	S	SN53KHZ	32	S	SN53KJV

VA6-10

Volvo Olympian YN2RV18Z4 | Alexander RH | B45/29F | 1996

6	TV	N136YRW	8	TV	N138YRW	9	TV	N139YRW	10	TV	N140YRW
7	TV	N137YRW									

VA17 | u | XDZ5917 | Volvo Olympian | | Alexander RH | B47/25D | 1997

VA45-54

Volvo Olympian | Alexander RH | B47/25F | 1998

45	TV	R945YOV	49	TV	R949YOV	51	V	R951YOV	53	V	R953YOV
46	TV	R946YOV	50	V	R950YOV	52	V	R952YOV	54	TV	R954YOV
48	TV	R948YOV									

VA60-104

Volvo B7TL 10.1m | Alexander ALX400 4.4m | N43/20D | 2000

60	S	V176OOE	72	S	V188OOE	83	S	V206OOE	94	AV	W128EON
61	S	V177OOE	73	S	V189OOE	84	S	V207OOE	95	AV	W129EON
62	S	V178OOE	74	S	V190OOE	85	S	V208OOE	96	AV	W131EON
63	S	V179OOE	75	S	V191OOE	86	S	W116EON	97	AV	W132EON
64	S	V180OOE	76	S	V192OOE	87	S	W117EON	98	AV	W133EON
65	S	V181OOE	77	S	V193OOE	88	S	W118EON	99	AV	W134EON
66	S	V182OOE	78	S	V194OOE	89	S	W119EON	100	AV	W136EON
67	S	V183OOE	79	S	V202OOE	90	S	W122EON	101	AV	W137EON
68	S	V184OOE	80	S	V203OOE	91	AV	W124EON	102	AV	W138EON
69	S	V185OOE	81	S	V204OOE	92	AV	W126EON	103	AV	W139EON
70	S	V186OOE	82	S	V205OOE	93	AV	W127EON	104	AV	W141EON
71	S	V187OOE									

VP105-130 — Volvo B7TL 10m — Plaxton President 4.4m — N41/21D — 2000

105	BT	W448BCW	112	AV	W458BCW	119	AV	W466BCW	125	AV	W473BCW
106	AV	W449BCW	113	AV	W459BCW	120	AV	W467BCW	126	AV	W474BCW
107	AV	W451BCW	114	AV	W461BCW	121	AV	W468BCW	127	AV	W475BCW
108	AV	W452BCW	115	AV	W462BCW	122	AV	W469BCW	128	AV	W476BCW
109	AV	W453BCW	116	AV	W463BCW	123	AV	W471BCW	129	AV	W477BCW
110	AV	W454BCW	117	AV	W464BCW	124	AV	W472BCW	130	AV	W478BCW
111	AV	W457BCW	118	AV	W465BCW						

TA201-225 — Dennis Trident 9.9m — Alexander ALX400 4.4m — N43/20D* — 2000-01 — *215-25 are N43/19D

201	AV	X201UMS	208	TV	SN51SYG	214	S	SN51SYT	220	FW	SN51SYZ
202	AV	X202UMS	209	TV	SN51SYH	215	FW	SN51SYU	221	FW	SN51SZC
203	AV	X203UMS	210	AV	SN51SYJ	216	FW	SN51SYV	222	FW	SN51SZD
204	AV	SN51SYA	211	AV	SN51SYO	217	FW	SN51SYW	223	FW	SN51SZE
205	TV	SN51SYC	212	AV	SN51SYR	218	FW	SN51SYX	224	FW	SN51SZT
206	TV	SN51SYE	213	S	SN51SYS	219	FW	SN51SYY	225	FW	SN51SZU
207	TV	SN51SYF									

VR226	S	BD51YCR	Volvo B7TL 10.1m	Wrightbus Eclipse Gemini	N41/23D	2002
VR227	S	BD51YCS	Volvo B7TL 10.1m	Wrightbus Eclipse Gemini	N41/23D	2002
VR228	S	BD51YCT	Volvo B7TL 10.1m	Wrightbus Eclipse Gemini	N41/23D	2002

TA229-292 — Dennis Trident 9.9m — Alexander ALX400 4.4m — N43/20D — 2002

229	FW	LG02FAA	245	FW	LG02FBN	261	FW	LG02FCO	277	TV	LG02FDP
230	FW	LG02FAF	246	FW	LG02FBO	262	FW	LG02FCP	278	TV	LG02FDU
231	FW	LG02FAJ	247	FW	LG02FBU	263	FW	LG02FCU	279	TV	LG02FDV
232	FW	LG02FAK	248	FW	LG02FBV	264	TV	LG02FCX	280	TV	LG02FDX
233	FW	LG02FAM	249	FW	LG02FBX	265	TV	LG02FCY	281	TV	LG02FDY
234	FW	LG02FAO	250	FW	LG02FBY	266	TV	LG02FCZ	282	TV	LG02FDZ
235	FW	LG02FAU	251	FW	LG02FBZ	267	TV	LG02FDA	283	TV	LG02FEF
236	FW	LG02FBA	252	FW	LG02FCA	268	TV	LG02FDC	284	TV	LG02FEH
237	FW	LG02FBB	253	FW	LG02FCC	269	TV	LG02FDD	285	TV	LG02FEJ
238	FW	LG02FBC	254	FW	LG02FCD	270	TV	LG02FDF	286	TV	LG02FEK
239	FW	LG02FBD	255	FW	LG02FCE	271	TV	LG02FDJ	287	TV	LG02FEM
240	FW	LG02FBE	256	FW	LG02FCF	272	TV	LG02FDK	288	TV	LG02FEO
241	FW	LG02FBF	257	FW	LG02FCJ	273	TV	LG02FDL	289	TV	LG02FEP
242	FW	LG02FBJ	258	FW	LG02FCL	274	TV	LG02FDM	290	TV	LG02FET
243	FW	LG02FBK	259	FW	LG02FCM	275	TV	LG02FDO	291	TV	LG02FEU
244	FW	LG02FBL	260	FW	LG02FCN	276	TV	LG02FDO	292	TV	LG02FEV

VA293-311 — Volvo B7TL 10.1m — Alexander ALX400 4.4m — N43/20D — 2002-03

293	S	SK52MKV	298	S	SK52MPY	303	S	SK52URZ	308	S	SK52USG
294	S	SK52MSO	299	S	SK52URV	304	S	SK52USB	309	S	SK52USH
295	S	SK52MPU	300	S	SK52URW	305	S	SK52USC	310	S	SK52USJ
296	S	SK52MPV	301	S	SK52URX	306	S	SK52USD	311	S	SK52USL
297	S	SK52MPX	302	S	SK52URY	307	S	SK52USF			

TA312-346 — TransBus Trident 9.9m — TransBus ALX400 4.4m — N45/20D — 2003

312	AV	SN03DZJ	321	FW	SN03DZX	330	FW	SN03EAW	339	FW	SN03EBL
313	AV	SN03DZK	322	FW	SN03EAA	331	FW	SN03EAX	340	FW	SN03EBM
314	AV	SN03DZM	323	FW	SN03EAC	332	FW	SN03EBA	341	FW	SN03LFL
315	TV	SN03DZP	324	FW	SN03EAE	333	FW	SN03EBC	342	FW	SN03LFM
316	AV	SN03DZR	325	FW	SN03EAF	334	FW	SN03EBD	343	FW	SN03LFP
317	AV	SN03DZS	326	FW	SN03EAG	335	FW	SN03EBF	344	FW	SN03LFR
318	FW	SN03DZT	327	FW	SN03EAJ	336	FW	SN03EBG	345	FW	SN03LFS
319	FW	SN03DZV	328	FW	SN03EAM	337	FW	SN03EBJ	346	FW	SN03LFT
320	FW	SN03DZW	329	FW	SN03EAP	338	FW	SN03EBK			

VE1-10 — Volvo B7TL 10.4m — East Lancs Vyking 4.4m — N45/19D — 2004

1	S	PG04WGN	4	S	PG04WGV	7	S	PG04WGY	9	S	PG04WHA
2	S	PG04WGP	5	S	PG04WGW	8	S	PG04WGZ	10	S	PG04WHB
3	S	PG04WGU	6	S	PG04WGX						

Stamford Brook depot operates route 9 using twenty-six 11m Volvo B7TLs with East Lancs Vyking bodies. Operating a short working to Hyde Park Corner in June 2006 is VLE11, PG04WHP. *Mark Lyons*

VLE1-45

	Volvo B7TL 11m			East Lancs Vyking 4.4m			N47/22D	2004		

1	V	PG04WHC	13	V	PG04WHS	24	V	PA04CYG	35	BT	PO54ACU
2	V	PG04WHD	14	V	PG04WHT	25	S	PA04CYH	36	BT	PO54ACV
3	V	PG04WHE	15	V	PG04WHU	26	V	PA04CYJ	37	BT	PO54ACX
4	V	PG04WHF	16	V	PG04WHV	27	BT	PA04CYK	38	BT	PO54ACY
5	V	PG04WHH	17	V	PG04WHW	28	BT	PA04CYL	39	BT	PO54ACZ
6	V	PG04WHJ	18	V	PG04WHX	29	BT	PA04CYP	40	u	PO54ADU
7	V	PG04WHK	19	V	PG04WHY	30	BT	PA04CYS	41	u	PO54ADV
8	V	PG04WHL	20	V	PG04WJA	31	BT	PA04CYT	42	u	PO54OOD
9	V	PG04WHM	21	V	PA04CYC	32	BT	PO54ABZ	43	u	PO54OOE
10	V	PG04WHN	22	V	PA04CYE	33	BT	PO54ACF	44	u	PO54OOF
11	V	PG04WHP	23	V	PA04CYF	34	BT	PO54ACJ	45	u	PO54OOG
12	V	PG04WHR									

VLP1-17

	Volvo B7TL 10.6m			Plaxton President 4.4m		N43/24D	2001-02	Blazefield Holdings, 2002	

1	BT	LN51AZA	6	BT	LN51AZG	10	BT	LN51AZR	14	BT	LN51AZW
2	BT	LN51AZB	7	BT	LN51AZJ	11	BT	LN51AZT	15	BT	LN51AYX
3	BT	LN51AZC	8	BT	LN51AZL	12	BT	LN51AZU	16	BT	LN51AYY
4	BT	LN51AZD	9	BT	LN51AZP	13	BT	LN51AZV	17	BT	LN51AYZ
5	BT	LN51AZF									

VLP18-27

	Volvo B7TL 10.6m			TransBus President 4.4m		N45/23D	2003	

18	BT	PJ53OUN	21	BT	PJ53OUU	24	BT	PJ53OUX	26	BT	PJ53OVA
19	BT	PJ53OUO	22	BT	PJ53OUV	25	BT	PJ53OUY	27	BT	PJ53OVB
20	BT	PJ53OUP	23	BT	PJ53OUW						

Special event vehicle:

RML880	TV	WLT880	AEC Routemaster RH2H1	Park Royal	B40/32R	1961

Ancillary vehicles:

DRL107 FW	K107SAG	Dennis Dart 9m	Plaxton Pointer	Staff	1993
DR131 u	J131DUV	Dennis Dart 8.5m	Plaxton Pointer	TV	1992

MV1-8   MAN 11.190   Optare Vecta   TV   1995

1	Vt	N281DWY	**3**	Vt	N283DWY	**5**	Vt	N285DWY	**7**	Vt	N287DWY
2	Vt	N282DWY	**4**	Vt	N284DWY	**6**	Vt	N286DWY	**8**	Vt	N288DWY

M46	BTt	WYW46T	MCW Metrobus DR101/8	MCW	TV	1978
M147	Vt	BYX147V	MCW Metrobus DR101/12	MCW	TV	1980

M1006-1029   MCW Metrobus DR101/12   MCW   TV   1980

1006	Vt	A706THV	**1019**	Vt	A719THV	**1026**	Vt	A726THV	**1029**	Vt	A729THV
1015	BTt	A715THV	**1024**	Vt	A724THV						

Depots and allocations:

Edgware (Station Road) - BT

Olympian	VA11	VA12	VA13	VA14	VA15	VA16	VA17	VA18
	VA19	VA20	VA42					
DB250	DLP34	DLP35	DLP36	DLP37	DLP38	DLP39		
Volvo B7TL	VLP1	VLP2	VLP3	VLP4	VLP5	VLP6	VLP7	VLP8
	VLP9	VLP10	VLP11	VLP12	VLP13	VLP14	VLP15	VLP16
	VLP17	VLP18	VLP19	VLP20	VLP21	VLP22	VLP23	VLP24
	VLP25	VLP26	VLP27	VLE27	VLE28	VLE29	VLE30	VLE31
	VLE32	VLE33	VLE34	VLE35	VLE36	VLE37	VLE38	VLE39

Training buses	DRL166	M147

Fulwell (Wellington Road) - FW

Dart	DPS511	DPS512	DPS513	DPS514	DPS516	DPS517	DPS518	DPS519
	DPS521	DPS522	DPS523	DPS524	DPS526	DPS527	DPS529	DPS531
	DPS532	DPS533	SPD539	DPS579	DPS580	DPS581	DPS582	DPS583
	DPS584	DPS585	DPS586					
Olympian	VA41	VA52	VA53	VA54				
Trident	TA205	TA207	TA208	TA209	TA210	TA211	TA212	TA213
	TA214	TA215	TA216	TA217	TA218	TA219	TA220	TA221
	TA222	TA223	TA224	TA225	TA229	TA230	TA231	TA232
	TA233	TA234	TA235	TA236	TA237	TA238	TA239	TA240
	TA241	TA242	TA243	TA244	TA245	TA246	TA247	TA248
	TA249	TA250	TA251	TA252	TA253	TA254	TA255	TA256
	TA257	TA258	TA259	TA260	TA261	TA262	TA263	TA318
	TA319	TA320	TA321	TA322	TA323	TA324	TA325	TA326
	TA327	TA328	TA329	TA330	TA331	TA332	TA333	TA334
	TA335	TA336	TA337	TA338	TA339	TA340	TA341	TA342
	TA343	TA344	TA345	TA346				

Harrow (Pinner Road) - SO

Dart	SDP503	SDP504	SDP506	SDP507	SDP508	SDP509	SDP510	SDP511
	SDP512	SDP513	SDP514	SDP515	SDP516	SDP517	SDP518	SDP519
	SDP520	SDP521	SDP522	SDP523	SDP524	SDP525	SDP526	SDP527
	SDP528	SDP529	SDP530	SDP531	SDP532	SDP533	SDP534	SDP535
	SDP536	SDP537	SDP538	SDP551	SDP552	SDP553	SDP556	SDP557
	DPF558	DPF559	DPF560	DPF561	DPF562	DPS602	DPS637	DPS673

In 2003 ten TransBus President-bodied Volvo B7TLs were added to the seventeen similar buses acquired with the London Sovereign operation. Together, the twenty-seven examples form the Edgware allocated VLP class represented here by VLP21, PJ53OUU. *Dave Heath*

Hounslow (Kingsley Road) - AV

Dart								
	DP12	DP13	DP14	DP15	DP16	DP17	DP18	DP26
	DP27	DP28	DP31	DP32	DP34	DP35	DP36	DP37
	DP38	DP39	DP40	DP41	DP42	DP43	DP44	DP45
	DP46	DP47	DP48	DP49	DP50	DP51	DP52	DP53
	DP54	DP55	DP56	DP57	DP58	DP59	DP60	DP61
	DP62	DP63	DP64	DP65	DP66	DP67	DP68	DP69
	DP70	DP71	DP72	DP73	DP74	DP75	DP76	DP77
	DP78	DP79	DP81	DP86	DP90	DP93	DP500	DP501
	DP502	DP503	DP504	DP505	DP506	DP507	DP508	DP509
	DP681	DP682	DP683	DP684	DP685			
Trident	TA201	TA202	TA203	TA204	TA312	TA313	TA314	TA315
	TA316	TA317						
Volvo B7TL	VA90	VA91	VA92	VA93	VA94	VA95	VA96	VA97
	VA98	VA99	VA100	VA101	VA102	VA103	VA104	VP105
	VP106	VP107	VP108	VP109	VP110	VP111	VP112	VP113
	VP114	VP115	VP116	VP117	VP118	VP119	VP120	VP121
	VP122	VP123	VP124	VP125	VP126	VP127	VP128	VP129
	VP130							

Hounslow Heath (Pulborough Way) - HH

Dart								
	DP1	DP2	DP3	DP4	DP5	DP6	DP7	DP8
	DP9	DP10	DP11	DP19	DP20	DP21	DP22	DP23
	DP24	DP25	DP33	DP80	DP83	DP84	DP85	DP91
	DP94	DP97	DPS558	DPS559	DPS560	DPS561	DPS562	DPS563
	DPS564	DPS565	DPS566	DPS567	DPS568	DPS569	DPS570	DPS571
	DPS572	DPS573	DPS574	DPS575	DPS576	DPS577	DPS578	DP686
	DP687	DP688	DP689	DP690	DP691	DP692	DP693	
Lance	LLW1	LLW2	LLW3	LLW4	LLW5	LLW6	LLW7	LLW8
	LLW9	LLW10						
Olympian	VA6	VA7	VA8	VA9	VA10	VA43	VA44	

Shepherd's Bush (Wells Road) - S

Dart	DPS1	DPS2	DPS3	DPS4	DPS5	DPS6	DPS7	DPS8
	DPS9	DPS10	DPS11	DPS12	DPS13	DPS14	DPS15	DPS16
	DRL102							
Trident	TLA1	TLA2	TLA3	TLA4	TLA5	TLA6	TLA7	TLA8
	TLA9	TLA10	TLA11	TLA12	TLA13	TLA14	TLA15	TLA16
	TLA17	TLA18	TLA19	TLA20	TLA21	TLA22	TLA23	TLA24
	TLA25	TLA26	TLA27	TLA28	TLA29	TLA30	TLA31	TLA32
Volvo B7TL	VA60	VA61	VA62	VA63	VA64	VA65	VA66	VA67
	VA68	VA69	VA70	VA71	VA72	VA73	VA74	VA75
	VA76	VA77	VA78	VA79	VA80	VA81	VA82	VA83
	VA84	VA85	VA86	VA87	VA88	VA89	VA226	VA227
	VA228	VA293	VA294	VA295	VA296	VA297	VA298	VA299
	VA300	VA301	VA302	VA303	VA304	VA305	VA306	VA307
	VA308	VA309	VA310	VA311	VE1	VE2	VE3	VE4
	VE5	VE6	VE7	VE8	VE9	VE10		
Scania OmniDekka	SP1	SP2	SP3	SP4	SP5	SP6	SP7	

Stamford Brook (Chiswick High Road, Chiswick) - V

Dart	CD1	CD2	CD3	CD4	CD5	CD6	CD7	CD8
	DP29	DP30	DP87	DP88	DP89	DP95	DP97	DP99
	DP162	DPK616	DPK617	DPK618	DPK619	DPK620	DPK621	DPK622
	DPK623	DPS624	DPS625	DPS626	DPS627	DPS628	DPS629	DPS630
	DPS631	DPS632	DPS633	DPS634	DPS635	DPS636	DPS638	DPS639
	DPS640	DPS660	DPS661	DPS662	DPS663	DPS664	DPS665	DPS666
	DPS667	DPS668	DPS669	DPS670	DPS671	DPS672	DPS674	DPS675
	DPS676	DPS677	DPS678	DPS679	DPS680	DPS694		
Routemaster	RML880							
Volvo B7TL	VLE1	VLE2	VLE3	VLE4	VLE5	VLE6	VLE7	VLE8
	VLE9	VLE10	VLE11	VLE12	VLE13	VLE14	VLE15	VLE16
	VLE17	VLE18	VLE19	VLE20	VLE21	VLE22	VLE23	VLE24
	VLE25	VLE26						
Trainers	DRL165	MV1	MV2	MV3	MV4	MV5	MV6	MV7
	MV8	M36	M46	M157	M204	M1006	M1014	M1015
	M1019	M1022	M1023	M1024	M1026	M1027	M1028	M1029

Tolworth (Kingston Goods Yard, Kingston Road) - TV

Dart	DRL107	DPS534	DPS536	DPS537	DPS538	DPS539	DPS541	DPS542
	DPS543	DPS544	DPS546	DPS547	DPS548	DPS549	DPS551	DPS552
	DPS553	DPS554	DPS556	DPS557	DPS587	DPS588	DPS589	DPS590
	DPS591	DPS592	DPS593	DPS594	DPS595	DPS596	DPS597	DPS598
	DPS599	DPS600	DPS601	DPK603	DPK604	DPK605	DPK606	DPK607
	DPK608	DPK609	DPK610	DPK611	DPK612	DPK613	DPK614	DPK615
	DPS641	DPS642	DPS643	DPS644	DPS645	DPS646	DPS647	DPS648
	DPS649	DPS650	DPS651	DPS652	DPS653	DPS654	DPS655	DPS656
	DPS657	DPS658	DPS659					
Trident	TA264	TA265	TA266	TA267	TA268	TA269	TA270	TA271
	TA272	TA273	TA274	TA275	TA276	TA277	TA278	TA279
	TA280	TA281	TA282	TA283	TA284	TA285	TA286	TA287
	TA288	TA289	TA290	TA291	TA292			
Olympian	VA45	VA46	VA47	VA48	VA49	VA50	VA51	

Unallocated and reserve - u

Dart	DT12	DLS21	DR131					
National	LS297	LS431						
Routemaster	RM848	RML891						
DAF Spectra	DLO24	DLO25	DLO26	DLO27	DLO28	DLO29		
DAF President	DLP30	DLP31	DLP32	DLP33				
Volvo B7TL	VLE40	VLE41	VLE42	VLE43	VLE44	VLE45		
Scania OmniDekka	SP8	SP9	SP10	SP11	SP12	SP13	SP14	SP15

TRAVEL LONDON

Travel London Ltd, Waterloo Business Centre, Waterloo Road, London, SE1 8UL

Part of the National Express Group.

MB1	u	E460ANC	Mercedes-Benz 507D	Made-to-Measure	B16F	1988	
MB2	TG	R705MJH	Mercedes-Benz Vario 0814	Plaxton Beaver 2	B31F	1997	
MB3	TG	R706MJH	Mercedes-Benz Vario 0814	Plaxton Beaver 2	B31F	1997	
MB4	TF	S549BNV	Mercedes-Benz Vario 0814	Plaxton Beaver 2	B31F	1999	
MB5	TG	S707JJH	Mercedes-Benz Vario 0814	Plaxton Beaver 2	B31F	1998	
MB6	TG	S708TCF	Mercedes-Benz Vario 0814	Plaxton Beaver 2	B31F	1998	
MB7	TG	S107HGF	Mercedes-Benz Vario 0814	Plaxton Beaver 2	B27F	1998	
MB8	u	R246XDA	Mercedes-Benz Vario 0814	Alexander ALX100	B27F	1997	

DA5-8

Dennis Dart SLF 8.9m — Alexander ALX200 — N28F — 2001

5	TF	Y215HWF	6	TF	Y116HWB	7	TF	Y117HWB	8	TG	Y118HWB

DH19	TG	4019MW	Dennis Dart 9m	Plaxton Pointer	B34F	1993	London United, 2003
DH25	TG	8325MW	Dennis Dart 9m	Plaxton Pointer	B34F	1993	London United, 2003
DH35	u	1335MW	Dennis Dart 9.8m	Northern Counties Paladin	B39F	1995	Choice Travel, Willenhall, 2000
DH39	u	7639MW	Dennis Dart 9m	Plaxton Pointer	B34F	1993	London United, 2003
DH48	TG	5948MW	Dennis Dart 9m	Plaxton Pointer	B34F	1993	London United, 2003
DH67	TG	4967MW	Dennis Dart 9.8m	Northern Counties Paladin	B39F	1995	Choice Travel, Willenhall, 2000

DP1-4

ADL Dart 8.8m — ADL Mini Pointer — NC24F — 2006

1	TF	LJ56ONH	2	TF	LJ56ONK	3	TF	LJ56ONL	4	TF	LJ56ONM

Passing St Leonard's Church in Streatham, Travel London's DP22, BU05HDV, is one of the short Mini Pointer Darts operated. Travel London's operations were recently extended with the purchase of the bus interests of Tellings-Golden Miller. *Colin Lloyd*

Following the replacement of Optare Solo buses on central London route C1 with Dennis Darts, the surplus Solos were relocated within the Group, both within London and in the West Midlands. Here in Hersham S244, YT51EBA, shows its new red and white livery used for Surrey County Council tendered routes. *Mark Lyons*

DP13-20

			ADL Dart 8.8m			ADL Mini Pointer		N29F	2004	
13	WL	BX54DLZ	15	WL	BX54DMF	17	WL	BX54DMU	19	WL	BX54DMY
14	WL	BX54DME	16	WL	BX54DMO	18	WL	BX54DMV	20	WL	BX54DMZ

DP21-39

			ADL Dart 8.8m			ADL Mini Pointer		N29F	2005	
21	QB	BU05HDO	26	QB	BU05HFA	31	QB	BU05HFK	36	QB	BU05HFW
22	QB	BU05HDV	27	QB	BU05HFB	32	QB	BU05HFM	37	QB	BU05HFX
23	QB	BU05HDX	28	QB	BU05HFC	33	QB	BU05HFN	38	QB	BU05HFY
24	QB	BU05HDY	29	QB	BU05HFD	34	QB	BU05HFT	39	QB	BU05HFZ
25	QB	BU05HEJ	30	QB	BU05HFG	35	QB	BU05HFV			

DP41-61

			Dennis Dart SLF 8.8m			Plaxton Pointer MPD		N24F*	2000-01	*51-7/9 are N27F
41	TF	V301MDP	46	TF	V306MDP	52	TF	X312KRX	58	TF	1068MW
42	TF	V302MDP	47	TF	V307MDP	53	TF	X313KRX	59	TF	X319KRX
43	TF	V303MDP	48	TF	V308MDP	54	TF	X314KRX	60	TF	X371CUY
44	TF	V304MDP	49	TF	V309MDP	55	TF	X315KRX	61	TF	X322KRX
45	TF	V305MDP	51	TF	X311KRX	57	TF	X317KRX			

DP62	TF	Y38YVV	Dennis Dart SLF 8.8m	Plaxton Pointer MPD	N24F	2001	Countryliner, Guildford, 2003
DP63	TF	KP51SXY	Dennis Dart SLF 8.8m	Plaxton Pointer MPD	N24F	2001	
DP64	TG	RA51KVS	Dennis Dart SLF 8.8m	Plaxton Pointer MPD	N27F	2002	

DP65-74

			Dennis Dart 8.8m			Plaxton Pointer MPD		N26F	2002	Wings Buses, 2004
65	TM	SX02TZN	68	TM	SX02TZR	71	TM	SX02TZU	73	TM	SX02TZW
66	TM	SX02TZO	69	TM	SX02TZS	72	TM	SX02TZV	74	TM	SX02TZX
67	TM	SX02TZP	70	TM	SX02TZT						

DP75-85

			Dennis Dart SLF 8.8m			Plaxton Pointer MPD		N29F	2002	
75	TG	KN52NFO	78	TG	KN52NFT	81	TG	KN52NFX	84	TG	KN52NFD
76	TG	KN52NFP	79	TG	KN52NFU	82	TG	KN52NFY	85	TG	KN52NFE
77	TG	KN52NFR	80	TG	KN52NFV	83	TG	KN52NFC			

The London Bus Handbook

DP86-95 | TransBus Dart 8.8m | TransBus Mini Pointer | N29F* | 2003 | *93-5 are N24F

86	TG	KV03ZFM	89	TG	KV03ZFR	92	TG	KV03ZFU	94	TF	KV03ZFX
87	TG	KV03ZFN	90	TG	KV03ZFS	93	TF	KV03ZFW	95	TF	KV03ZFY
88	TG	KV03ZFP	91	TG	KV03ZFT						

DP101-120 | ADL Dart 9.3m | ADL Pointer | N27D | 2004

101	WL	BX54DKA	106	WL	BX54DKK	111	WL	BX54DKY	116	WL	BX54DLN
102	WL	BX54DKD	107	WL	BX54DKL	112	WL	BX54DLD	117	WL	BX54DLO
103	WL	BX54DKE	108	WL	BX54DKO	113	WL	BX54DLF	118	WL	BX54DLU
104	WL	BX54DKF	109	WL	BX54DKU	114	WL	BX54DLJ	119	WL	BX54DLV
105	WL	BX54DKJ	110	WL	BX54DKV	115	WL	BX54DLK	120	WL	BX54DLY

S241-252 | Optare Solo M850 | Optare | N28F | 2001-02

241	u	YT51EAW	244	u	YT51EBA	249	WL	YP02LCA	251	WL	YP02LCE
242	u	YT51EAX	247	TF	YT51EBF	250	WL	YP02LCC	252	WL	YP02LCF
243	u	YT51EAY	248	WL	YT51EBG						

DP401-413 | Dennis Dart SLF 10.1m | Plaxton Pointer 2 | N28D | 2000

401	TF	W401UGM	404	TF	W404UGM	409	TF	W409UGM	412	TF	W412UGM
402	TF	W402UGM	407	TF	W407UGM	411	TF	W411UGM	413	TF	W413UGM
403	TF	W403UGM	408	TF	W408UGM						

DE414-420 | Dennis Dart SLF 10.5m | East Lancs Spryte | N30D | 2000-01

414	TM	V336MBV	416	TM	V338MBV	418	BC	W436CRN	420	BC	W438CRN
415	TM	V337MBV	417	BC	W435CRN	419	BC	W437CRN			

DC433 | TF | X93FOR | Dennis Dart SLF 10.2m | Caetano Nimbus | N29D | 2000

DP434-440 | Dennis Dart SLF 10.1m | Plaxton Pointer 2 | N30D | 2001

434	TF	RX51FGG	436	TF	RX51FGK	438	TF	RX51FGN	440	TF	RX51FGP
435	TF	RX51FGJ	437	TF	RX51FGM	439	TF	RX51FGO			

DP441-452 | Dennis Dart SLF 10.1m | Plaxton Pointer 2 | N30D | 2002

441	TF	KM02HFP	444	TF	KM02HFT	447	TF	RD02BJK	450	TF	RD02BJV
442	TF	KM02HFR	445	TF	KM02HFU	448	TF	RD02BJO	451	TF	RD02BJX
443	TF	KM02HFS	446	TF	KM02HFV	449	TF	RD02BJU	452	TF	RD02BJZ

DE418, W436CRN, is one of seven East Lancs Spryte-bodies Darts acquired along with the services of Wings Buses in 2004. Now repainted into the TfL all-red livery, it is seen at Mitcham Common. *Colin Lloyd*

In June 2005 the buses and routes of Tellings-Golden Miller were transferred to Travel London. As with DP446, KM02HFV, many of the buses received new transfers over the top of the old livery. Formerly 439 in the Tellings fleet, the vehicle is seen in Richmond in August 2006. *Mark Lyons*

DC453-465

Dennis Dart SLF 10.5m · Caetano Nimbus · N25D · 2001-02

453	TF	RA51KGE	**457**	TF	RA51KKG	**460**	TF	RL02FOT	**463**	TF	RL02FVN
454	TF	RA51KKD	**458**	TF	RA51KKH	**461**	TF	RL02FOU	**464**	TF	RL02ZTB
455	TF	RA51KKE	**459**	TF	RA51KLE	**462**	TF	RL02FVM	**465**	TF	RL02ZTC
456	TF	RA51KKF									

DC466	TF	GM03TGM	TransBus Dart SLF 10.5m		Caetano Nimbus		N29D	2003

DC467-472

TransBus Dart SLF 10.5m · Caetano Nimbus · N32D · 2004

467	TM	HX04HTP	**469**	TM	HX04HTU	**471**	TM	HX04HTY	**472**	TM	HX04HTZ
468	TM	HX04HTT	**470**	TM	HX04HTV						

DP473-477

ADL Dart 10.1m · ALD Pointer · N28D · 2006

473	WL	LF06YRJ	**475**	WL	LF06YRL	**476**	WL	LF06YRM	**477**	WL	LF06YRN
474	WL	LF06YRK									

DP701-710

Dennis Dart SLF 10.6m · Plaxton Pointer · N36F · 1998

701	TG	R501SJM	**704**	TG	R504SJM	**707**	TG	R507SJM	**709**	TG	R509SJM
702	TG	R502SJM	**705**	TG	R505SJM	**708**	TG	R508SJM	**710**	TG	R510SJM
703	TG	R503SJM	**706**	TG	R506SJM						

No.	Dep	Reg	Model	Body	Type	Year	Notes
711	TG	N305DHE	Dennis Dart SLF 10.6m	Plaxton Pointer	N41F	1996	Country Lion, Northampton, '01
715	TG	S515JJH	Dennis Dart SLF 10.7m	Plaxton Pointer 2	N39F	1998	
716	TG	S516JJH	Dennis Dart SLF 10.7m	Plaxton Pointer 2	N39F	1998	
717	TG	S517JJH	Dennis Dart SLF 10.7m	Plaxton Pointer 2	N39F	1998	
718	TG	S518TCF	Dennis Dart SLF 10.7m	Plaxton Pointer 2	N39F	1998	
719	TG	S519TCF	Dennis Dart SLF 10.7m	Plaxton Pointer 2	N39F	1998	

DP721-732

Dennis Dart SLF 10.7m · Plaxton Pointer 2 · N32D · 2000

721	TF	W601UGM	**724**	TF	W604UGM	**727**	TF	W607UGM	**731**	TF	W611UGM
722	TF	W602UGM	**725**	TF	W605UGM	**728**	TF	W608UGM	**732**	TF	W612UGM
723	TF	W603UGM	**726**	TF	W606UGM	**729**	TF	W609UGM			

Another Travel London bus fully repainted into TfL all red is TA24, V324KGW. The usual vehicle type to be allocated to route 3 from Beddington depot, it is seen southbound while passing the National Gallery en route to Crystal Palace. *Colin Lloyd*

DC733-753

		Dennis Dart SLF 10.9m			Caetano Nimbus		N33D	2003	
733	TF	RN52EOB	739	TF	RN52EOX	744	TF	RN52EYL	749	TF	RN52FVR
734	TF	RN52EOC	740	TF	RN52ERO	745	TF	RN52FPA	750	TF	RN52FVS
735	TF	RN52EOD	741	TF	RN52ERU	746	TF	RN52FPC	751	TF	RN52FXD
736	TF	RN52EOE	742	TF	RN52ERV	747	TF	RN52FRD	752	TF	RN52FYO
737	TF	RN52EOV	743	TF	RN52EYK	748	TF	RN52FRF	753	TF	RN52FZA
738	TF	RN52EOW									

TA1-20

		Dennis Trident 9.9m			Alexander ALX400 4.4m		N45/20D	2000	
1	BC	V301KGW	6	BC	V306KGW	11	BC	V311KGW	16	BC	V316KGW
2	BC	V302KGW	7	BC	V307KGW	12	BC	V312KGW	17	BC	V317KGW
3	BC	V303KGW	8	BC	V308KGW	13	BC	V313KGW	18	BC	V318KGW
4	BC	V304KGW	9	BC	V309KGW	14	BC	V314KGW	19	BC	V319KGW
5	BC	V305KGW	10	BC	V310KGW	15	BC	V315KGW	20	BC	V320KGW

TA21	QB	T135AUA	DAF DB250 10.5m		Plaxton President 4.4m		N45/19D	1999	London Sovereign, 2005

TA22-30

		Dennis Trident 9.9m			Alexander ALX400 4.4m		N45/20D	2000	
22	BC	V322KGW	25	BC	V325KGW	27	TF	V327KGW	29	BC	V329KGW
23	BC	V323KGW	26	TF	V326KGW	28	TF	V328KGW	30	BC	V330KGW
24	BC	V324KGW									

TA31-72

		Dennis Trident 9.9m			Alexander ALX400 4.4m		N43/20D	2001	
31	QB	Y131HWB	42	BC	YN51KUX	53	BC	YN51KVK	63	BC	YN51KVW
32	QB	Y32HWB	43	BC	YN51KUY	54	BC	YN51KVL	64	BC	YN51KVX
33	QB	Y133HWB	44	BC	YN51KVA	55	BC	YN51KVM	65	BC	YN51KVZ
34	QB	Y134HWB	46	BC	YN51KVC	56	BC	YN51KVO	66	BC	YN51KWA
35	QB	Y235HWB	47	BC	YN51KVD	57	BC	YN51KVP	67	BC	YN51KWB
36	QB	Y36HWB	48	BC	YN51KVE	58	BC	YN51KVR	68	BC	YN51KWC
37	QB	Y37HWB	49	BC	YN51KVF	59	BC	YN51KVS	69	BC	YN51KWD
38	QB	Y38HWB	50	BC	YN51KVG	60	BC	YN51KVT	70	BC	YN51KWE
39	BC	YN51KUU	51	BC	YN51KVH	61	BC	YN51KVU	71	BC	YN51KWF
40	BC	YN51KUV	52	BC	YN51KVJ	62	BC	YN51KVV	72	BC	YN51KWG
41	BC	YN51KUW									

TA73-129 — Dennis Trident 9.9m — Alexander ALX400 4.4m — N43/20D — 2002

73	QB	KU02YBH	88	QB	KV02USD	102	QB	KV02USW	116	QB	LG52XYK
74	BC	KU02YBJ	89	QB	KV02USE	103	QB	KV02URL	117	QB	LG52XYM
75	QB	KU02YBK	90	QB	KV02USF	104	QB	KV02URM	118	QB	LG52XYP
76	QB	KU02YBL	91	QB	KV02USG	105	QB	KV02URN	119	QB	LG52XYO
77	QB	KU02YBM	92	QB	KV02USH	106	QB	KV02URO	120	QB	LG52XYN
78	QB	KU02YBN	93	QB	KV02USJ	107	QB	KV02URR	121	QB	LG52XYY
79	QB	KU02YBO	94	QB	KV02USL	108	QB	KV02URP	122	QB	LG52XYZ
80	QB	KU02YBP	95	QB	KV02USM	109	QB	KV02URS	123	QB	LG52XZA
81	QB	KU02YBR	96	QB	KV02USN	110	QB	KV02URT	124	QB	LG52XZS
82	QB	KU02YBS	97	QB	KV02USO	111	QB	KV02URU	125	QB	LG52XZR
83	QB	KV02URX	98	QB	KV02USP	112	QB	LG52HWN	126	QB	LG52XYL
84	QB	KV02URY	99	QB	KV02USS	113	QB	LG52XZB	127	QB	LG52XZT
85	QB	KV02URZ	100	QB	KV02UST	114	QB	LB52URZ	128	QB	LG52XYJ
86	QB	KV02USB	101	QB	KV02USU	115	QB	LG52XWE	129	QB	LG52XWD
87	QB	KV02USC									

V1-20 — Volvo B7TL 10.6m — Wrightbus Eclipse Gemini — N45/24D — 2004

1	WL	BX54DHJ	6	WL	BX54DHO	11	WL	BX54DJD	16	WL	BX54DJO
2	WL	BX54DHK	7	WL	BX54DHP	12	WL	BX54DJE	17	WL	BX54DJU
3	WL	BX54DHL	8	WL	BX54DHV	13	WL	BX54DJF	18	WL	BX54DJV
4	WL	BX54DHM	9	WL	BX54DHY	14	WL	BX54DJJ	19	WL	BX54DJY
5	WL	BX54DHN	10	WL	BX54DHZ	15	WL	BX54DJK	20	WL	BX54DJZ

V21-65 — Volvo B7TL 10.6m — Wrightbus Eclipse Gemini — N45/24D — 2005

21	WL	BX55XLS	33	WL	BX55XMG	44	WL	BX55XMV	55	WL	BX55XNJ
22	WL	BX55XLT	34	WL	BX55XMH	45	WL	LF55CZA	56	WL	BX55XNK
23	WL	BX55XLU	35	WL	BX55XMJ	46	WL	BX55XMW	57	WL	BX55XNL
24	WL	BX55XLV	36	WL	BX55XMK	47	WL	BX55XMZ	58	WL	BX55XNM
25	WL	BX55XLW	37	WL	BX55XML	48	WL	LF55CYZ	59	WL	BX55XNN
26	WL	BX55XLY	38	WL	BX55XMM	49	WL	LF55CYY	60	WL	BX55XNO
27	WL	BX55XLZ	39	WL	BX55XMP	50	WL	LF55CYX	61	WL	BX55XNP
28	WL	BX55XMA	40	WL	BX55XMR	51	WL	LF55CYW	62	WL	BX55XNR
29	WL	BX55XMB	41	WL	BX55XMS	52	WL	LF55CYV	63	WL	BX55XNS
30	WL	BX55XMC	42	WL	BX55XMT	53	WL	LF55CZB	64	WL	BX55XNT
31	WL	BX55XMD	43	WL	BX55XMU	54	WL	BX55XNG	65	WL	BX55XNU
32	WL	BX55XME									

This new Wrightbus Eclipse Gemini-bodied Volvo B7TL at Hayes shows the changing image of London's buses including the all-red livery and simpler destination displays. Also now standard are yellow mirror backs and the provision of tree deflectors on the front upper-deck nearside corners. Travel London's V69, BX55XNZ, was captured in June 2006.
Colin Lloyd

V66-73 Volvo B7TL 10.6m Wrightbus Eclipse Gemini N45/23D 2006

66	TM	BX55XNV	68	TM	BX55XNY	70	QB	LF06YRC	72	QB	LF06YRE
67	TM	BX55XNW	69	TM	BX55XNZ	71	QB	LF06YRD	73	QB	LF06YRG

ED1-27 ADL Trident 2 ADL Enviro 400 N-/- On order

1	-	-	8	-	-	15	-	-	22	-	-
2	-	-	9	-	-	16	-	-	23	-	-
3	-	-	10	-	-	17	-	-	24	-	-
4	-	-	11	-	-	18	-	-	25	-	-
5	-	-	12	-	-	19	-	-	26	-	-
6	-	-	13	-	-	20	-	-	27	-	-
7	-	-	14	-	-	21	-	-			

Ancillary vehicles:

L2	QB	A102SYE	Leyland Olympian ONTL11/1R	Eastern Coach Works	TV	1984	Arriva London, 2000
L3	BC	A103SYE	Leyland Olympian ONTL11/1R	Eastern Coach Works	TV	1984	Arriva London, 2000
2922	WL	D922NDA	MCW Metrobus DR109/59	MCW	TV	1986	Travel West Midlands, 2004
2928	WL	D928NDA	MCW Metrobus DR109/59	MCW	TV	1986	Travel West Midlands, 2004
2942	WL	D942NDA	MCW Metrobus DR109/59	MCW	TV	1986	Travel West Midlands, 2004
2948	WL	D948NDA	MCW Metrobus DR109/59	MCW	TV	1986	Travel West Midlands, 2004
2951	WL	D951NDA	MCW Metrobus DR109/59	MCW	TV	1986	Travel West Midlands, 2004
2955	WL	D955NDA	MCW Metrobus DR109/59	MCW	TV	1986	Travel West Midlands, 2004
9072	WL	F72DDA	Leyland Lynx LX2R11C15Z4R	Leyland Lynx	TV	1989	Travel West Midlands, 2004
9266	WL	G266EOG	Leyland Lynx LX2R11C15Z4R	Leyland Lynx	TV	1989	Travel West Midlands, 2004

On order: Four Alexander Dennis Dart/Pointer (DP1-4); six Alexander Dennis Enviro200s (ES1-6); six Alexander Dennis Enviro200s (ES401-6).

Depots and allocations:

Battersea (Silverthorne Road) - QB

Dart	DP21	DP22	DP23	DP24	DP25	DP26	DP27	DP28
	DP29	DP30	DP31	DP32	DP33	DP34	DP35	DP36
	DP37	DP38	DP39					
Trident	TA21	TA31	TA32	TA33	TA34	TA35	TA36	TA37
	TA38	TA73	TA75	TA76	TA77	TA78	TA79	TA80
	TA81	TA82	TA83	TA84	TA85	TA86	TA87	TA88
	TA89	TA90	TA91	TA92	TA93	TA94	TA95	TA96
	TA97	TA98	TA99	TA100	TA101	TA102	TA103	TA104
	TA105	TA106	TA107	TA108	TA109	TA110	TA111	TA113
	TA115	TA116	TA117	TA118	TA119	TA120	TA121	TA122
	TA123	TA124	TA125	TA126	TA127	TA128	TA129	
Volvo B7TL	V70	V71	V72	V73				

Ancillary vehicle L2

Beddington (Beddington Farm Road) - BC

Dart	DE417	DE418	DE419	DE420				
Trident	TA1	TA2	TA3	TA4	TA5	TA6	TA7	TA8
	TA9	TA10	TA11	TA12	TA13	TA14	TA15	TA16
	TA17	TA18	TA19	TA20	TA22	TA23	TA24	TA25
	TA29	TA30	TA39	TA40	TA41	TA42	TA43	TA44
	TA46	TA47	TA48	TA49	TA50	TA51	TA52	TA53
	TA54	TA55	TA56	TA57	TA58	TA59	TA60	TA61
	TA62	TA63	TA64	TA65	TA66	TA67	TA68	TA69
	TA70	TA71	TA72	TA74				

Ancillary L3

Byfleet (Wintersells Road) - TG

Vario	MB2	MB3	MB5	MB6	MB7		
Dart	DA8	DH19	DH25	DH48	DP64	DH67	DP75	DP76
	DP77	DP78	DP79	DP80	DP81	DP82	DP83	DP84
	DP85	DP86	DP87	DP88	DP89	DP90	DP91	DP92
	DP701	DP702	DP703	DP704	DP705	DP706	DP707	DP708
	DP709	DP710	DP715	DP716	DP717	DP718	DP719	DP720

Hayes (Springfield Road) - TM

Dart	DP65	DP66	DP67	DP68	DP69	DP70	DP71	DP72
	DP73	DP74	DP65	DE414	DE415	DE416	DC467	DC468
	DC469	DC470	DC471	DC472				
Volvo B7TL	V66	V67	V68	V69				

Twickenham (Stanley Road) - TF

Mercedes-Benz	MB4						
Optare Solo	S247						
Dart	DP1	DP2	DP3	DP4	DA5	DA6	DA7	DP41
	DP42	DP43	DP44	DP45	DP46	DP47	DP48	DP49
	DP51	DP52	DP53	DP54	DP55	DP57	DP58	DP59
	DP60	DP61	DP63	DP62	DP63	DP93	DP94	DP95
	DC193	DP401	DP402	DP403	DP404	DP407	DP408	DP409
	DP411	DP412	DP413	DP434	DP435	DP436	DP437	DP438
	DP439	DP440	DP441	DP442	DP443	DP444	DP445	DP446
	DP447	DP448	DP449	DP450	DP451	DP452	DC453	DC454
	DC455	DC456	DC457	DC58	DC459	DC460	DC461	DC462
	DC463	DC464	DC465	DC466	DP721	DP722	DP723	DP724
	DP725	DP726	DP727	DP728	DP729	DP730	DP731	DP732
	DC733	DC734	DC735	DC736	DC737	DC738	DC739	DC740
	DC741	DC742	DC743	DC744	DC745	DC746	DC747	DC748
	DC749	DC750	DC751	DC752	DC753			
Trident	TA26	TA27	TA28					

Walworth (Walworth Road) - WL

Optare Solo	S248	S249	S250	S251	S252		
Dart	DP13	DP14	DP15	DP16	DP17	DP18	DP19	DP20
	DP101	DP102	DP103	DP104	DP105	DP106	DP107	DP108
	DP109	DP110	DP111	DP112	DP113	DP114	DP115	DP116
	DP117	DP118	DP119	DP120	DP473	DP474	DP475	DP476
	DP477							
Volvo B7TL	V1	V2	V3	V4	V5	V6	V7	V8
	V9	V10	V11	V12	V13	V14	V15	V16
	V17	V18	V19	V20	V21	V22	V23	V24
	V25	V26	V27	V28	V29	V30	V31	V32
	V33	V34	V35	V36	V37	V38	V39	V40
	V41	V42	V43	V44	V45	V46	V47	V48
	V49	V50	V51	V52	V53	V54	V55	V56
	V57	V58	V59	V60	V61	V62	V63	V64
	V65							
Ancillary	2922	2928	2942	2948	2951	2955	9072	9266

Unallocated and reserve - u

Mercedes-Benz	MB1	MB8					
Solo	S241	S242	S243	S244			
Dart	DH35	DH39					
Trident 2/Enviro	ED1	ED2	ED3	ED4	ED5	ED6	ED7	ED8
	ED9	ED10	ED11	ED12	ED13	ED14	ED15	ED16
	ED17	ED18	ED19	ED20	ED21	ED22	ED23	ED24
	ED25	ED26	ED27					

WESTBUS

Armchair - Westbus

Westbus Coach Services Ltd, 27a Spring Grove Road, Hounslow, TW3 4BE
Armchair Passenger Transport Co Ltd, Armchair House, Commerce Rd, Brentford, TW8 8LW

WB	G806BPG	Volvo B10M-60	Plaxton Paramount 3500 III	C53F	1990	Airlinks, Feltham, 2000
WB	G807BPG	Volvo B10M-60	Plaxton Paramount 3500 III	C53F	1990	Airlinks, Feltham, 2000
WB	G808BPG	Volvo B10M-60	Plaxton Paramount 3500 III	C53F	1990	Airlinks, Feltham, 2000
WB	MUI4841	DAF DB250	Optare Spectra	C(72)F	1993	JG Coaches, Heathfield, 2006
AR	XAZ774	Volvo B10M-62	Van Hool Alizée HE	C48FT	1997	Metroline, Harrow, 2006
AR	XAZ807	Volvo B10M-62	Van Hool Alizée HE	C48FT	1997	Metroline, Harrow, 2006
WB	WIB255	Volvo B10M-62	Berkhof Axial 50	C51FT	1997	
WB	WIB300	Volvo B10M-62	Berkhof Axial 50	C51FT	1997	
WB	WIB117	Mercedes-Benz O404	Hispano Vita	C49FT	1999	
AR	T2APT	Volvo B10M-62	Van Hool T9 Alizée	C40FT	1999	
AR	T3APT	Volvo B10M-62	Van Hool T9 Alizée	C48FT	1999	
AR	T4APT	Volvo B10M-62	Van Hool T9 Alizée	C48FT	1999	
AR	BIG2114	Volvo B10M-62	Van Hool T9 Alizée	C48FT	1999	
AR	BIG2115	Volvo B10M-62	Van Hool T9 Alizée	C48FT	1999	
AR	BIG2116	Volvo B10M-62	Van Hool T9 Alizée	C49FT	1999	
AR	BIG2117	Volvo B10M-62	Van Hool T9 Alizée	C49FT	1999	
WB	WIB150	DAF SB3000	Van Hool T9 Alizée	C49FT	2000	
WB	W228CDN	DAF SB3000	Van Hool T9 Alizée	C53F	2000	
WB	W229CDN	DAF SB3000	Van Hool T9 Alizée	C53F	2000	
AR	W18APT	Toyota Coaster BB50R	Caetano Optimo V	C18F	2000	
WB	Y816HHE	Mercedes-Benz Vario O814	Plaxton Cheetah	C25F	2001	

Westbus operates a fleet of high-specification coaches, most of which were new to the operation. The present fleet now has a mix of Volvo, DAF and Bova products. One of the DAF SB3000s is W229CDN, seen here at Holborn Circus and it features Van Hool T9 Alizée coachwork. The Westbus business was acquired recently by Singapore-based Comfort del Gro from its Australian-based owners. *Dave Heath*

Carrying the simple orange and white colours of Armchair is Volvo B10M T2APT, one of the first with the Van Hool T9 Alizée bodywork. *Colin Lloyd*

WB	Y461HUA	DAF SB3000	Van Hool T9 Alizée	C51FT	2001
WB	Y462HUA	DAF SB3000	Van Hool T9 Alizée	C51FT	2001
WB	Y463HUA	DAF SB3000	Van Hool T9 Alizée	C51FT	2001
WB	Y464HUA	DAF SB3000	Van Hool T9 Alizée	C51FT	2001
AR	Y22APT	Volvo B9M	Van Hool T9 Alizée	C28FT	2001
WB	WJ02VRL	Volvo B12M	Van Hool T9 Alizée	C53F	2002
AR	WJ02VRM	Volvo B12M	Van Hool T9 Alizée	C53F	2002
WB	WJ02VRN	Volvo B12M	Van Hool T9 Alizée	C53F	2002
WB	YN03WXW	Mercedes-Benz Vario 0814	TransBus Cheetah	C25F	2003
WB	WE52BUS	DAF SB4000	Van Hool T9 Alizée	C49FT	2003
WB	WE53BUS	DAF SB4000	Van Hool T9 Alizée	C49FT	2003
WB	YJ53VHA	DAF SB4000	Van Hool T9 Alizée	C49FT	2003
WB	YJ53VHB	DAF SB4000	Van Hool T9 Alizée	C49FT	2003
AR	WA03HRG	Bova FHD10.340	Bova Futura	C36FT	2003
AR	WA03HRK	Bova FHD10.340	Bova Futura	C36FT	2003
AR	WA04EWS	Bova FHD10.340	Bova Futura	C36FT	2004
WB	YJ04HVS	VDL Bus SB4000	Van Hool T9 Alizée	C49FT	2004
WB	YJ04HVU	VDL Bus SB4000	Van Hool T9 Alizée	C49FT	2004
WB	BU06CUO	Setra S415 GT-HD	Setra	C49FT	2006
WB	BU06CUV	Setra S415 GT-HD	Setra	C49FT	2006
WB	WA06NCC	Mercedes-Benz Vario 0815	Sitcar Beluga 2	C25F	2006
WB	YJ06LDD	VDL Bus SB4000	Van Hool T9 Alizée	C49FT	2006
WB	YJ06LDE	VDL Bus SB4000	Van Hool T9 Alizée	C49FT	2006

Previous registrations:

BIG2114	W14APT	WIB150	W227CDN
BIG2115	W15APT	WIB255	P116HCF
BIG2116	W16APT	WIB300	P117HCF
BIG217	W17APT	XAZ774	P846WUG
WIB117	V385NOA	XAZ807	P845WUG

Web: www.westbus.co.uk

The London Bus Handbook

WESTWAY

Westway - Aspen Bussing

D J West, 7A Rainbow Industrial Estate, Station Approach, Raynes Park, SW20 0JY
C Gash, 56 Little Bookham Street, Little Bookham, Leatherhead, KT23 3AQ

WW	17EJU	Volvo B10M-61	Van Hool Astral	C47/10DT	1984	Shorey, Maulden, 2001
WW	TIL8795	Volvo B10M-61	Plaxton Paramount 3200 II	C53F	1985	Young, Bearstead, 2002
AB	CCG376	Van Hool T824	Van Hool Astromega	C57/27F	1985	Oakwood, Grassendale, 2006
AB	CCG706	Volvo B10M-53	Jonckheere Jubilee P95	C49/12FT	1987	
WW	VSC16	Volvo B10M-61	Jonckheere Jubilee P599	C28FT	1988	Hilton's, Newton-le-Willows, '01
WW	F85GGC	Mercedes-Benz 811	Robin Hood	BC29F	1989	Windle, Newton-le-Willows, '04
AB	45CG	Volvo B10M-50	Van Hool Astral	C8/7FT	1989	Len Wright Travel, Watford, '04
WW	715ATV	Volvo B12(T)	Van Hool Astrobel	C57/14CT	1993	Berry, Taunton, 1998
WW	B19WCS	Volvo B12(T)	Jonckheere Monaco	C57/14CT	1994	Turner, Bristol, 2003
WW	449GTU	Volvo B12(T)	Van Hool Astrobel	C57/14CT	1994	Trathens, Plymouth, 2001
WW	B16WSC	Volvo B12(T)	Van Hool Astrobel	C57/14CT	1995	Berry, Taunton, 1998
WW	WET476	Setra S210H	Setra Optimal	C24FT	1995	
WW	P27TTX	Volvo B12(T)	Jonckheere Mistral 70	C48FT	1996	Ferris, Nantgarw, 2002
WW	B16WCS	Volvo B10M-62	Van Hool Alizée	C53F	1996	
WW	B19WCS	Volvo B12(T)	Jonckheere Monaco	C57/14CT	1997	Clarke's of London, 2004
WW	BSK853	Volvo B12(T)	Jonckheere Monaco	C57/14CT	1997	Clarke's of London, 2004
WW	45DG	EOS E230Z	EOS	C20FT	1998	Go-Goodwin, Eccles, 2004
WW	R778WSB	Volvo B10M-62	Van Hool T9 Alizée	C53F	1998	Highland Heritage, Dalmally, '05
WW	644RU	Volvo B9M	Van Hool T9 Alizée	C32FT	1999	
WW	LIB378	Volvo B9M	Van Hool T9 Alizée	C34FT	1999	
WW	W629WMA	Volvo B10M-55	Van Hool T9 Alizée	C53F	1998	Barratt, Nantwich, 2005
WW	WE51WAY	Volvo B12M	Van Hool T9 Alizée	C48FT	2003	
WW	WA03UEE	Mercedes-Benz Vario O815	Sitcar Beluga	C29F	2003	
WW	WJ55EWF	Mercedes-Benz Vario O815	Sitcar Beluga 2	C29F	2005	
WW	WA06GSO	Volvo B12T	Van Hool T925 Astrobel	C61/18DT	2006	
WW	WA06JGU	Volvo B12T	Van Hool T925 Astrobel	C61/18DT	2006	

Previous registrations:

45CG	G96VMM, A19LWB, CCG376	CCG376	C256FHJ, A4HWD, 201SC, A20HWD, AIG1907
45DG	R127GNW, GSU489, TIL8795	CCG706	D105BNV, WIB7190, UVF47
449GTU	M863TYC	F85GGC	F85GGC, TIL1253
644RU	T519PYD	LIB378	W152RYB
715ATV	L116NYB	TIL8795	C509HGF, MIL9311, C509HGF, LIB378
B16WCS	N991BWJ	VSC16	YR3939, E218WWW, 300CUH, E804WEP, OHH19
B16WSC	N320BYA	W629WMA	W11BCL
B19WSC	P88COL, BIL1816	WE51WAY	WA03HRF
BSK853	P77COL, TAN1A, P799TMY		

Depot: 7A Rainbow Industrial Estate, Station Approach, Raynes Park
Web: www.westway-coaches.co.uk; www.aspenbussing.co.uk

Westway's fleet includes a high proportion of double-deck coaches. Two new double-deck Volvo B12Ts bodied by Van Hool to the Astrobel design were taken into stock in 2006. One of these was pictured passing Painshill fire station.
Dave Heath

WINGS

Wings Luxury Travel Ltd, The West London Coach Centre, North Hyde Gardens, Hayes, Hillingdon, UB3 4QT

WET342	Mercedes-Benz 308D	Devon Conversions	M14	1992	Felix, Long Melford, 2000
WLT560	Mercedes-Benz 308D	Devon Conversions	M8	1994	Alamo, West Drayton, 1998
P501PTM	Ford Transit VE6	Ford	M11	1995	private owner, 2000
WLT746	Mercedes-Benz 0814 Vario	Autobus Nouvelle 2	C33F	1998	Reay, Wigton, 2000
WLT982	Mercedes-Benz 0814 Vario	Autobus Nouvelle 2	C33F	1998	Westway, Belmont, 1999
WET590	Mercedes-Benz 0814 Vario	Autobus Nouvelle 2	C20FT	1999	
S580ACT	Mercedes-Benz 0814 Vario	Autobus Nouvelle 2	C29F	1999	MCH, Uxbridge, 2004
S590ACT	Mercedes-Benz 0814 Vario	Autobus	C24F	1999	Bookham Coaches, 2004
WLT891	Ford Transit Tourneo	Ford	M8	1999	
W1NGS	Mercedes-Benz 0814 Vario	Autobus Nouvelle 2	C16FT	2000	
W11NGS	Mercedes-Benz 0814 Vario	Autobus Nouvelle 2	C16FT	2000	
WET725	Ford Transit Tourneo	Ford	M8	2001	private owner, 2003
EY02WFK	Ford Transit Tourneo	Ford	M8	2002	private owner, 2006
WLT931	Ford Galaxy	Ford	M6	2002	
WLT852	Mercedes-Benz Vario 0814	Autobus Nouvelle SR	C29F	2002	
WLT987	Mercedes-Benz Sprinter 413cdi	Ferqui/Optare Soroco	M16	2003	
YX05DHN	Mercedes-Benz Sprinter 413cdi	Ferqui/Optare Soroco	M16	2005	
YX05DHO	Mercedes-Benz Sprinter 413cdi	Ferqui/Optare Soroco	M16	2005	
BX55FYY	Mercedes-Benz Tourino 0510	Mercedes-Benz	C34F	2005	
BX55FYZ	Mercedes-Benz Tourino 0510	Mercedes-Benz	C34F	2005	
BX06UMY	Mercedes-Benz Tourino 0510	Mercedes-Benz	C24FT	2006	
BX06UMZ	Mercedes-Benz Tourino 0510	Mercedes-Benz	C24FT	2006	

Previous registrations:

W1NGS	W837PPD	WLT746	S302JRM
W11NGS	W836PPD	WLT852	FY02LEU
WET342	K142PLP, WET342, K142PLP	WLT891	WET880
WET590	T350EJM	WLT931	From new
WET725	LR51YMC	WLT982	R636FCT, WLT982
WLT560	L464VLX	WLT987	FX03GJZ

Liveries: White with red, orange and yellow (Wings coaches and minibuses); white and blue (Allied); white and orange (Allied); Eurolines (BF52SYX/SYY).
Depot: Swallowfield Way, Hayes.

High specification mini and midi-sized vehicles are the norm in the Wings fleet. Typical is WLT852, an Autobus Nouvelle SR-bodied Mercedes-Benz Vario seen on Hayes station bridge.
Colin Lloyd

Vehicle index

Reg	Operator	Reg	Operator	Reg	Operator	Reg	Operator
6MCH	MCH	A9HRR	Epsom Coaches	ALD941B	East London	BSK853	Westway
7MCH	MCH	A20YAL	Royale European	ALD968B	East London	BT04BUS	Blue Triangle
9MCH	MCH	A56THX	Big Bus Company	ALM50B	East London	BU03LYS	Clarkes of London
17EJU	Westway	A60THX	Big Bus Company	ALM60B	East London	BU04EXT	Epsom Coaches
33LUG	Metroline	A72THX	Big Bus Company	ALM71B	East London	BU04EXV	Epsom Coaches
45CG	Westway	A73THX	Big Bus Company	ALM89B	East London	BU04EXW	Epsom Coaches
45DG	Westway	A102SYE	Travel London	ALS975B	Blue Triangle	BU04EXX	Epsom Coaches
70CLT	Arriva	A103SYE	Travel London	B14BUS	Big Bus Company	BU04EYR	Redwing
124CLT	Arriva	A112KFX	Arriva Original Tour	B16BSS	Big Bus Company	BU04EYS	Redwing
133CLT	First London	A605THV	Big Bus Company	B16WCS	Westway	BU04EYT	Redwing
166CLT	Go-Ahead London	A614THV	Big Bus Company	B16WSC	Westway	BU04EYW	Allied
185CLT	Arriva	A624THV	Big Bus Company	B19WCS	Westway	BU04EYX	Redwing
197CLT	Go-Ahead London	A638THV	Big Bus Company	B19WCS	Westway	BU04EYY	Allied
202UXJ	Go-Ahead London	A640THV	Big Bus Company	B20DMS	Big Bus Company	BU04EYZ	Allied
204CLT	First London	A644THV	Big Bus Company	B95WUV	Blue Triangle	BU04EZA	City Circle
205CLT	Arriva	A667XDA	Arriva Original Tour	B101WUV	Blue Triangle	BU04EZB	City Circle
215UXJ	Blue Triangle	A706THV	Transdev	B124WUL	Arriva	BU04EZC	City Circle
217CLT	Arriva	A710THV	East Thames	B126WUL	Arriva	BU04EZD	City Circle
218CLT	First London	A715THV	Transdev	B130WUL	Arriva	BU04EZE	City Circle
280CLT	First London	A719THV	Transdev	B136WUL	Arriva	BU04EZK	Go-Ahead London
292CLT	First London	A724THV	Transdev	B140WUL	Arriva	BU04UTM	Go-Ahead London
319CLT	Arriva	A726THV	Transdev	B152WUL	Arriva Original Tour	BU04UTN	Metrobus
324CLT	Arriva	A729THV	Transdev	B170WUL	Arriva	BU04UTP	Metrobus
330CLT	Arriva	A735WEV	Arriva Original Tour	B200WUL	Blue Triangle	BU05HDO	Travel London
361CLT	Arriva	A737WEV	Arriva Original Tour	B225VHW	Arriva Original Tour	BU05HDV	Travel London
398CLT	Arriva	A831SUL	Big Bus Company	B227WUL	Arriva Original Tour	BU05HDX	Travel London
449GTU	Westway	A835SUL	Big Bus Company	B231WUL	Arriva	BU05HDY	Travel London
453CLT	Arriva	A839SUL	Big Bus Company	B239WUL	Arriva Original Tour	BU05HEJ	Travel London
464CLT	Arriva	A844SUL	Big Bus Company	B241LRA	Arriva Original Tour	BU05HFA	Travel London
480CLT	Arriva	A851SUL	Big Bus Company	B248WUL	Arriva	BU05HFB	Travel London
503CLT	First London	A852SUL	Big Bus Company	B253WUL	Arriva	BU05HFC	Travel London
510CLT	First London	A870SUL	Big Bus Company	B260WUL	First London	BU05HFD	Travel London
513CLT	Metroline	A875SUL	Big Bus Company	B265WUL	Arriva Original Tour	BU05HFG	Travel London
519CLT	Arriva	A895SUL	Arriva Original Tour	B300WUL	Arriva	BU05HFK	Travel London
527CLT	East London	A903SUL	Arriva	BD51YCR	Transdev	BU05HFM	Travel London
545CLT	Go-Ahead London	A908SYE	Blue Triangle	BD51YCS	Transdev	BU05HFN	Travel London
562CLT	First London	A919SYE	Big Bus Company	BD51YCT	Transdev	BU05HFT	Travel London
593CLT	Arriva	A927SUL	Arriva Original Tour	BD52LMO	Go-Ahead London	BU05HFV	Travel London
627DYE	First London	A928SYE	Big Bus Company	BD52LMU	Go-Ahead London	BU05HFW	Travel London
640DYE	First London	A931SYE	Big Bus Company	BD52LMV	Go-Ahead London	BU05HFX	Travel London
644RU	Westway	A956SYE	Big Bus Company	BD52LMX	Go-Ahead London	BU05HFY	Travel London
650DYE	First London	A981SYF	Blue Triangle	BD52LMY	Go-Ahead London	BU05HFZ	Travel London
656DYE	Arriva	A991SYE	Big Bus Company	BD52LNA	Go-Ahead London	BU05VFE	Arriva
676DYE	First London	AB03BUS	Isleworth	BD52LNC	Go-Ahead London	BU05VFF	Arriva
715ATV	Westway	AB04BUS	Isleworth	BD52LNE	Go-Ahead London	BU05VFG	Arriva
725DYE	Arriva	AB05BUS	Isleworth	BD52LNF	Go-Ahead London	BU05VFH	Arriva
734DYE	Arriva	AB06BUS	Isleworth	BD52LNG	Go-Ahead London	BU05VFJ	Arriva
735DYE	First London	AB52BUS	Isleworth	BD52LNO	Go-Ahead London	BU06CSF	Epsom Coaches
776DYE	First London	AB55BUS	Isleworth	BD52LNP	Go-Ahead London	BU06CSO	Epsom Coaches
801DYE	Arriva	AE05EFF	MCH	BD52LNR	Go-Ahead London	BU06CUO	Westbus
809DYE	First London	AE05EFG	MCH	BD52LNT	Go-Ahead London	BU06CUV	Westbus
810DYE	First London	AE06HCA	Go-Ahead (Docklands)	BD52LNU	Go-Ahead London	BU06CVC	Allied
811DYE	First London	AE06HCC	Go-Ahead (Docklands)	BIG2114	Westbus	BU53AWW	Epsom Coaches
822DYE	Arriva	AE06HCD	Go-Ahead (Docklands)	BIG2115	Westbus	BU53AWX	Epsom Coaches
1068MW	Travel London	AE06HCF	Go-Ahead (Docklands)	BIG2116	Westbus	BU53AWY	Epsom Coaches
1335MW	Travel London	AE06HCG	Go-Ahead (Docklands)	BIG2117	Westbus	BU53AWZ	Epsom Coaches
3262MW	Tellings-Golden Miller	AE06HCH	Go-Ahead (Docklands)	BL52ODK	Go-Ahead London	BU53AXA	Epsom Coaches
3401MW	Tellings-Golden Miller	AE06HCJ	Go-Ahead (Docklands)	BL52ODM	Go-Ahead London	BU53ZWN	Epsom Coaches
4019MW	Travel London	AE06HCK	Go-Ahead (Docklands)	BL52ODN	Go-Ahead London	BU53ZWP	Epsom Coaches
4967MW	Travel London	AG02AWP	Hamiltons	BL52ODP	Go-Ahead London	BU53ZWR	Epsom Coaches
5141MW	Tellings-Golden Miller	AJ02ZRY	Metroline	BL52ODR	Go-Ahead London	BU55UCT	Blue Triangle
5579MW	Tellings-Golden Miller	AK52LYV	Hamiltons	BL52ODT	Go-Ahead London	BU55UCU	Blue Triangle
5877MW	Tellings-Golden Miller	AL03ASH	Ashford Luxury	BL52ODU	Go-Ahead London	BU55UCW	Blue Triangle
5948MW	Travel London	AL04ASH	Ashford Luxury	BL52ODV	Go-Ahead London	BU55UCX	Blue Triangle
6764MW	Tellings-Golden Miller	AL05ASH	Ashford Luxury	BN52GVU	Go-Ahead London	BU55UCY	Blue Triangle
6963MW	Tellings-Golden Miller	AL06ASH	Ashford Luxury	BN52GWC	Go-Ahead London	BW03ZMY	Epsom Coaches
7639MW	Travel London	ALD913B	First London	BN52GWD	Go-Ahead London	BW03ZMZ	Epsom Coaches
8325MW	Travel London	ALD933B	East London	BN52GWE	Go-Ahead London	BX02CMO	Epsom Coaches

Reg	Operator	Reg	Operator	Reg	Operator	Reg	Operator
BX02CMU	Epsom Coaches	BX04MYD	Arriva	BX06UMF	Redwing	BX54UCR	Go-Ahead London
BX02YYJ	Go-Ahead London	BX04MYF	Arriva	BX06UMG	Redwing	BX54UCT	Go-Ahead London
BX02YYK	Go-Ahead London	BX04MYG	Arriva	BX06UMH	Redwing	BX54UCU	Go-Ahead London
BX02YYL	Go-Ahead London	BX04MYH	Arriva	BX06UMJ	Redwing	BX54UCV	Go-Ahead London
BX02YYM	Go-Ahead London	BX04MYJ	Arriva	BX06UMK	Redwing	BX54UCW	Go-Ahead London
BX02YYN	Go-Ahead London	BX04MYK	Arriva	BX06UML	Redwing	BX54UCZ	Go-Ahead London
BX02YYO	Go-Ahead London	BX04MYL	Arriva	BX06UMY	Wings	BX54UDB	Go-Ahead London
BX02YYP	Go-Ahead London	BX04MYM	Arriva	BX06UMZ	Wings	BX54UDD	Go-Ahead London
BX02YYR	Go-Ahead London	BX04MYN	Arriva	BX06UNE	Allied	BX54UDE	Go-Ahead London
BX02YYS	Go-Ahead London	BX04MYR	Arriva	BX06UNF	MCH	BX54UDG	Go-Ahead London
BX02YYT	Go-Ahead London	BX04MYS	Arriva	BX54DHJ	Travel London	BX54UDH	Go-Ahead London
BX02YYU	Go-Ahead London	BX04MYT	Arriva	BX54DHK	Travel London	BX54UDJ	Go-Ahead London
BX02YYV	Go-Ahead London	BX04MYU	Arriva	BX54DHL	Travel London	BX54UDK	Go-Ahead London
BX02YYW	Go-Ahead London	BX04MYV	Arriva	BX54DHM	Travel London	BX54UDL	Go-Ahead London
BX02YYZ	Go-Ahead London	BX04MYW	Arriva	BX54DHN	Travel London	BX54UDM	Go-Ahead London
BX02YZA	Go-Ahead London	BX04MYY	Arriva	BX54DHO	Travel London	BX54UDN	Go-Ahead London
BX02YZB	Go-Ahead London	BX04MYZ	Arriva	BX54DHP	Travel London	BX54UDO	Go-Ahead London
BX02YZC	Go-Ahead London	BX04MZD	Arriva	BX54DHV	Travel London	BX54UDP	Go-Ahead London
BX02YZD	Go-Ahead London	BX04MZE	Arriva	BX54DHY	Travel London	BX54UDT	Go-Ahead London
BX02YZE	Go-Ahead London	BX04MZG	Arriva	BX54DHZ	Travel London	BX54UDU	Go-Ahead London
BX02YZG	Go-Ahead London	BX04MZJ	Arriva	BX54DJD	Travel London	BX54UDV	Go-Ahead London
BX02YZH	Go-Ahead London	BX04MZL	Arriva	BX54DJE	Travel London	BX54UDW	Go-Ahead London
BX02YZJ	Go-Ahead London	BX04MZN	Arriva	BX54DJF	Travel London	BX54UDY	Go-Ahead London
BX02YZK	Go-Ahead London	BX04NBD	Go-Ahead London	BX54DJJ	Travel London	BX54UDZ	Go-Ahead London
BX02YZL	Go-Ahead London	BX04NBK	Arriva	BX54DJK	Travel London	BX54UEA	Go-Ahead London
BX02YZM	Go-Ahead London	BX04NCF	Arriva	BX54DJO	Travel London	BX54UEB	Go-Ahead London
BX02YZN	Go-Ahead London	BX04NCJ	Arriva	BX54DJU	Travel London	BX55FUH	Arriva
BX02YZO	Go-Ahead London	BX04NCN	Arriva	BX54DJV	Travel London	BX55FUJ	Arriva
BX02YZP	Go-Ahead London	BX04NCU	Arriva	BX54DJY	Travel London	BX55FUO	Arriva
BX02YZR	Go-Ahead London	BX04NCV	Arriva	BX54DKA	Travel London	BX55FUP	Arriva
BX02YZS	Go-Ahead London	BX04NCY	Arriva	BX54DKD	Travel London	BX55FUT	Arriva
BX02YZT	Go-Ahead London	BX04NCZ	Arriva	BX54DKE	Travel London	BX55FUU	Arriva
BX04AZU	East Thames	BX04NDC	Arriva	BX54DKF	Travel London	BX55FUW	Arriva
BX04AZV	East Thames	BX04NDD	Arriva	BX54DKJ	Travel London	BX55FUY	Arriva
BX04AZW	East Thames	BX04NDF	Arriva	BX54DKK	Travel London	BX55FVA	Arriva
BX04AZZ	East Thames	BX04NDG	Arriva	BX54DKL	Travel London	BX55FVB	Arriva
BX04BAA	East Thames	BX04NDJ	Arriva	BX54DKO	Travel London	BX55FVC	Arriva
BX04BAU	East Thames	BX04NDK	Arriva	BX54DKU	Travel London	BX55FVD	Arriva
BX04BAV	East Thames	BX04NDL	Arriva	BX54DKV	Travel London	BX55FVE	Allied
BX04BBE	East Thames	BX04NDN	Arriva	BX54DKY	Travel London	BX55FVF	Arriva
BX04BBF	East Thames	BX04NDU	Arriva	BX54DKZ	Travel London	BX55FVG	Arriva
BX04BBJ	East Thames	BX04NDV	Arriva	BX54DLD	Travel London	BX55FVH	Arriva
BX04BJF	Cavalier	BX04NDY	Arriva	BX54DLF	Travel London	BX55FVJ	Arriva
BX04BKJ	East Thames	BX04NDZ	Arriva	BX54DLJ	Travel London	BX55FVK	Arriva
BX04BKK	East Thames	BX04NEF	Arriva	BX54DLK	Travel London	BX55FVL	Arriva
BX04BKL	East Thames	BX04NEJ	Arriva	BX54DLN	Travel London	BX55FVM	Arriva
BX04BXL	East Thames	BX04NEN	Arriva	BX54DLO	Travel London	BX55FVN	Arriva
BX04BXM	East Thames	BX05UUY	MCH	BX54DLU	Travel London	BX55FVP	Arriva
BX04BXN	East Thames	BX05UVC	Redwing	BX54DLV	Travel London	BX55FVQ	Arriva
BX04BXP	East Thames	BX05UVD	Redwing	BX54DLY	Travel London	BX55FVR	Arriva
BX04MWW	Arriva	BX05UVE	Redwing	BX54DLZ	Travel London	BX55FVS	Arriva
BX04MWY	Arriva	BX05UVG	Redwing	BX54DME	Travel London	BX55FVT	Arriva
BX04MWZ	Arriva	BX05UVH	Redwing	BX54DMF	Travel London	BX55FVU	Arriva
BX04MXA	Arriva	BX05UVJ	Clarkes of London	BX54DMO	Travel London	BX55FVW	Arriva
BX04MXC	Arriva	BX05UVK	Clarkes of London	BX54DMU	Travel London	BX55FVY	Arriva
BX04MXD	Arriva	BX05UVL	City Circle	BX54DMV	Travel London	BX55FVZ	Arriva
BX04MXE	Arriva	BX05UVM	City Circle	BX54DMY	Travel London	BX55FWA	Arriva
BX04MXG	Arriva	BX05UVN	City Circle	BX54DMZ	Travel London	BX55FWB	Arriva
BX04MXH	Arriva	BX05UVO	City Circle	BX54ECF	First London	BX55FWG	Arriva
BX04MXJ	Arriva	BX05UVP	City Circle	BX54ECF	Epsom Coaches	BX55FWH	Arriva
BX04MXK	Arriva	BX05UWA	Allied	BX54ECJ	Epsom Coaches	BX55FWJ	Arriva
BX04MXL	Arriva	BX05UWB	Allied	BX54EDL	Redwing	BX55FWK	Arriva
BX04MXM	Arriva	BX05UWD	Allied	BX54EDO	Redwing	BX55FWL	Arriva
BX04MXN	Arriva	BX05UWV	Arriva	BX54EDP	Redwing	BX55FWM	Arriva
BX04MXP	Arriva	BX05UWW	Arriva	BX54EDR	Redwing	BX55FWN	Arriva
BX04MXS	Arriva	BX05UWY	Arriva	BX54EDU	Redwing	BX55FWP	Arriva
BX04MXU	Arriva	BX05UXC	Arriva	BX54EFB	Go-Ahead London	BX55FWR	Arriva
BX04MXV	Arriva	BX05UXD	Arriva	BX54EFC	Go-Ahead London	BX55FWS	Arriva
BX04MXW	Arriva	BX06BTF	Go-Ahead London	BX54EFD	Go-Ahead London	BX55FWT	Arriva
BX04MXY	Arriva	BX06UMB	Redwing	BX54UCM	Go-Ahead London	BX55FWU	Arriva
BX04MYA	Arriva	BX06UMC	Redwing	BX54UCN	Go-Ahead London	BX55FWV	Arriva
BX04MYB	Arriva	BX06UMD	Redwing	BX54UCO	Go-Ahead London	BX55FWW	Arriva
BX04MYC	Arriva	BX06UME	Redwing	BX54UCP	Go-Ahead London	BX55FWY	Arriva

BX55FWZ	Arriva	C327BVU	Arriva	ESL660	Duck Tours	FJ54ZDC	East Thames
BX55FXB	Arriva	C328BUV	First London	ESL679	Duck Tours	FJ54ZDP	East Thames
BX55FXC	Arriva	C332BVU	Arriva	EU04BVD	Blue Triangle	FJ54ZDR	East Thames
BX55FXE	Arriva	C335BUV	First London	EU04BVF	Blue Triangle	FJ54ZDT	East Thames
BX55FXF	Arriva	C367BVU	Arriva	EU05DVW	Arriva Original Tour	FJ54ZDU	East Thames
BX55FXG	Arriva	C384BUV	First London	EU05DVX	Arriva Original Tour	FJ54ZDV	East Thames
BX55FXH	Arriva	C405BUV	Arriva	EU53PXY	Blue Triangle	FJ54ZDW	East Thames
BX55FXJ	Arriva	C412BUV	First London	EU53PXZ	Blue Triangle	FJ54ZDX	East Thames
BX55FXK	Arriva	C418BUV	First London	EU53PYA	Blue Triangle	FJ54ZDY	East Thames
BX55FXL	Arriva	C422BUV	First London	EU53PYB	Blue Triangle	FJ54ZDZ	East Thames
BX55FXM	Arriva	C907GUD	Arriva Original Tour	EU53PYD	Blue Triangle	FJ54ZFA	East Thames
BX55FXO	Arriva	CCG376	Westway	EU53PYF	Blue Triangle	FJ54ZTU	East Thames
BX55FXP	Arriva	CCG706	Westway	EU53PYG	Blue Triangle	FJ54ZTW	East Thames
BX55FXR	Arriva	CE52UWW	Tellings-Golden Miller	EU53PYH	Blue Triangle	FJ54ZTX	East Thames
BX55FXS	Arriva	CSU992	East London	EU53PYJ	Blue Triangle	FJ54ZTY	East Thames
BX55FXT	Arriva	CUV217C	Arriva	EU53PYL	Blue Triangle	FJ54ZTZ	East Thames
BX55FXU	Arriva	CUV260C	Blue Triangle	EU53PYO	Blue Triangle	FJ54ZUA	East Thames
BX55FXV	Arriva	CUV305C	Go-Ahead London	EU53PYP	Blue Triangle	FJ54ZUC	East Thames
BX55FXW	Arriva	CUV317C	Metrobus	EY02WFK	Wings	FJ54ZUD	East Thames
BX55FXY	Arriva	CUV318C	Go-Ahead London	EY03FNK	Blue Triangle	FJ54ZVA	East Thames
BX55FYG	Redwing	CUV355C	Arriva	EY03FNL	Blue Triangle	FJ54ZVB	East Thames
BX55FYY	Wings	CUV360C	Arriva	F59SYE	Big Bus Company	FJ55BXM	Hamiltons
BX55FYZ	Wings	D512UGT	Big Bus Company	F67SYE	Big Bus Company	FJ55BXR	Excalibur
BX55XLS	Travel London	D514UGT	Big Bus Company	F69SYE	Big Bus Company	FJ55BXS	Excalibur
BX55XLT	Travel London	D553YNO	Arriva Original Tour	F72DDA	Travel London	FL02ZXR	P & J Ellis
BX55XLU	Travel London	D675YNO	Arriva Original Tour	F85GGC	Westway	FL02ZXT	P & J Ellis
BX55XLV	Travel London	D690UGT	Big Bus Company	F137FCC	Excalibur	FN52GUC	Cavalier
BX55XLW	Travel London	D692UGT	Big Bus Company	F153UJN	Big Bus Company	FN52GUG	Redwing
BX55XLY	Travel London	D922NDA	Travel London	F326UJN	Big Bus Company	FN52GUH	Redwing
BX55XLZ	Travel London	D928NDA	Travel London	F355UJN	Big Bus Company	FP51EUR	Clarkes of London
BX55XMA	Travel London	D942NDA	Travel London	F418UJN	Big Bus Company	FP53JYO	P & J Ellis
BX55XMB	Travel London	D948NDA	Travel London	F601XMS	First London	FX03GJJ	Cavalier
BX55XMC	Travel London	D951NDA	Travel London	FD03YOH	Redwing	FX04EEP	Cavalier
BX55XMD	Travel London	D955NDA	Travel London	FD03YOJ	Redwing	FY03WZT	Cavalier
BX55XME	Travel London	DB52BUS	Isleworth	FD03YOK	Redwing	G32FWC	Big Bus Company
BX55XMG	Travel London	E336NUV	Big Bus Company	FD03YOL	Redwing	G34FWC	Big Bus Company
BX55XMH	Travel London	E337NUV	Big Bus Company	FD03YON	Redwing	G42FWC	Big Bus Company
BX55XMJ	Travel London	E338NUV	Big Bus Company	FD03YOP	Redwing	G43FWC	Big Bus Company
BX55XMK	Travel London	E340NUV	Big Bus Company	FJ03ABU	P & J Ellis	G159FWC	Big Bus Company
BX55XML	Travel London	E460ANC	Travel London	FJ03ACU	P & J Ellis	G266EOG	Travel London
BX55XMM	Travel London	E568JVV	Ealing CT	FJ03ACY	P & J Ellis	G515VBB	Arriva
BX55XMP	Travel London	E764JAR	Big Bus Company	FJ03ZZN	Redwing	G517VBB	Arriva
BX55XMR	Travel London	E767JAR	Arriva Original Tour	FJ03ZZP	Redwing	G520VBB	Arriva
BX55XMS	Travel London	E768JAR	Arriva Original Tour	FJ03ZZS	Redwing	G521VBB	Arriva
BX55XMT	Travel London	E769JAR	Arriva Original Tour	FJ03ZZU	Redwing	G538VBB	Arriva
BX55XMU	Travel London	E770JAR	Arriva Original Tour	FJ03ZZY	Redwing	G551VBB	Arriva
BX55XMV	Travel London	E771JAR	Arriva Original Tour	FJ04ERK	P & J Ellis	G554VBB	Arriva
BX55XMW	Travel London	E772JAR	Arriva Original Tour	FJ04ERU	P & J Ellis	G806BPG	Westbus
BX55XMZ	Travel London	E773JAR	Arriva Original Tour	FJ04ETZ	P & J Ellis	G807BPG	Westbus
BX55XNG	Travel London	E869JAR	Big Bus Company	FJ05AOA	P & J Ellis	G808BPG	Westbus
BX55XNJ	Travel London	E881JAR	Big Bus Company	FJ05AOB	P & J Ellis	G938FVX	Big Bus Company
BX55XNK	Travel London	E901JAR	Big Bus Company	FJ05APO	Anderson	G939FVX	Big Bus Company
BX55XNL	Travel London	E949JAR	Big Bus Company	FJ05APV	Anderson	G943FVX	Big Bus Company
BX55XNM	Travel London	E964JAR	Arriva Original Tour	FJ05APX	Anderson	G952FVX	Big Bus Company
BX55XNN	Travel London	E965JAR	Arriva Original Tour	FJ05APY	Anderson	G953FVX	Big Bus Company
BX55XNO	Travel London	EJ52WXC	Blue Triangle	FJ05HYN	Hamiltons	G954FVX	Big Bus Company
BX55XNP	Travel London	EJ52WXD	Blue Triangle	FJ05HYO	Hamiltons	G956FVX	Big Bus Company
BX55XNR	Travel London	EJ52WXE	Blue Triangle	FJ05HYP	Hamiltons	G964FVX	Big Bus Company
BX55XNS	Travel London	EJ52WXF	Blue Triangle	FJ06BOF	P & J Ellis	G969FVX	Big Bus Company
BX55XNT	Travel London	EO02FKZ	First London	FJ06BOH	P & J Ellis	G96SGO	Big Bus Company
BX55XNU	Travel London	EO02FLA	First London	FJ06GGV	Hamiltons	G991FVX	Big Bus Company
BX55XNV	Travel London	EO02FLB	First London	FJ06GGX	Hamiltons	GB03LLC	Tellings-Golden Miller
BX55XNW	Travel London	EO02FLC	First London	FJ06GGY	Hamiltons	GB03TGM	Tellings-Golden Miller
BX55XNY	Travel London	EO02FLD	First London	FJ06GGZ	Hamiltons	GB04LLC	Tellings-Golden Miller
BX55XNZ	Travel London	EO02FLE	First London	FJ06URB	Clarkes of London	GB04TGM	Tellings-Golden Miller
BYX147V	Transdev	EO02FLF	First London	FJ06URC	Clarkes of London	GG04ONE	Clarkes of London
BYX271V	Blue Triangle	EO02FLG	First London	FJ06URD	Clarkes of London	GG04TWO	Clarkes of London
C89NNV	Tellings-Golden Miller	EO02FLH	First London	FJ06URE	Clarkes of London	GM03TGM	Travel London
C310BUV	Arriva Original Tour	EO02FLJ	First London	FJ06ZLZ	Redwing	GS05TGM	Tellings-Golden Miller
C312BUV	Arriva	EO02FLK	First London	FJ06ZMO	Redwing	GV53RHU	Metrobus
C313BUV	Arriva	EO02NVW	Excalibur	FJ06ZMU	Redwing	GV53RHY	Metrobus
C320BUV	Arriva	EO52OZT	Tellings-Golden Miller	FJ06ZMV	Redwing	GV53RHZ	Metrobus
C326BVU	Arriva	ESL636	Duck Tours	FJ51JYG	Anderson	GV53RJJ	Metrobus

Reg	Operator	Reg	Operator	Reg	Operator	Reg	Operator
GYE463W	Blue Triangle	J342BSH	Arriva Original Tour	KN52NEO	Metroline	KU52YKP	Metroline
GYE468W	Blue Triangle	J343BSH	Arriva Original Tour	KN52NEU	Metroline	KU52YKR	Metroline
GYE500W	Arriva Original Tour	J344BSH	Arriva Original Tour	KN52NEY	Metroline	KU52YKS	Metroline
GYE525W	Arriva Original Tour	J345BSH	Arriva Original Tour	KN52NFA	Metroline	KU52YKT	Metroline
GYE555W	Arriva Original Tour	J346BSH	Arriva Original Tour	KN52NFC	Travel London	KU52YKV	Metroline
GYE573W	Arriva	J347BSH	Arriva Original Tour	KN52NFD	Travel London	KU52YKX	Metroline
H129FLX	First London	J348BSH	Arriva Original Tour	KN52NFE	Travel London	KU52YKY	Metroline
H130FLX	First London	J349BSH	Arriva Original Tour	KN52NFO	Travel London	KU52YKZ	Metroline
H135FLX	First London	J350BSH	Arriva Original Tour	KN52NFP	Travel London	KU52YLA	Metroline
H136FLX	First London	J351BSH	Arriva Original Tour	KN52NFR	Travel London	KU52YLB	Metroline
H137FLX	First London	J352BSH	Arriva Original Tour	KN52NFT	Travel London	KU52YLC	Metroline
H139FLX	First London	J401LKO	East London	KN52NFU	Travel London	KU52YLD	Metroline
H140FLX	First London	J403LKO	East London	KN52NFV	Travel London	KU52YLE	Metroline
H142FLX	First London	J433BSH	Arriva Original Tour	KN52NFX	Travel London	KU52YLF	Metroline
H144FLX	First London	J711CYG	East London	KN52NFY	Travel London	KU52YLG	Metroline
H145FLX	First London	J716CYG	East London	KP02PUF	Metroline	KU52YLH	Metroline
H392MAR	First London	J724CYG	East London	KP02PUH	Metroline	KV02URL	Travel London
HV02OZS	Go-Ahead (Docklands)	J729CYG	East London	KP02PUJ	Metroline	KV02URM	Travel London
HV02OZT	Go-Ahead (Docklands)	J916WVC	First London	KP02PUK	Metroline	KV02URN	Travel London
HV02OZU	Go-Ahead (Docklands)	JDZ2407	East Thames	KP02PUO	Metroline	KV02URO	Travel London
HV02OZW	Go-Ahead (Docklands)	JDZ2408	East Thames	KP02PVD	Metroline	KV02URP	Travel London
HV02OZX	Go-Ahead (Docklands)	JF56JFN	Metrobus	KP02PVE	Metroline	KV02URR	Travel London
HV02PCO	Go-Ahead (Docklands)	JF56JFU	Metrobus	KP02PVF	Metroline	KV02URS	Travel London
HV02PCU	Go-Ahead (Docklands)	JJD403D	Arriva	KP02PVJ	Metroline	KV02URT	Travel London
HV02PCX	Go-Ahead (Docklands)	JJD472D	Go-Ahead London	KP02PVK	Metroline	KV02URU	Travel London
HV02PCY	Go-Ahead (Docklands)	JJD520D	Go-Ahead London	KP02PVL	Metroline	KV02URX	Travel London
HV02PCZ	Go-Ahead (Docklands)	JO56JFF	Metrobus	KP02PVN	Metroline	KV02URY	Travel London
HV02PDK	Go-Ahead (Docklands)	JO56JFG	Metrobus	KP02PVO	Metroline	KV02URZ	Travel London
HV02PDO	Go-Ahead (Docklands)	K107SAG	Transdev	KP02PVT	Metroline	KV02USB	Travel London
HX03MGJ	CT Plus	K131SRH	Go-Ahead (Dock-lands)	KP02PVU	Metroline	KV02USC	Travel London
HX03MGU	CT Plus	K321GEW	Epsom Coaches	KP02PWN	Metroline	KV02USD	Travel London
HX03MGV	CT Plus	K634HWX	East London	KP02PWO	Metroline	KV02USE	Travel London
HX03MGY	CT Plus	K904CVW	First London	KP02PWU	Metroline	KV02USF	Travel London
HX03MGZ	CT Plus	K906CVW	First London	KP02PWV	Metroline	KV02USG	Travel London
HX04HTP	Travel London	KC06EVN	Tellings-Golden Miller	KP51SXY	Travel London	KV02USH	Travel London
HX04HTT	Travel London	KC06EVP	Tellings-Golden Miller	KP51SXY	Travel London	KV02USJ	Travel London
HX04HTU	Travel London	KE55DCV	MCH	KP51SYF	Tellings-Golden Miller	KV02USL	Travel London
HX04HTV	Travel London	KGK575	Blue Triangle	KP51UEV	Tellings-Golden Miller	KV02USM	Travel London
HX04HTY	Travel London	KM02HDJ	Metroline	KP51UEW	Tellings-Golden Miller	KV02USN	Travel London
HX04HTZ	Travel London	KM02HDK	Metroline	KP51UEX	Tellings-Golden Miller	KV02USO	Travel London
HX04HUH	Tellings-Golden Miller	KM02HFK	Metroline	KP51UEY	Tellings-Golden Miller	KV02USP	Travel London
HX04HUK	Tellings-Golden Miller	KM02HFL	Metroline	KP51UEZ	Tellings-Golden Miller	KV02USS	Travel London
HY06CJO	Epsom Coaches	KM02HFN	Metroline	KU02YBH	Travel London	KV02UST	Travel London
J131DUV	Transdev	KM02HFO	Metroline	KU02YBJ	Travel London	KV02USU	Travel London
J131YRM	First London	KM02HFP	Travel London	KU02YBK	Travel London	KV02USW	Travel London
J135PVC	First London	KM02HFR	Travel London	KU02YBL	Travel London	KV03ZFE	CT Plus
J135YRM	First London	KM02HFS	Travel London	KU02YBM	Travel London	KV03ZFF	CT Plus
J315BSH	Arriva Original Tour	KM02HFT	Travel London	KU02YBN	Travel London	KV03ZFG	CT Plus
J316BSH	Arriva Original Tour	KM02HFU	Travel London	KU02YBO	Travel London	KV03ZFH	CT Plus
J317BSH	Arriva Original Tour	KM02HFV	Travel London	KU02YBP	Travel London	KV03ZFM	Travel London
J318BSH	Arriva Original Tour	KM02HGD	Metroline	KU02YBR	Travel London	KV03ZFN	Travel London
J319BSH	Arriva Original Tour	KM02HGE	Metroline	KU02YBS	Travel London	KV03ZFP	Travel London
J320BSH	Arriva Original Tour	KM02HGF	Metroline	KU02YUB	Metroline	KV03ZFR	Travel London
J321BSH	Arriva Original Tour	KN05KFW	Ealing CT	KU02YUC	Metroline	KV03ZFS	Travel London
J322BSH	Arriva Original Tour	KN52NCD	Metroline	KU02YUD	Metroline	KV03ZFT	Travel London
J323BSH	Arriva Original Tour	KN52NCE	Metroline	KU02YUE	Metroline	KV03ZFU	Travel London
J324BSH	Arriva Original Tour	KN52NDC	Metroline	KU02YUF	Tellings-Golden Miller	KV03ZFW	Travel London
J325BSH	Arriva Original Tour	KN52NDD	Metroline	KU02YUG	Tellings-Golden Miller	KV03ZFX	Travel London
J326BSH	Arriva Original Tour	KN52NDE	Metroline	KU02YUJ	Metroline	KV03ZFY	Travel London
J327BSH	Arriva Original Tour	KN52NDF	Metroline	KU02YUK	Metroline	KX03HZE	Ealing CT
J328BSH	Arriva Original Tour	KN52NDG	Metroline	KU52YKA	Metroline	KX03HZF	Ealing CT
J329BSH	Arriva Original Tour	KN52NDJ	Metroline	KU52YKB	Metroline	KX03HZG	Ealing CT
J330BSH	Arriva Original Tour	KN52NDK	Metroline	KU52YKC	Metroline	KX03HZN	Ealing CT
J331BSH	Arriva Original Tour	KN52NDL	Metroline	KU52YKD	Metroline	KX03HZP	Ealing CT
J332BSH	Arriva Original Tour	KN52NDO	Metroline	KU52YKE	Metroline	KX03HZR	Ealing CT
J334BSH	Arriva Original Tour	KN52NDU	Metroline	KU52YKF	Metroline	KX03HZS	Ealing CT
J335BSH	Arriva Original Tour	KN52NDV	Metroline	KU52YKG	Metroline	KX03HZT	Ealing CT
J336BSH	Arriva Original Tour	KN52NDX	Metroline	KU52YKH	Metroline	KX03HZU	Ealing CT
J337BSH	Arriva Original Tour	KN52NDY	Metroline	KU52YKJ	Metroline	KX03HZV	Ealing CT
J338BSH	Arriva Original Tour	KN52NDZ	Metroline	KU52YKK	Metroline	KX03HZW	Ealing CT
J339BSH	Arriva Original Tour	KN52NEF	Metroline	KU52YKL	Metroline	KX03HZY	Ealing CT
J340BSH	Arriva Original Tour	KN52NEJ	Metroline	KU52YKN	Metroline	KX03HZZ	Ealing CT
J341BSH	Arriva Original Tour			KU52YKO	Metroline	KX04HRD	Metrobus

Reg	Operator	Reg	Operator	Reg	Operator	Reg	Operator	Reg	Operator
KX04HRE	Metrobus	LF02PNL	Arriva	LF52UOH	Arriva	LF52USX	Arriva
KX04HRF	Metrobus	LF02PNN	Arriva	LF52UOJ	Arriva	LF52USY	Arriva
KX04HRG	Metrobus	LF02PNO	Arriva	LF52UOK	Arriva	LF52USZ	Arriva
KX04HSJ	Tellings-Golden Miller	LF02PNU	Arriva	LF52UOL	Arriva	LF52UTA	Arriva
KX53SDU	Metroline	LF02PNV	Arriva	LF52UOM	Arriva	LF52UTB	Arriva
KX53SDV	Metroline	LF02PNX	Arriva	LF52UON	Arriva	LF52UTC	Arriva
KX54NJO	Metroline	LF02PNY	Arriva	LF52UOO	Arriva	LF52UTE	Arriva
KXW171	Blue Triangle	LF02POA	Arriva	LF52UOP	Arriva	LF52UTG	Arriva
KYV512X	Blue Triangle	LF02POH	Arriva	LF52UOR	Arriva	LF52UTH	Arriva
KYV693X	Blue Triangle	LF02PSO	Arriva	LF52UOS	Arriva	LF52UTL	Arriva
KYV710X	Arriva Original Tour	LF02PSU	Arriva	LF52UOT	Arriva	LF52UTM	Arriva
KYV801X	Blue Triangle	LF02PSY	Arriva	LF52UOU	Arriva	LF52ZLZ	Go-Ahead London
L58UNS	Metrobus	LF02PSZ	Arriva	LF52UOV	Arriva	LF52ZMO	Go-Ahead London
L59UNS	Metrobus	LF02PTO	Arriva	LF52UOW	Arriva	LF52ZMU	Go-Ahead London
L201SKD	Metroline	LF02PTU	Arriva	LF52UOX	Arriva	LF52ZND	Go-Ahead London
L202SKD	Metroline	LF02PTX	Arriva	LF52UOY	Arriva	LF52ZNE	Go-Ahead London
L203SKD	Metroline	LF02PTY	Arriva	LF52UPA	Arriva	LF52ZNG	Go-Ahead London
L204SKD	Metroline	LF02PTZ	Arriva	LF52UPB	Arriva	LF52ZNH	Go-Ahead London
L205SKD	Metroline	LF02PVE	Arriva	LF52UPC	Arriva	LF52ZNJ	Go-Ahead London
L206SKD	Metroline	LF02PVJ	Arriva	LF52UPD	Arriva	LF52ZNK	Go-Ahead London
L207SKD	Metroline	LF02PVK	Arriva	LF52UPG	Arriva	LF52ZNL	Go-Ahead London
L208SKD	Metroline	LF02PVL	Arriva	LF52UPH	Arriva	LF52ZNM	Go-Ahead London
L209SKD	Metroline	LF02PVN	Arriva	LF52UPK	Arriva	LF52ZNN	Go-Ahead London
L210SKD	Metroline	LF02PVO	Arriva	LF52UPM	Arriva	LF52ZNO	Go-Ahead London
L212TWM	Metroline	LF06YRC	Travel London	LF52UPN	Arriva	LF52ZNP	Go-Ahead London
L213TWM	Metroline	LF06YRD	Travel London	LF52UPO	Arriva	LF52ZNR	Go-Ahead London
L214TWM	Metroline	LF06YRE	Travel London	LF52UPP	Arriva	LF52ZNS	Go-Ahead London
L215TWM	Metroline	LF06YRG	Travel London	LF52UPR	Arriva	LF52ZNT	Go-Ahead London
L216TWM	Metroline	LF06YRJ	Travel London	LF52UPS	Arriva	LF52ZNU	Go-Ahead London
L217TWM	Metroline	LF06YRK	Travel London	LF52UPT	Arriva	LF52ZNV	Go-Ahead London
L227BUT	Ashford Luxury	LF06YRL	Travel London	LF52UPV	Arriva	LF52ZNW	Go-Ahead London
L377NMV	Ashford Luxury	LF06YRM	Travel London	LF52UPW	Arriva	LF52ZNX	Go-Ahead London
LB02YWX	East Thames	LF06YRN	Travel London	LF52UPX	Arriva	LF52ZNY	Go-Ahead London
LB02YWY	East Thames	LF51CYC	Go-Ahead London	LF52UPZ	Arriva	LF52ZNZ	Go-Ahead London
LB02YWZ	East Thames	LF52TGN	East Thames	LF52URA	Arriva	LF52ZPB	Go-Ahead London
LB02YXA	East Thames	LF52TGO	East Thames	LF52URB	Arriva	LF52ZPC	Go-Ahead London
LB02YXD	East Thames	LF52TGU	East Thames	LF52URC	Arriva	LF52ZPD	Go-Ahead London
LB02YXE	East Thames	LF52TGV	East Thames	LF52URD	Arriva	LF52ZPE	Go-Ahead London
LB02YXF	East Thames	LF52TGX	East Thames	LF52URE	Arriva	LF52ZPG	Go-Ahead London
LB02YXG	East Thames	LF52TGY	East Thames	LF52URG	Arriva	LF52ZPH	Go-Ahead London
LB02YXH	East Thames	LF52TGZ	East Thames	LF52URH	Arriva	LF52ZPJ	Go-Ahead London
LB02YXJ	East Thames	LF52THG	East Thames	LF52URJ	Arriva	LF52ZPK	Go-Ahead London
LB02YXK	East Thames	LF52THK	East Thames	LF52URK	Arriva	LF52ZPL	Go-Ahead London
LB02YXL	East Thames	LF52THN	East Thames	LF52URL	Arriva	LF52ZPM	Go-Ahead London
LB02YXM	East Thames	LF52THU	East Thames	LF52URM	Arriva	LF52ZPN	Go-Ahead London
LB02YXN	East Thames	LF52THV	East Thames	LF52URN	Arriva	LF52ZPO	Go-Ahead London
LB51OCL	Epsom Coaches	LF52THX	East Thames	LF52URO	Arriva	LF52ZPR	Go-Ahead London
LB52URZ	Travel London	LF52THZ	East Thames	LF52URP	Arriva	LF52ZPS	Go-Ahead London
LB52UYK	Tellings-Golden Miller	LF52TJO	East Thames	LF52URR	Arriva	LF52ZPU	Go-Ahead London
LF02PKA	Arriva	LF52TJU	East Thames	LF52URS	Arriva	LF52ZPV	Go-Ahead London
LF02PKC	Arriva	LF52TJV	East Thames	LF52URT	Arriva	LF52ZPW	Go-Ahead London
LF02PKD	Arriva	LF52TJX	East Thames	LF52URU	Arriva	LF52ZPX	Go-Ahead London
LF02PKE	Arriva	LF52TJY	East Thames	LF52URV	Arriva	LF52ZPY	Go-Ahead London
LF02PKJ	Arriva	LF52TKA	East Thames	LF52URW	Arriva	LF52ZPZ	Go-Ahead London
LF02PKO	Arriva	LF52TKC	East Thames	LF52URX	Arriva	LF52ZRA	Go-Ahead London
LF02PKU	Arriva	LF52TKD	East Thames	LF52URY	Arriva	LF52ZRC	Go-Ahead London
LF02PKV	Arriva	LF52TKE	East Thames	LF52URZ	Arriva	LF52ZRD	Go-Ahead London
LF02PKX	Arriva	LF52TKJ	East Thames	LF52USB	Arriva	LF52ZRE	Go-Ahead London
LF02PKY	Arriva	LF52TKK	East Thames	LF52USC	Arriva	LF52ZRG	Go-Ahead London
LF02PLJ	Arriva	LF52TKN	East Thames	LF52USD	Arriva	LF52ZRJ	Go-Ahead London
LF02PLN	Arriva	LF52TKO	East Thames	LF52USE	Arriva	LF52ZRK	Go-Ahead London
LF02PLO	Arriva	LF52TKT	East Thames	LF52USG	Arriva	LF52ZRL	Go-Ahead London
LF02PLU	Arriva	LF52UNV	Arriva	LF52USH	Arriva	LF52ZRN	Go-Ahead London
LF02PLV	Arriva	LF52UNW	Arriva	LF52USJ	Arriva	LF52ZRO	Go-Ahead London
LF02PLX	Arriva	LF52UNX	Arriva	LF52USL	Arriva	LF52ZRR	Go-Ahead London
LF02PLZ	Arriva	LF52UNY	Arriva	LF52USM	Arriva	LF52ZRT	Go-Ahead London
LF02PMO	Arriva	LF52UNZ	Arriva	LF52USN	Arriva	LF52ZRU	Go-Ahead London
LF02PMV	Arriva	LF52UOA	Arriva	LF52USO	Arriva	LF52ZRV	Go-Ahead London
LF02PMX	Arriva	LF52UOB	Arriva	LF52USS	Arriva	LF52ZRX	Go-Ahead London
LF02PMY	Arriva	LF52UOC	Arriva	LF52UST	Arriva	LF52ZRY	Go-Ahead London
LF02PNE	Arriva	LF52UOD	Arriva	LF52USU	Arriva	LF52ZRZ	Go-Ahead London
LF02PNJ	Arriva	LF52UOE	Arriva	LF52USV	Arriva		
LF02PNK	Arriva	LF52UOG	Arriva	LF52USW	Arriva		

Reg	Operator	Reg	Operator	Reg	Operator	Reg	Operator
LF52ZSD	Go-Ahead London	LG02FDX	Transdev	LG02KHL	Go-Ahead London	LG52DDL	Arriva
LF52ZSO	Go-Ahead London	LG02FDY	Transdev	LG02KHM	Go-Ahead London	LG52HWN	Travel London
LF52ZSP	Go-Ahead London	LG02FDZ	Transdev	LG02KHO	Go-Ahead London	LG52XWD	Travel London
LF52ZSR	Go-Ahead London	LG02FEF	Transdev	LG02KHP	Go-Ahead London	LG52XWE	Travel London
LF52ZST	Go-Ahead London	LG02FEH	Transdev	LG02KHR	Go-Ahead London	LG52XYJ	Travel London
LF52ZTG	Go-Ahead London	LG02FEJ	Transdev	LG02KHT	Go-Ahead London	LG52XYK	Travel London
LF52ZTH	Go-Ahead London	LG02FEK	Transdev	LG02KHU	Go-Ahead London	LG52XYL	Travel London
LF52ZTJ	Go-Ahead London	LG02FEM	Transdev	LG02KHV	Go-Ahead London	LG52XYM	Travel London
LF52ZTK	Go-Ahead London	LG02FEO	Transdev	LG02KHW	Go-Ahead London	LG52XYN	Travel London
LF52ZTL	Go-Ahead London	LG02FEP	Transdev	LG02KHX	Go-Ahead London	LG52XYO	Travel London
LF52ZTM	Go-Ahead London	LG02FET	Transdev	LG02KHY	Go-Ahead London	LG52XYP	Travel London
LF52ZTN	Go-Ahead London	LG02FEU	Transdev	LG02KHZ	Go-Ahead London	LG52XYY	Travel London
LF52ZTO	Go-Ahead London	LG02FEV	Transdev	LG02KJA	Go-Ahead London	LG52XYZ	Travel London
LF52ZTP	Go-Ahead London	LG02FEX	Transdev	LG02KJE	Go-Ahead London	LG52XZA	Travel London
LF52ZTR	Go-Ahead London	LG02FFA	Transdev	LG02KJF	Go-Ahead London	LG52XZB	Travel London
LF55CYV	Travel London	LG02FFB	Transdev	LG03MBF	Arriva	LG52XZR	Travel London
LF55CYW	Travel London	LG02FFC	Transdev	LG03MBU	Arriva	LG52XZS	Travel London
LF55CYX	Travel London	LG02FFD	Transdev	LG03MBV	Arriva	LG52XZT	Travel London
LF55CYY	Travel London	LG02FFE	Transdev	LG03MBX	Arriva	LIB378	Westway
LF55CYZ	Travel London	LG02FFH	Transdev	LG03MBY	Arriva	LJ03MDV	Arriva
LF55CZA	Travel London	LG02FFJ	Transdev	LG03MDE	Arriva	LJ03MDX	Arriva
LF55CZB	Travel London	LG02FFK	Transdev	LG03MDF	Arriva	LJ03MDY	Arriva
LG02FAA	Transdev	LG02FFL	Transdev	LG03MDK	Arriva	LJ03MDZ	Arriva
LG02FAF	Transdev	LG02FFM	Transdev	LG03MDN	Arriva	LJ03MEU	Arriva
LG02FAJ	Transdev	LG02FFN	Transdev	LG03MDU	Arriva	LJ03MFN	Arriva
LG02FAK	Transdev	LG02FFO	Transdev	LG03MEV	Arriva	LJ03MFP	Arriva
LG02FAM	Transdev	LG02FFP	Transdev	LG03MFA	Arriva	LJ03MFU	Arriva
LG02FAO	Transdev	LG02FFR	Transdev	LG03MFE	Arriva	LJ03MFV	Arriva
LG02FAU	Transdev	LG02FFS	Transdev	LG03MFF	Arriva	LJ03MFX	Arriva
LG02FBA	Transdev	LG02FFT	Transdev	LG03MFK	Arriva	LJ03MFY	Arriva
LG02FBB	Transdev	LG02FFU	Transdev	LG03MLL	Arriva	LJ03MFZ	Arriva
LG02FBC	Transdev	LG02FFV	Transdev	LG03MLN	Arriva	LJ03MGE	Arriva
LG02FBD	Transdev	LG02FFW	Transdev	LG03MLV	Arriva	LJ03MGU	Arriva
LG02FBE	Transdev	LG02FFX	Transdev	LG03MMU	Arriva	LJ03MGV	Arriva
LG02FBF	Transdev	LG02FFY	Transdev	LG03MMV	Arriva	LJ03MGX	Arriva
LG02FBJ	Transdev	LG02FFZ	Transdev	LG03MMX	Arriva	LJ03MGY	Arriva
LG02FBK	Transdev	LG02FGA	Transdev	LG03MOA	Arriva	LJ03MGZ	Arriva
LG02FBL	Transdev	LG02FGC	Transdev	LG03MOF	Arriva	LJ03MHA	Arriva
LG02FBN	Transdev	LG02FGD	Transdev	LG03MOV	Arriva	LJ03MHE	Arriva
LG02FBO	Transdev	LG02FGE	Transdev	LG03MPF	Arriva	LJ03MHF	Arriva
LG02FBU	Transdev	LG02FGF	Transdev	LG03MPU	Arriva	LJ03MHK	Arriva
LG02FBV	Transdev	LG02FGJ	Transdev	LG03MPV	Arriva	LJ03MHL	Arriva
LG02FBX	Transdev	LG02FGK	Transdev	LG03MPX	Arriva	LJ03MHM	Arriva
LG02FBY	Transdev	LG02FGM	Transdev	LG03MPY	Arriva	LJ03MHN	Arriva
LG02FBZ	Transdev	LG02FGN	Transdev	LG03MPZ	Arriva	LJ03MHU	Arriva
LG02FCA	Transdev	LG02FGO	Transdev	LG03MRU	Arriva	LJ03MHV	Arriva
LG02FCC	Transdev	LG02FGP	Transdev	LG03MRV	Arriva	LJ03MHX	Arriva
LG02FCD	Transdev	LG02FGU	Transdev	LG03MRX	Arriva	LJ03MHY	Arriva
LG02FCE	Transdev	LG02FGV	Transdev	LG03MRY	Arriva	LJ03MHZ	Arriva
LG02FCF	Transdev	LG02FGX	Transdev	LG03MSU	Arriva	LJ03MJE	Arriva
LG02FCJ	Transdev	LG02FGZ	Transdev	LG03MSV	Arriva	LJ03MJF	Arriva
LG02FCL	Transdev	LG02FHA	Transdev	LG03MSX	Arriva	LJ03MJK	Arriva
LG02FCM	Transdev	LG02FHB	Transdev	LG52DAA	Arriva	LJ03MJU	Arriva
LG02FCN	Transdev	LG02FHC	Transdev	LG52DAO	Arriva	LJ03MJV	Arriva
LG02FCO	Transdev	LG02FHD	Transdev	LG52DAU	Arriva	LJ03MJX	Arriva
LG02FCP	Transdev	LG02FHE	Transdev	LG52DBO	Arriva	LJ03MJY	Arriva
LG02FCU	Transdev	LG02FHF	Transdev	LG52DBU	Arriva	LJ03MKA	Arriva
LG02FCX	Transdev	LG02FHH	Transdev	LG52DBV	Arriva	LJ03MKC	Arriva
LG02FCY	Transdev	LG02FHJ	Transdev	LG52DBY	Arriva	LJ03MKD	Arriva
LG02FCZ	Transdev	LG02FHK	Transdev	LG52DBZ	Arriva	LJ03MKE	Arriva
LG02FDA	Transdev	LG02FHL	Transdev	LG52DCE	Arriva	LJ03MKF	Arriva
LG02FDC	Transdev	LG02KGP	Go-Ahead London	LG52DCF	Arriva	LJ03MKG	Arriva
LG02FDD	Transdev	LG02KGU	Go-Ahead London	LG52DCO	Arriva	LJ03MKK	Arriva
LG02FDF	Transdev	LG02KGV	Go-Ahead London	LG52DCU	Arriva	LJ03MKL	Arriva
LG02FDJ	Transdev	LG02KGX	Go-Ahead London	LG52DCV	Arriva	LJ03MKM	Arriva
LG02FDK	Transdev	LG02KGY	Go-Ahead London	LG52DCX	Arriva	LJ03MKN	Arriva
LG02FDL	Transdev	LG02KGZ	Go-Ahead London	LG52DCY	Arriva	LJ03MKU	Arriva
LG02FDM	Transdev	LG02KHA	Go-Ahead London	LG52DCZ	Arriva	LJ03MKV	Arriva
LG02FDN	Transdev	LG02KHE	Go-Ahead London	LG52DDA	Arriva	LJ03MKX	Arriva
LG02FDO	Transdev	LG02KHF	Go-Ahead London	LG52DDE	Arriva	LJ03MKZ	Arriva
LG02FDP	Transdev	LG02KHH	Go-Ahead London	LG52DDF	Arriva	LJ03MLE	Arriva
LG02FDU	Transdev	LG02KHJ	Go-Ahead London	LG52DDJ	Arriva	LJ03MLF	Arriva
LG02FDV	Transdev	LG02KHK	Go-Ahead London	LG52DDK	Arriva	LJ03MLK	Arriva

The London Bus Handbook

LJ03MLX	Arriva	LJ03MYU	Arriva	LJ05BHX	Arriva	LJ51DCZ	Arriva
LJ03MLY	Arriva	LJ03MYV	Arriva	LJ05BHY	Arriva	LJ51DDA	Arriva
LJ03MLZ	Arriva	LJ03MYX	Arriva	LJ05BHZ	Arriva	LJ51DDE	Arriva
LJ03MMA	Arriva	LJ03MYY	Arriva	LJ05BJV	Arriva	LJ51DDF	Arriva
LJ03MME	Arriva	LJ03MYZ	Arriva	LJ05BJX	Arriva	LJ51DDK	Arriva
LJ03MMF	Arriva	LJ03MZD	Arriva	LJ05BJY	Arriva	LJ51DDL	Arriva
LJ03MMK	Arriva	LJ03MZE	Arriva	LJ05BJZ	Arriva	LJ51DDN	Arriva
LJ03MSY	Arriva	LJ03MZF	Arriva	LJ05BKA	Arriva	LJ51DDO	Arriva
LJ03MTE	Arriva	LJ03MZG	Arriva	LJ05BKD	Arriva	LJ51DDU	Arriva
LJ03MTF	Arriva	LJ03MZL	Arriva	LJ05BKF	Arriva	LJ51DDV	Arriva
LJ03MTK	Arriva	LJ04LDA	Arriva	LJ05BKY	Arriva	LJ51DDX	Arriva
LJ03MTU	Arriva	LJ04LDC	Arriva	LJ05BKZ	Arriva	LJ51DDY	Arriva
LJ03MTV	Arriva	LJ04LDD	Arriva	LJ05BLF	Arriva	LJ51DDZ	Arriva
LJ03MTY	Arriva	LJ04LDF	Arriva	LJ05BLK	Arriva	LJ51DEU	Arriva
LJ03MTZ	Arriva	LJ04LDK	Arriva	LJ05BLN	Arriva	LJ51DFA	Arriva
LJ03MUA	Arriva	LJ04LDL	Arriva	LJ05BLV	Arriva	LJ51DFC	Arriva
LJ03MUB	Arriva	LJ04LDN	Arriva	LJ05BLX	Arriva	LJ51DFD	Arriva
LJ03MUW	Arriva	LJ04LDU	Arriva	LJ05BLY	Arriva	LJ51DFE	Arriva
LJ03MUY	Arriva	LJ04LDX	Arriva	LJ05BMO	Arriva	LJ51DFF	Arriva
LJ03MVC	Arriva	LJ04LDY	Arriva	LJ05BMU	Arriva	LJ51DFG	Arriva
LJ03MVD	Arriva	LJ04LDZ	Arriva	LJ05BMV	Arriva	LJ51DFK	Arriva
LJ03MVE	Arriva	LJ04LEF	Arriva	LJ05BMY	Arriva	LJ51DFL	Arriva
LJ03MVF	Arriva	LJ04LEU	Arriva	LJ05BMZ	Arriva	LJ51DFN	Arriva
LJ03MVG	Arriva	LJ04LFB	Arriva	LJ05BNA	Arriva	LJ51DFO	Arriva
LJ03MVT	Arriva	LJ04LFD	Arriva	LJ05BNB	Arriva	LJ51DFP	Arriva
LJ03MVV	Arriva	LJ04LFE	Arriva	LJ05BND	Arriva	LJ51DFU	Arriva
LJ03MVW	Arriva	LJ04LFF	Arriva	LJ05BNE	Arriva	LJ51DFX	Arriva
LJ03MVX	Arriva	LJ04LFG	Arriva	LJ05BNF	Arriva	LJ51DFY	Arriva
LJ03MVY	Arriva	LJ04LFH	Arriva	LJ05BNK	Arriva	LJ51DFZ	Arriva
LJ03MVZ	Arriva	LJ04LFK	Arriva	LJ05BNL	Arriva	LJ51DGE	Arriva
LJ03MWA	Arriva	LJ04LFL	Arriva	LJ05GKX	Arriva	LJ51DGF	Arriva
LJ03MWC	Arriva	LJ04LFM	Arriva	LJ05GKY	Arriva	LJ51DGO	Arriva
LJ03MWD	Arriva	LJ04LFN	Arriva	LJ05GKZ	Arriva	LJ51DGU	Arriva
LJ03MWE	Arriva	LJ04LFP	Arriva	LJ05GLF	Arriva	LJ51DGV	Arriva
LJ03MWF	Arriva	LJ04LFR	Arriva	LJ05GLK	Arriva	LJ51DGX	Arriva
LJ03MWG	Arriva	LJ04LFS	Arriva	LJ05GLV	Arriva	LJ51DGY	Arriva
LJ03MWK	Arriva	LJ04LFT	Arriva	LJ05GLY	Arriva	LJ51DGZ	Arriva
LJ03MWL	Arriva	LJ04LFU	Arriva	LJ05GLZ	Arriva	LJ51DHA	Arriva
LJ03MWN	Arriva	LJ04LFV	Arriva	LJ05GME	Arriva	LJ51DHC	Arriva
LJ03MWP	Arriva	LJ04LFW	Arriva	LJ05GMF	Arriva	LJ51DHD	Arriva
LJ03MWU	Arriva	LJ04LFX	Arriva	LJ05GOP	Arriva	LJ51DHF	Arriva
LJ03MWV	Arriva	LJ04LFZ	Arriva	LJ05GOU	Arriva	LJ51DHG	Arriva
LJ03MWX	Arriva	LJ04LGA	Arriva	LJ05GOX	Arriva	LJ51DHK	Arriva
LJ03MXH	Arriva	LJ04LGC	Arriva	LJ05GPF	Arriva	LJ51DHL	Arriva
LJ03MXK	Arriva	LJ04LGD	Arriva	LJ05GPK	Arriva	LJ51DHO	Arriva
LJ03MXL	Arriva	LJ04LGE	Arriva	LJ05GPO	Arriva	LJ51DHP	Arriva
LJ03MXM	Arriva	LJ04LGF	Arriva	LJ05GPU	Arriva	LJ51DHV	Arriva
LJ03MXN	Arriva	LJ04LGG	Arriva	LJ05GPX	Arriva	LJ51DHX	Arriva
LJ03MXP	Arriva	LJ04LGK	Arriva	LJ05GPY	Arriva	LJ51DHY	Arriva
LJ03MXR	Arriva	LJ04LGL	Arriva	LJ05GPZ	Arriva	LJ51DHZ	Arriva
LJ03MXS	Arriva	LJ04LGN	Arriva	LJ05GRF	Arriva	LJ51DJD	Arriva
LJ03MXT	Arriva	LJ04LGV	Arriva	LJ05GRK	Arriva	LJ51DJE	Arriva
LJ03MXU	Arriva	LJ04LGW	Arriva	LJ05GRU	Arriva	LJ51DJF	Arriva
LJ03MXV	Arriva	LJ04LGX	Arriva	LJ05GRX	Arriva	LJ51DJK	Arriva
LJ03MXW	Arriva	LJ04LGY	Arriva	LJ05GRZ	Arriva	LJ51DJO	Arriva
LJ03MXX	Arriva	LJ04YWE	Arriva	LJ05GSO	Arriva	LJ51DJU	Arriva
LJ03MXY	Arriva	LJ04YWS	Arriva	LJ05GSU	Arriva	LJ51DJV	Arriva
LJ03MXZ	Arriva	LJ04YWT	Arriva	LJ51DAA	Arriva	LJ51DJX	Arriva
LJ03MYA	Arriva	LJ04YWU	Arriva	LJ51DAO	Arriva	LJ51DJY	Arriva
LJ03MYB	Arriva	LJ04YWV	Arriva	LJ51DAU	Arriva	LJ51DJZ	Arriva
LJ03MYC	Arriva	LJ04YWW	Arriva	LJ51DBO	Arriva	LJ51DKA	Arriva
LJ03MYD	Arriva	LJ04YWX	Arriva	LJ51DBU	Arriva	LJ51DKD	Arriva
LJ03MYF	Arriva	LJ04YWY	Arriva	LJ51DBV	Arriva	LJ51DKE	Arriva
LJ03MYG	Arriva	LJ04YWZ	Arriva	LJ51DBX	Arriva	LJ51DKF	Arriva
LJ03MYH	Arriva	LJ04YXA	Arriva	LJ51DBY	Arriva	LJ51DKK	Arriva
LJ03MYK	Arriva	LJ04YXB	Arriva	LJ51DBZ	Arriva	LJ51DKL	Arriva
LJ03MYL	Arriva	LJ05BHL	Arriva	LJ51DCE	Arriva	LJ51DKN	Arriva
LJ03MYM	Arriva	LJ05BHN	Arriva	LJ51DCF	Arriva	LJ51DKO	Arriva
LJ03MYN	Arriva	LJ05BHO	Arriva	LJ51DCO	Arriva	LJ51DKU	Arriva
LJ03MYP	Arriva	LJ05BHP	Arriva	LJ51DCU	Arriva	LJ51DKV	Arriva
LJ03MYR	Arriva	LJ05BHU	Arriva	LJ51DCV	Arriva	LJ51DKX	Arriva
LJ03MYS	Arriva	LJ05BHV	Arriva	LJ51DCX	Arriva	LJ51DKY	Arriva
LJ03MYT	Arriva	LJ05BHW	Arriva	LJ51DCY	Arriva	LJ51DLD	Arriva

LJ51DLF	Arriva	LJ53NFX	Arriva	LJ54BFV	Arriva	LJ56ARF	Arriva
LJ51DLK	Arriva	LJ53NFY	Arriva	LJ54BFY	Arriva	LJ56ARO	Arriva
LJ51DLN	Arriva	LJ53NFZ	Arriva	LJ54BFZ	Arriva	LJ56ARU	Arriva
LJ51DLU	Arriva	LJ53NGE	Arriva	LJ54BGE	Arriva	LJ56ARX	Arriva
LJ51DLV	Arriva	LJ53NGF	Arriva	LJ54BGF	Arriva	LJ56ARZ	Arriva
LJ51DLX	Arriva	LJ53NGG	Arriva	LJ54BGK	Arriva	LJ56ASO	Arriva
LJ51DLY	Arriva	LJ53NGN	Arriva	LJ54BGO	Arriva	LJ56ASU	Arriva
LJ51DLZ	Arriva	LJ53NGU	Arriva	LJ54BJE	Arriva	LJ56ASV	Arriva
LJ51ORA	Arriva	LJ53NGV	Arriva	LJ54BJF	Arriva	LJ56ASX	Arriva
LJ51ORC	Arriva	LJ53NGX	Arriva	LJ54BJK	Arriva	LK03CDA	Metroline
LJ51ORF	Arriva	LJ53NGY	Arriva	LJ54BJO	Arriva	LK03CDD	Metroline
LJ51ORG	Arriva	LJ53NGZ	Arriva	LJ54BJU	Arriva	LK03CDE	Metroline
LJ51ORH	Arriva	LJ53NHA	Arriva	LJ54BKG	Arriva	LK03CDF	Metroline
LJ51ORK	Arriva	LJ53NHB	Arriva	LJ54BKK	Arriva	LK03CDG	Metroline
LJ51ORL	Arriva	LJ53NHC	Arriva	LJ54BKL	Arriva	LK03CDJ	Metroline
LJ51OSK	Arriva	LJ53NHD	Arriva	LJ54BKN	Arriva	LK03CDL	Metroline
LJ51OSX	Arriva	LJ53NHE	Arriva	LJ54BKO	Arriva	LK03CDM	Metroline
LJ51OSY	Arriva	LJ53NHF	Arriva	LJ54BKU	Arriva	LK03CDN	Metroline
LJ51OSZ	Arriva	LJ53NHG	Arriva	LJ54BKV	Arriva	LK03CDP	Metroline
LJ53BAA	Arriva	LJ53NHH	Arriva	LJ54BKX	Arriva	LK03CDU	Metroline
LJ53BAO	Arriva	LJ53NHK	Arriva	LJ54LGV	Arriva	LK03CDV	Metroline
LJ53BAU	Arriva	LJ53NHL	Arriva	LJ54LHF	Arriva	LK03CDX	Metroline
LJ53BAV	Arriva	LJ53NHN	Arriva	LJ54LHG	Arriva	LK03CDY	Metroline
LJ53BBE	Arriva	LJ53NHO	Arriva	LJ54LHH	Arriva	LK03CDZ	Metroline
LJ53BBF	Arriva	LJ53NHP	Arriva	LJ54LHK	Arriva	LK03CEJ	Metroline
LJ53BBK	Arriva	LJ53NHT	Arriva	LJ54LHL	Arriva	LK03CEN	Metroline
LJ53BBN	Arriva	LJ53NHV	Arriva	LJ54LHM	Arriva	LK03CEU	Metroline
LJ53BBO	Arriva	LJ53NHY	Arriva	LJ54LHN	Arriva	LK03CEV	Metroline
LJ53BBU	Arriva	LJ53NHZ	Arriva	LJ54LHO	Arriva	LK03CEX	Metroline
LJ53BBV	Arriva	LJ53NJF	Arriva	LJ54LHP	Arriva	LK03CEY	Metroline
LJ53BBX	Arriva	LJ53NJK	Arriva	LJ54LHR	Arriva	LK03CGE	Metroline
LJ53BBZ	Arriva	LJ53NJN	Arriva	LJ55BPZ	Arriva	LK03CGF	Metroline
LJ53BCF	Arriva	LJ54BAA	Arriva	LJ55BRV	Arriva	LK03CGG	Metroline
LJ53BCK	Arriva	LJ54BAO	Arriva	LJ55BRX	Arriva	LK03CGU	Metroline
LJ53BCO	Arriva	LJ54BAU	Arriva	LJ55BRZ	Arriva	LK03CGV	Metroline
LJ53BCU	Arriva	LJ54BAV	Arriva	LJ55BSO	Arriva	LK03GFU	Metroline
LJ53BCV	Arriva	LJ54BBE	Arriva	LJ55BSU	Arriva	LK03GFV	Metroline
LJ53BCX	Arriva	LJ54BBF	Arriva	LJ55BSV	Arriva	LK03GFX	Metroline
LJ53BCY	Arriva	LJ54BBK	Arriva	LJ55BSX	Arriva	LK03GFY	Metroline
LJ53BCZ	Arriva	LJ54BBN	Arriva	LJ55BSY	Arriva	LK03GFZ	Metroline
LJ53BDE	Arriva	LJ54BBO	Arriva	LJ55BSZ	Arriva	LK03GGA	Metroline
LJ53BDF	Arriva	LJ54BBU	Arriva	LJ55BTE	Arriva	LK03GGF	Metroline
LJ53BDO	Arriva	LJ54BBV	Arriva	LJ55BTF	Arriva	LK03GGJ	Metroline
LJ53BDU	Arriva	LJ54BBX	Arriva	LJ55BTO	Arriva	LK03GGP	Metroline
LJ53BDV	Arriva	LJ54BBZ	Arriva	LJ55BTU	Arriva	LK03GGU	Metroline
LJ53BDX	Arriva	LJ54BCE	Arriva	LJ55BTV	Arriva	LK03GGV	Metroline
LJ53BDY	Arriva	LJ54BCF	Arriva	LJ55BTX	Arriva	LK03GGX	Metroline
LJ53BDZ	Arriva	LJ54BCK	Arriva	LJ55BTY	Arriva	LK03GGY	Metroline
LJ53BEO	Arriva	LJ54BCO	Arriva	LJ55BTZ	Arriva	LK03GGZ	Metroline
LJ53BEU	Arriva	LJ54BCU	Arriva	LJ55BUA	Arriva	LK03GHA	Metroline
LJ53BEY	Arriva	LJ54BCV	Arriva	LJ55BUE	Arriva	LK03GHB	Metroline
LJ53BFA	Arriva	LJ54BCX	Arriva	LJ55BUP	Arriva	LK03GHD	Metroline
LJ53BFE	Arriva	LJ54BCY	Arriva	LJ55BUR	Arriva	LK03GHF	Metroline
LJ53BFF	Arriva	LJ54BCZ	Arriva	LJ55BUS	Arriva	LK03GHG	Metroline
LJ53BFK	Arriva	LJ54BDE	Arriva	LJ55BUT	Arriva	LK03GHH	Metroline
LJ53BFL	Arriva	LJ54BDF	Arriva	LJ55BUU	Arriva	LK03GHJ	Metroline
LJ53BFM	Arriva	LJ54BDO	Arriva	LJ55BUV	Arriva	LK03GHU	Metroline
LJ53BFN	Arriva	LJ54BDU	Arriva	LJ55BUW	Arriva	LK03GHU	Metroline
LJ53BFO	Arriva	LJ54BDV	Arriva	LJ55BUX	Arriva	LK03GHV	Metroline
LJ53BFP	Arriva	LJ54BDX	Arriva	LJ55BUY	Arriva	LK03GHX	Metroline
LJ53BFU	Arriva	LJ54BDY	Arriva	LJ55BUZ	Arriva	LK03GHY	Metroline
LJ53BFX	Arriva	LJ54BDZ	Arriva	LJ55BVD	Arriva	LK03GHZ	Metroline
LJ53BFY	Arriva	LJ54BEO	Arriva	LJ55BVE	Arriva	LK03GJF	Metroline
LJ53BGF	Arriva	LJ54BEU	Arriva	LJ55BVF	Arriva	LK03GJG	Metroline
LJ53BGK	Arriva	LJ54BFA	Arriva	LJ55BVG	Arriva	LK03GJU	Metroline
LJ53BGO	Arriva	LJ54BFE	Arriva	LJ55BVH	Arriva	LK03GJV	Metroline
LJ53BGU	Arriva	LJ54BFF	Arriva	LJ55BVK	Arriva	LK03GJX	Metroline
LJ53NFE	Arriva	LJ54BFK	Arriva	LJ55BVL	Arriva	LK03GJY	Metroline
LJ53NFF	Arriva	LJ54BFL	Arriva	LJ55BVM	Arriva	LK03GJZ	Metroline
LJ53NFG	Arriva	LJ54BFM	Arriva	LJ56AOW	Arriva	LK03GKA	Metroline
LJ53NFT	Arriva	LJ54BFN	Arriva	LJ56AOX	Arriva	LK03GKC	Metroline
LJ53NFU	Arriva	LJ54BFO	Arriva	LJ56AOY	Arriva	LK03GKD	Metroline
LJ53NFV	Arriva	LJ54BFP	Arriva	LJ56APZ	Arriva	LK03GKE	Metroline

LK03GKF	Metroline	LK03NJY	First London	LK04CTZ	Metroline	LK04HYC	First London
LK03GKG	Metroline	LK03NJZ	First London	LK04CUA	Metroline	LK04HYF	First London
LK03GKJ	Metroline	LK03NKA	First London	LK04CUC	Metroline	LK04HYG	First London
LK03GKL	Metroline	LK03NKC	First London	LK04CUG	Metroline	LK04HYH	First London
LK03GKN	Metroline	LK03NKD	First London	LK04CUH	Metroline	LK04HYJ	First London
LK03GKP	Metroline	LK03NKE	First London	LK04CUJ	Metroline	LK04HYL	First London
LK03GKU	Metroline	LK03NKF	First London	LK04CUU	Metroline	LK04HYM	First London
LK03GKV	Metroline	LK03NKG	First London	LK04CUW	Metroline	LK04HYN	First London
LK03GKX	Metroline	LK03NKH	First London	LK04CUX	Metroline	LK04HYP	First London
LK03GKY	Metroline	LK03NKJ	First London	LK04CUY	Metroline	LK04HYS	First London
LK03GKZ	Metroline	LK03NKL	First London	LK04CVA	Metroline	LK04HYT	First London
LK03GLF	Metroline	LK03NKM	First London	LK04CVB	Metroline	LK04HYU	First London
LK03GLJ	Metroline	LK03NKN	First London	LK04CVC	Metroline	LK04HYV	First London
LK03GLV	Metroline	LK03NKP	First London	LK04CVD	Metroline	LK04HYW	First London
LK03GLY	Metroline	LK03NKR	First London	LK04CVE	Metroline	LK04HYX	First London
LK03GLZ	Metroline	LK03NKS	First London	LK04CVF	Metroline	LK04HYY	First London
LK03GME	Metroline	LK03NKT	First London	LK04CVG	Metroline	LK04HYZ	First London
LK03GMF	Metroline	LK03NKU	First London	LK04CVH	Metroline	LK04HZA	First London
LK03GMG	Metroline	LK03NKW	First London	LK04CVJ	Metroline	LK04HZB	First London
LK03GMU	Metroline	LK03NKX	First London	LK04CVL	Metroline	LK04HZC	First London
LK03GMV	Metroline	LK03NKZ	First London	LK04CVM	Metroline	LK04HZD	First London
LK03GMX	Metroline	LK03NLA	First London	LK04CVN	Metroline	LK04HZE	First London
LK03GMY	Metroline	LK03NLC	First London	LK04CVP	Metroline	LK04HZF	First London
LK03GMZ	Metroline	LK03NLD	First London	LK04CVR	Metroline	LK04HZG	First London
LK03GNF	Metroline	LK03NLE	First London	LK04CVS	Metroline	LK04HZH	First London
LK03GNJ	Metroline	LK03NLF	First London	LK04CVT	Metroline	LK04HZJ	First London
LK03GNN	Metroline	LK03NLG	First London	LK04CVU	Metroline	LK04HZL	First London
LK03GNP	Metroline	LK03NLJ	First London	LK04CVV	Metroline	LK04HZM	First London
LK03LLX	First London	LK03NLL	First London	LK04CVW	Metroline	LK04HZN	First London
LK03LLZ	First London	LK03NLM	First London	LK04CVX	Metroline	LK04HZP	First London
LK03LME	First London	LK03NLN	First London	LK04EKU	Metroline	LK04HZS	First London
LK03LMF	First London	LK03NLP	First London	LK04EKV	Metroline	LK04HZT	First London
LK03LMJ	First London	LK03NLR	First London	LK04EKW	Metroline	LK04HZU	First London
LK03LNU	First London	LK03NLT	First London	LK04EKX	Metroline	LK04HZV	First London
LK03LNV	First London	LK03UEX	First London	LK04EKY	Metroline	LK04HZW	First London
LK03LNW	First London	LK03UEY	First London	LK04EKZ	Metroline	LK04HZX	First London
LK03LNX	First London	LK03UEZ	First London	LK04ELC	Metroline	LK04HZY	First London
LK03NFY	First London	LK03UFA	First London	LK04ELH	Metroline	LK04HZZ	First London
LK03NFZ	First London	LK03UFB	First London	LK04ELJ	Metroline	LK04JBE	First London
LK03NGE	First London	LK03UFC	First London	LK04ELU	Metroline	LK04JBU	First London
LK03NGF	First London	LK03UFD	First London	LK04ELV	Metroline	LK04JBV	First London
LK03NGG	First London	LK03UFE	First London	LK04ELW	Metroline	LK04JBX	First London
LK03NGJ	First London	LK03UFG	First London	LK04ELX	Metroline	LK04JBY	First London
LK03NGN	First London	LK03UFJ	First London	LK04EMF	Metroline	LK04JBZ	First London
LK03NGU	First London	LK03UFL	First London	LK04EMJ	Metroline	LK04JCJ	First London
LK03NGV	First London	LK03UFM	First London	LK04EMV	Metroline	LK04JCU	First London
LK03NGX	First London	LK03UFN	First London	LK04EMX	Metroline	LK04JCV	First London
LK03NGY	First London	LK03UFP	First London	LK04ENE	Metroline	LK04JCX	First London
LK03NGZ	First London	LK03UFR	First London	LK04ENF	Metroline	LK04JCZ	First London
LK03NHA	First London	LK03UFS	First London	LK04ENH	Metroline	LK04NLZ	Metroline
LK03NHB	First London	LK03UFT	First London	LK04ENJ	Metroline	LK04NMA	Metroline
LK03NHC	First London	LK03UFU	First London	LK04HXA	First London	LK04NME	Metroline
LK03NHD	First London	LK03UFV	First London	LK04HXB	First London	LK04NMF	Metroline
LK03NHE	First London	LK03UFW	First London	LK04HXC	First London	LK04NMJ	Metroline
LK03NHF	First London	LK03UFX	First London	LK04HXD	First London	LK04NMM	Metroline
LK03NHG	First London	LK04CPY	Metroline	LK04HXE	First London	LK04NMU	Metroline
LK03NHH	First London	LK04CPZ	Metroline	LK04HXF	First London	LK04NMV	Metroline
LK03NHJ	First London	LK04CRF	Metroline	LK04HXG	First London	LK04NMX	Metroline
LK03NHL	First London	LK04CRJ	Metroline	LK04HXH	First London	LK04NMY	Metroline
LK03NHM	First London	LK04CRU	Metroline	LK04HXJ	First London	LK04NMZ	Metroline
LK03NHN	First London	LK04CRV	Metroline	LK04HXL	First London	LK04NNA	Metroline
LK03NHP	First London	LK04CRZ	Metroline	LK04HXM	First London	LK04NNB	Metroline
LK03NHT	First London	LK04CSF	Metroline	LK04HXN	First London	LK04NNC	Metroline
LK03NHV	First London	LK04CSU	Metroline	LK04HXP	First London	LK04NND	Metroline
LK03NHX	First London	LK04CSV	Metroline	LK04HXR	First London	LK04NNE	Metroline
LK03NHY	First London	LK04CSY	Metroline	LK04HXS	First London	LK04NNF	Metroline
LK03NHZ	First London	LK04CSZ	Metroline	LK04HXT	First London	LK04NNG	Metroline
LK03NJE	First London	LK04CTE	Metroline	LK04HXU	First London	LK04NNH	Metroline
LK03NJF	First London	LK04CTF	Metroline	LK04HXV	First London	LK04NNJ	Metroline
LK03NJJ	First London	LK04CTF	Metroline	LK04HXW	First London	LK04NNL	Metroline
LK03NJN	First London	LK04CTU	Metroline	LK04HXX	First London	LK04NNM	Metroline
LK03NJV	First London	LK04CTV	Metroline	LK04HYA	First London	LK04NNP	Metroline
LK03NJX	First London	LK04CTX	Metroline	LK04HYB	First London	LK04UWJ	Metroline

LK04UWL	Metroline	LK05GHH	Metroline	LK51XGR	Metroline	LK53FCF	First London
LK04UWM	Metroline	LK06F	Metroline	LK51XGS	Metroline	LK53FCG	First London
LK04UWN	Metroline	LK06F	Metroline	LK51XGT	Metroline	LK53FCJ	First London
LK04UWF	Metroline	LK06F	Metroline	LK51XGU	Metroline	LK53FCL	First London
LK04UWR	Metroline	LK06FLA	Metroline	LK51XGV	Metroline	LK53FCM	First London
LK04UWS	Metroline	LK51DWJ	First London	LK51XGW	Metroline	LK53FCN	First London
LK04UWT	Metroline	LK51DWK	First London	LK51XGX	Metroline	LK53FCO	First London
LK04UWU	Metroline	LK51DWL	First London	LK51XGY	Metroline	LK53FCP	First London
LK04UWV	Metroline	LK51DWM	First London	LK51XGZ	Metroline	LK53FCU	First London
LK04UWW	Metroline	LK51DWO	First London	LK51XHA	Metroline	LK53FCV	First London
LK04UWX	Metroline	LK51DWP	First London	LK51XHB	Metroline	LK53FCX	First London
LK04UWY	Metroline	LK51DWU	First London	LK53EXT	First London	LK53FCY	First London
LK04UWZ	Metroline	LK51DWY	First London	LK53EXU	First London	LK53FCZ	First London
LK04UXA	Metroline	LK51DWZ	First London	LK53EXV	First London	LK53FDA	First London
LK04UXB	Metroline	LK51DXA	First London	LK53EXW	First London	LK53FDC	First London
LK04UXC	Metroline	LK51DXB	First London	LK53EXX	First London	LK53FDD	First London
LK04UXD	Metroline	LK51DXC	First London	LK53EXZ	First London	LK53FDE	First London
LK04UXE	Metroline	LK51DXD	First London	LK53EYA	First London	LK53FDF	First London
LK04UXF	Metroline	LK51DXE	First London	LK53EYB	First London	LK53FDG	First London
LK04UXG	Metroline	LK51DXF	First London	LK53EYC	First London	LK53FDJ	First London
LK04UXH	Metroline	LK51DXG	First London	LK53EYD	First London	LK53FDM	First London
LK05DXP	First London	LK51DXH	First London	LK53EYF	First London	LK53FDN	First London
LK05DXR	First London	LK51JYJ	First London	LK53EYG	First London	LK53FDO	First London
LK05DXS	First London	LK51JYL	First London	LK53EYH	First London	LK53FDP	First London
LK05DXT	First London	LK51JYN	First London	LK53EYJ	First London	LK53FDU	First London
LK05DXU	First London	LK51JYO	First London	LK53EYL	First London	LK53FDV	First London
LK05DYO	First London	LK51UYD	First London	LK53EYM	First London	LK53FDX	First London
LK05EZW	First London	LK51UYE	First London	LK53EYO	First London	LK53FDY	First London
LK05EZX	First London	LK51UYF	First London	LK53EYP	First London	LK53FDZ	First London
LK05EZZ	First London	LK51UYG	First London	LK53EYR	First London	LK53FEF	First London
LK05FBY	First London	LK51UYH	First London	LK53EYT	First London	LK53FEG	First London
LK05FBZ	First London	LK51UYJ	First London	LK53EYU	First London	LK53FEH	First London
LK05FCA	First London	LK51UYL	First London	LK53EYV	First London	LK53FEJ	First London
LK05FCB	First London	LK51UYM	First London	LK53EYW	First London	LK53LXM	Metroline
LK05FCC	First London	LK51UYN	First London	LK53EYX	First London	LK53LXN	Metroline
LK05FCM	First London	LK51UYO	First London	LK53EYY	First London	LK53LXO	Metroline
LK05FCN	First London	LK51UYP	First London	LK53EYZ	First London	LK53LXP	Metroline
LK05FCO	First London	LK51UYR	First London	LK53EZA	First London	LK53LXR	Metroline
LK05FCP	First London	LK51UYS	First London	LK53EZB	First London	LK53LXT	Metroline
LK05FCU	First London	LK51UYT	First London	LK53EZC	First London	LK53LXU	Metroline
LK05FCV	First London	LK51UYU	First London	LK53EZD	First London	LK53LXV	Metroline
LK05FCX	First London	LK51UYV	First London	LK53EZE	First London	LK53LXW	Metroline
LK05FCY	First London	LK51UYW	First London	LK53EZF	First London	LK53LXX	Metroline
LK05FCZ	First London	LK51UYX	First London	LK53EZV	First London	LK53LXY	Metroline
LK05FDC	First London	LK51UYY	First London	LK53EZW	First London	LK53LXZ	Metroline
LK05FDD	First London	LK51UYZ	First London	LK53EZX	First London	LK53LYA	Metroline
LK05FDD	First London	LK51UZA	First London	LK53EZZ	First London	LK53LYC	Metroline
LK05FDE	First London	LK51UZB	First London	LK53FAA	First London	LK53LYD	Metroline
LK05FDF	First London	LK51UZC	First London	LK53FAF	First London	LK53LYF	Metroline
LK05FDG	First London	LK51UZD	First London	LK53FAJ	First London	LK53LYG	Metroline
LK05FDJ	First London	LK51UZE	First London	LK53FAM	First London	LK53LYH	First London
LK05FDL	First London	LK51UZF	First London	LK53FAO	First London	LK53LYJ	First London
LK05GFO	Metroline	LK51UZG	First London	LK53FAU	First London	LK53LYO	First London
LK05GFV	Metroline	LK51UZH	First London	LK53FBA	First London	LK53LYP	First London
LK05GFX	Metroline	LK51UZJ	First London	LK53FBB	First London	LK53LYR	First London
LK05GFY	Metroline	LK51UZL	First London	LK53FBC	First London	LK53LYT	First London
LK05GFZ	Metroline	LK51UZM	First London	LK53FBD	First London	LK53LYU	First London
LK05GGA	Metroline	LK51UZN	First London	LK53FBE	First London	LK53LYV	First London
LK05GGE	Metroline	LK51UZO	First London	LK53FBF	First London	LK53LYW	First London
LK05GGF	Metroline	LK51UZP	First London	LK53FBG	First London	LK53LYX	First London
LK05GGJ	Metroline	LK51UZS	First London	LK53FBJ	First London	LK53LYY	First London
LK05GGO	Metroline	LK51UZT	First London	LK53FBL	First London	LK53LYZ	First London
LK05GGP	Metroline	LK51XGD	Metroline	LK53FBN	First London	LK53LZA	First London
LK05GGU	Metroline	LK51XGE	Metroline	LK53FBO	First London	LK53LZB	First London
LK05GGV	Metroline	LK51XGF	Metroline	LK53FBU	First London	LK53LZC	First London
LK05GGX	Metroline	LK51XGG	Metroline	LK53FBV	First London	LK53LZD	First London
LK05GGY	Metroline	LK51XGH	Metroline	LK53FBX	First London	LK53LZE	First London
LK05GGZ	Metroline	LK51XGJ	Metroline	LK53FBY	First London	LK53LZF	First London
LK05GHA	Metroline	LK51XGL	Metroline	LK53FBZ	First London	LK53LZG	First London
LK05GHB	Metroline	LK51XGM	Metroline	LK53FCA	First London	LK53LZH	First London
LK05GHD	Metroline	LK51XGN	Metroline	LK53FCC	First London	LK53LZL	First London
LK05GHF	Metroline	LK51XGO	Metroline	LK53FCD	First London	LK53LZM	First London
LK05GHG	Metroline	LK51XGP	Metroline	LK53FCE	First London	LK53LZN	First London

The London Bus Handbook

LK53LZO	First London	LK55KMG	Metroline	LN51GJY	First London	LN51KYG	Metroline
LK53LZP	First London	LK55KMJ	Metroline	LN51GJZ	First London	LN51KYH	Metroline
LK53LZR	First London	LK55KMM	Metroline	LN51GKA	First London	LN51KYJ	Metroline
LK53LZT	First London	LK55KMO	Metroline	LN51GKD	First London	LN51KYK	Metroline
LK53LZU	First London	LK56FHE	Metroline	LN51GKE	First London	LN51KYO	Metroline
LK53LZV	First London	LK56FHF	Metroline	LN51GKF	First London	LN51KYP	Metroline
LK53LZW	First London	LK56FHG	Metroline	LN51GKG	First London	LN51KYR	Metroline
LK53LZX	First London	LK56FHH	Metroline	LN51GKJ	First London	LN51KYS	Metroline
LK53MBF	First London	LK56FHJ	Metroline	LN51GKK	First London	LN51KYT	Metroline
LK53MBO	First London	LK56FHM	Metroline	LN51GKL	First London	LN51KYU	Metroline
LK53MBU	First London	LK56FHN	Metroline	LN51GKO	First London	LN51KYV	Metroline
LK53MBV	First London	LK56FHO	Metroline	LN51GKP	First London	LN51KYW	Metroline
LK54FKW	First London	LK56FHP	Metroline	LN51GKU	First London	LN51KYY	Metroline
LK54FKX	First London	LK56FHR	Metroline	LN51GKV	First London	LN51KYY	Metroline
LK54FLA	First London	LK56FHS	Metroline	LN51GKX	First London	LN51KYZ	Metroline
LK54FLB	First London	LK56FHT	Metroline	LN51GKY	First London	LN51KZA	Metroline
LK54FLC	First London	LLU670	Blue Triangle	LN51GKZ	First London	LN51KZB	Metroline
LK54FLD	First London	LN51AYX	Transdev	LN51GLF	First London	LN51KZC	Metroline
LK54FLE	First London	LN51AYY	Transdev	LN51GLJ	First London	LN51KZD	Metroline
LK54FLF	First London	LN51AYZ	Transdev	LN51GLK	First London	LN51NRJ	First London
LK54FLG	First London	LN51AZA	Transdev	LN51GLV	First London	LN51NRK	First London
LK54FWE	Metroline	LN51AZB	Transdev	LN51GLY	First London	LN51NRL	First London
LK54FWF	Metroline	LN51AZC	Transdev	LN51GLZ	First London	LN51RZZ	First London
LK54FWG	Metroline	LN51AZD	Transdev	LN51GME	First London	LN51SBO	First London
LK54FWH	Metroline	LN51AZF	Transdev	LN51GMF	First London	LN51SBU	First London
LK54FWJ	Metroline	LN51AZG	Transdev	LN51GMG	First London	LN51SBV	First London
LK54FWL	Metroline	LN51AZJ	Transdev	LN51GMO	First London	LR02BAA	Metroline
LK54FWM	Metroline	LN51AZL	Transdev	LN51GMU	First London	LR02BAO	Metroline
LK54FWN	Metroline	LN51AZP	Transdev	LN51GMV	First London	LR02BAU	Metroline
LK54FWO	Metroline	LN51AZR	Transdev	LN51GMX	First London	LR02BAV	Metroline
LK54FWP	Metroline	LN51AZT	Transdev	LN51GMY	First London	LR02BBE	Metroline
LK54FWR	Metroline	LN51AZU	Transdev	LN51GMZ	First London	LR02BBF	Metroline
LK54FWT	Metroline	LN51AZV	Transdev	LN51GNF	First London	LR02BBJ	Metroline
LK54JFF	First London	LN51AZW	Transdev	LN51GNJ	First London	LR02BBK	Metroline
LK55KJV	Metroline	LN51DUA	First London	LN51GNK	First London	LR02BBN	Metroline
LK55KJX	Metroline	LN51DUH	First London	LN51GNP	First London	LR02BBO	Metroline
LK55KJY	Metroline	LN51DUJ	First London	LN51GNU	First London	LR02BBU	Metroline
LK55KJZ	Metroline	LN51DUU	First London	LN51GNV	First London	LR02BBV	Metroline
LK55KKA	Metroline	LN51DUV	First London	LN51GNX	First London	LR02BBX	Metroline
LK55KKB	Metroline	LN51DUY	First London	LN51GNY	First London	LR02BBZ	Metroline
LK55KKC	Metroline	LN51DVA	First London	LN51GNZ	First London	LR02BCE	Metroline
LK55KKD	Metroline	LN51DVB	First London	LN51GOA	First London	LR02BCF	Metroline
LK55KKE	Metroline	LN51DVC	First London	LN51GOC	First London	LR02BCK	Metroline
LK55KKF	Metroline	LN51DVF	First London	LN51GOE	First London	LR02BCO	Metroline
LK55KKG	Metroline	LN51DVG	First London	LN51GOH	First London	LR02BCU	Metroline
LK55KKH	Metroline	LN51DVH	First London	LN51GOJ	First London	LR02BCV	Metroline
LK55KKJ	Metroline	LN51DVK	First London	LN51GOK	First London	LR02BCX	Metroline
LK55KKL	Metroline	LN51DVL	First London	LN51GOP	First London	LR02BCY	Metroline
LK55KKM	Metroline	LN51DVM	First London	LN51GOU	First London	LR02BCZ	Metroline
LK55KKO	Metroline	LN51DVO	First London	LN51KXD	Metroline	LR02BDE	Metroline
LK55KKP	Metroline	LN51DVP	First London	LN51KXE	Metroline	LR02BDF	Metroline
LK55KKR	Metroline	LN51DVR	First London	LN51KXF	Metroline	LR02BDO	Metroline
LK55KKS	Metroline	LN51DVT	First London	LN51KXG	Metroline	LR02BDU	Metroline
LK55KKT	Metroline	LN51DVV	First London	LN51KXH	Metroline	LR02BDV	Metroline
LK55KKU	Metroline	LN51DVW	First London	LN51KXJ	Metroline	LR02BDX	Metroline
LK55KKV	Metroline	LN51DVX	First London	LN51KXK	Metroline	LR02BDY	Metroline
LK55KKY	Metroline	LN51DVY	First London	LN51KXL	Metroline	LR02BDZ	Metroline
LK55KKZ	Metroline	LN51DVZ	First London	LN51KXM	Metroline	LR02BEJ	Metroline
LK55KLE	Metroline	LN51DWA	First London	LN51KXO	Metroline	LR02BEO	Metroline
LK55KLF	Metroline	LN51DWC	First London	LN51KXP	Metroline	LR02BEU	Metroline
LK55KLJ	Metroline	LN51DWD	First London	LN51KXR	Metroline	LR02BEY	Metroline
LK55KLL	Metroline	LN51DWE	First London	LN51KXS	Metroline	LR02BFA	Metroline
LK55KLM	Metroline	LN51DWF	First London	LN51KXT	Metroline	LR02BFE	Metroline
LK55KLO	Metroline	LN51DWG	First London	LN51KXU	Metroline	LR02BFF	Metroline
LK55KLP	Metroline	LN51DWV	First London	LN51KXV	Metroline	LR02BFJ	Metroline
LK55KLS	Metroline	LN51DWW	First London	LN51KXW	Metroline	LR02LWW	First London
LK55KLU	Metroline	LN51DWX	First London	LN51KXY	Metroline	LR02LWX	First London
LK55KLV	Metroline	LN51GJJ	First London	LN51KXZ	Metroline	LR02LWY	First London
LK55KLX	Metroline	LN51GJK	First London	LN51KYA	Metroline	LR02LWZ	First London
LK55KLZ	Metroline	LN51GJO	First London	LN51KYB	Metroline	LR02LXA	First London
LK55KMA	Metroline	LN51GJU	First London	LN51KYC	Metroline	LR02LXB	First London
LK55KME	Metroline	LN51GJV	First London	LN51KYE	Metroline	LR02LXC	First London
LK55KMF	Metroline	LN51GJX	First London	LN51KYF	Metroline	LR02LXG	First London

Reg	Operator	Reg	Operator	Reg	Operator	Reg	Operator	Reg	Operator
LR02LXH	First London	LR52KVU	Metroline	LT02NUO	First London	LT02ZZG	Metroline	LT52WVA	First London
LR02LXJ	First London	LR52KVV	Metroline	LT02NUP	First London	LT02ZZH	Metroline	LT52WVA	First London
LR02LXK	First London	LR52KVW	Metroline	LT02NUU	First London	LT02ZZJ	Metroline	LT52WVB	First London
LR02LXL	First London	LR52KVX	Metroline	LT02NUV	First London	LT02ZZK	Metroline	LT52WVB	First London
LR02LXM	First London	LR52KVY	Metroline	LT02NVE	First London	LT02ZZL	Metroline	LT52WVC	First London
LR02LXN	First London	LR52KVZ	Metroline	LT02NVH	First London	LT02ZZM	Metroline	LT52WVC	First London
LR02LXO	First London	LR52KWA	Metroline	LT02NVJ	First London	LT02ZZN	Metroline	LT52WVD	First London
LR02LXP	First London	LR52KWB	Metroline	LT02NVK	First London	LT02ZZO	Metroline	LT52WVD	First London
LR02LXS	First London	LR52KWC	Metroline	LT02NVL	First London	LT02ZZP	Metroline	LT52WVE	First London
LR02LXT	First London	LR52KWD	Metroline	LT02NVM	First London	LT02ZZR	Metroline	LT52WVE	First London
LR02LXU	First London	LR52KWE	Metroline	LT02NVN	First London	LT02ZZS	Metroline	LT52WVF	First London
LR02LXV	First London	LR52KWF	Metroline	LT02NVO	First London	LT02ZZU	Metroline	LT52WVG	First London
LR02LXW	First London	LR52KWG	Metroline	LT02NVP	First London	LT02ZZV	Metroline	LT52WVG	First London
LR02LXX	First London	LR52KWH	Metroline	LT02NVR	First London	LT02ZZW	Metroline	LT52WVH	First London
LR02LXZ	First London	LR52KWJ	Metroline	LT02NVS	First London	LT02ZZX	Metroline	LT52WVH	First London
LR02LYA	First London	LR52KWK	Metroline	LT02NVU	First London	LT52WTE	First London	LT52WVJ	First London
LR02LYC	First London	LR52KWL	Metroline	LT02NVV	First London	LT52WTF	First London	LT52WVJ	First London
LR02LYD	First London	LR52KWM	Metroline	LT02NVW	First London	LT52WTG	First London	LT52WVK	First London
LR02LYF	First London	LR52KWN	Metroline	LT02NVX	First London	LT52WTJ	First London	LT52WVK	First London
LR02LYG	First London	LR52KWO	Metroline	LT02NVY	First London	LT52WTK	First London	LT52WVL	First London
LR02LYJ	First London	LR52KWP	Metroline	LT02NVZ	First London	LT52WTL	First London	LT52WVL	First London
LR02LYK	First London	LR52KWS	Metroline	LT02NWA	First London	LT52WTM	First London	LT52WVM	First London
LR02LYO	First London	LR52KWT	Metroline	LT02NWB	First London	LT52WTN	First London	LT52WVN	First London
LR02LYP	First London	LR52KWU	Metroline	LT02NWC	First London	LT52WTO	First London	LT52WVO	First London
LR02LYS	First London	LR52KWV	Metroline	LT02NWD	First London	LT52WTP	First London	LT52WVP	First London
LR02LYT	First London	LR52KWW	Metroline	LT02ZBX	First London	LT52WTR	First London	LT52WVY	First London
LR02LYU	First London	LR52KWX	Metroline	LT02ZBY	First London	LT52WTU	First London	LT52WVZ	First London
LR02LYV	First London	LR52KWY	Metroline	LT02ZBZ	First London	LT52WTV	First London	LT52WWA	First London
LR02LYW	First London	LR52KWZ	Metroline	LT02ZCA	First London	LT52WTW	First London	LT52WWB	First London
LR02LYX	First London	LR52KXA	Metroline	LT02ZCE	First London	LT52WTX	First London	LT52WWC	First London
LR02LYY	First London	LR52KXB	Metroline	LT02ZCF	First London	LT52WTY	First London	LT52WWD	First London
LR02LYZ	First London	LR52KXC	Metroline	LT02ZCJ	First London	LT52WTZ	First London	LT52WWE	First London
LR02LZA	First London	LR52KXD	Metroline	LT02ZCK	First London	LT52WUM	First London		
LR02LZB	First London	LR52KXE	Metroline	LT02ZCL	First London	LT52WUO	First London		
LR02LZC	First London	LR52KXF	Metroline	LT02ZCN	First London	LT52WUP	First London		
LR02LZD	First London	LR52KXG	Metroline	LT02ZCO	First London	LT52WUR	First London		
LR02LZE	First London	LR52KXH	Metroline	LT02ZCU	First London	LT52WUU	First London		
LR52BLK	Metroline	LR52KXJ	Metroline	LT02ZCV	First London	LT52WUV	First London		
LR52BLN	Metroline	LR52KXK	Metroline	LT02ZCX	First London	LT52WUW	First London		
LR52BLV	Metroline	LR52KXL	Metroline	LT02ZCY	First London	LT52WUX	First London		
LR52BLX	Metroline	LR52KXM	Metroline	LT02ZCZ	First London	LT52WUY	First London		
LR52BLZ	Metroline	LR52KXN	Metroline	LT02ZDA	First London				
LR52BMO	Metroline	LR52KXO	Metroline	LT02ZDC	First London				
LR52BMU	Metroline	LR52KXP	Metroline	LT02ZDD	First London				
LR52BMV	Metroline	LR52KXS	Metroline	LT02ZDE	First London				
LR52BMY	Metroline	LR52KXT	Metroline	LT02ZDF	First London				
LR52BMZ	Metroline	LR52KXU	Metroline	LT02ZDG	First London				
LR52BNA	Metroline	LR52KXV	Metroline	LT02ZDH	First London				
LR52BNB	Metroline	LR52KXW	Metroline	LT02ZDJ	First London				
LR52BND	Metroline	LR52KXX	Metroline	LT02ZDK	First London				
LR52BNE	Metroline	LR52LTF	CT Plus	LT02ZDL	First London				
LR52BNF	Metroline	LR52LTJ	CT Plus	LT02ZDM	First London				
LR52BNJ	Metroline	LR52LTK	CT Plus	LT02ZDN	First London				
LR52BNK	Metroline	LR52LTN	CT Plus	LT02ZDO	First London				
LR52BNL	Metroline	LR52LTO	CT Plus	LT02ZDP	First London				
LR52BNN	Metroline	LR52LWE	CT Plus	LT02ZDR	First London				
LR52BNO	Metroline	LR52LWF	CT Plus	LT02ZDS	First London				
LR52BNU	Metroline	LR52LWH	CT Plus	LT02ZDU	First London				
LR52BNV	Metroline	LR52LWJ	CT Plus	LT02ZDV	First London				
LR52BNX	Metroline	LR52LYC	CT Plus	LT02ZDW	First London				
LR52BNY	Metroline	LR52LYJ	CT Plus	LT02ZDX	First London				
LR52BNZ	Metroline	LT02NTV	First London	LT02ZDY	First London				
LR52BOF	Metroline	LT02NTX	First London	LT02ZDZ	First London				
LR52BOH	Metroline	LT02NTY	First London	LT02ZFA	First London				
LR52BOJ	Metroline	LT02NUA	First London	LT02ZFB	First London				
LR52BOU	Metroline	LT02NUB	First London	LT02ZFC	First London				
LR52BOV	Metroline	LT02NUC	First London	LT02ZFJ	First London				
LR52BPE	Metroline	LT02NUE	First London	LT02ZFK	First London				
LR52KVM	Metroline	LT02NUF	First London	LT02ZFL	First London				
LR52KVO	Metroline	LT02NUH	First London	LT02ZFM	First London				
LR52KVP	Metroline	LT02NUJ	First London	LT02ZZD	Metroline				
LR52KVS	Metroline	LT02NUK	First London	LT02ZZE	Metroline				
LR52KVT	Metroline	LT02NUM	First London	LT02ZZF	Metroline				

The London Bus Handbook

LT52WWF	First London	LV52HFR	East London	LX03BTU	East London	LX03BXY	East London
LT52WWG	First London	LV52HFS	East London	LX03BTV	East London	LX03BXZ	East London
LT52WWH	First London	LV52HFT	East London	LX03BTY	East London	LX03BYA	East London
LT52WWJ	First London	LV52HFU	East London	LX03BTZ	East London	LX03BYB	East London
LT52WWK	First London	LV52HFU	East London	LX03BUA	East London	LX03BYC	East London
LT52WWL	First London	LV52HFW	East London	LX03BUE	East London	LX03BYD	East London
LT52WWM	First London	LV52HFX	East London	LX03BUF	East London	LX03BYF	East London
LT52WWN	First London	LV52HFY	East London	LX03BUH	East London	LX03BYG	East London
LT52WWO	First London	LV52HFZ	East London	LX03BUJ	East London	LX03BYH	East London
LT52WWP	First London	LV52HGA	East London	LX03BUP	East London	LX03BYJ	East London
LT52WWR	First London	LV52HGC	East London	LX03BUU	East London	LX03BYL	East London
LT52WWS	First London	LV52HGD	East London	LX03BUV	East London	LX03BYM	East London
LT52WWU	First London	LV52HGE	East London	LX03BUW	East London	LX03BYN	East London
LT52WWV	First London	LV52HGF	East London	LX03BVA	East London	LX03BYP	East London
LT52WWX	First London	LV52HGG	East London	LX03BVB	East London	LX03BYR	East London
LT52WWY	First London	LV52HGJ	East London	LX03BVC	East London	LX03BYS	East London
LT52WWZ	First London	LV52HGK	East London	LX03BVD	East London	LX03BYT	East London
LT52WXC	First London	LV52HGL	East London	LX03BVE	East London	LX03BYU	East London
LT52WXD	First London	LV52HGM	East London	LX03BVF	East London	LX03BYV	East London
LT52WXE	First London	LV52HGN	East London	LX03BVG	East London	LX03BYW	East London
LT52WXF	First London	LV52HGO	East London	LX03BVH	East London	LX03BYY	East London
LT52WXG	First London	LV52HHA	East London	LX03BVJ	East London	LX03BYZ	East London
LT52WXH	First London	LV52HHB	East London	LX03BVK	East London	LX03BZA	East London
LT52WXJ	First London	LV52HHC	East London	LX03BVL	East London	LX03BZB	East London
LT52WXK	First London	LV52HHD	East London	LX03BVM	East London	LX03BZC	East London
LT52XAA	First London	LV52HHE	East London	LX03BVN	East London	LX03BZD	East London
LT52XAB	First London	LV52HHF	East London	LX03BVP	East London	LX03BZE	East London
LT52XAC	First London	LV52HHG	East London	LX03BVR	East London	LX03BZF	East London
LT52XAD	First London	LV52HHJ	East London	LX03BVS	East London	LX03BZG	East London
LT52XAE	First London	LV52HHK	East London	LX03BVT	East London	LX03BZH	East London
LT52XAF	First London	LV52HHL	East London	LX03BVU	East London	LX03BZJ	East London
LT52XAG	First London	LV52HHM	East London	LX03BVV	East London	LX03BZK	East London
LT52XAH	First London	LV52HHN	East London	LX03BVW	East London	LX03BZL	East London
LT52XAJ	First London	LV52HHO	East London	LX03BVY	East London	LX03BZM	East London
LT52XAK	First London	LV52HHP	East London	LX03BVZ	East London	LX03BZN	East London
LT52XAL	First London	LV52HHR	East London	LX03BWA	East London	LX03BZP	East London
LT52XAM	First London	LV52HHS	East London	LX03BWB	East London	LX03BZR	East London
LV51YCC	Metrobus	LV52HHT	East London	LX03BWC	East London	LX03BZS	East London
LV51YCD	Metrobus	LV52HHU	East London	LX03BWD	East London	LX03BZT	East London
LV51YCE	Metrobus	LV52HHW	East London	LX03BWE	East London	LX03BZU	East London
LV51YCF	Metrobus	LV52HHX	East London	LX03BWF	East London	LX03BZV	East London
LV51YCG	Metrobus	LV52HHY	East London	LX03BWG	East London	LX03BZW	East London
LV51YCH	Metrobus	LV52HHZ	East London	LX03BWH	East London	LX03BZY	East London
LV51YCJ	Metrobus	LV52HJA	East London	LX03BWJ	East London	LX03CAA	East London
LV51YCK	Metrobus	LV52HJY	East London	LX03BWK	East London	LX03CAE	East London
LV51YCL	Metrobus	LV52HJZ	East London	LX03BWL	East London	LX03CAU	East London
LV51YCM	Metrobus	LV52HKA	East London	LX03BWM	East London	LX03CAV	East London
LV51YCN	Metrobus	LV52HKB	East London	LX03BWN	East London	LX03CBF	East London
LV51YCO	Metrobus	LV52HKC	East London	LX03BWP	East London	LX03CBU	East London
LV51ZHJ	Clarkes of London	LV52HKD	East London	LX03BWU	East London	LX03CBV	East London
LV51ZHK	Clarkes of London	LV52HKE	East London	LX03BWV	East London	LX03CBY	East London
LV51ZHL	Clarkes of London	LV52HKF	East London	LX03BWW	East London	LX03ECV	Go-Ahead London
LV51ZHM	Clarkes of London	LV52HKG	East London	LX03BWY	East London	LX03ECW	Go-Ahead London
LV52HDO	East London	LV52HKH	East London	LX03BWZ	East London	LX03ECY	Go-Ahead London
LV52HDU	East London	LV52HKJ	East London	LX03BXA	East London	LX03EDR	Go-Ahead London
LV52HDX	East London	LV52HKK	East London	LX03BXB	East London	LX03EDU	Go-Ahead London
LV52HDY	East London	LV52HKL	East London	LX03BXC	East London	LX03EDV	Go-Ahead London
LV52HDZ	East London	LV52HKM	East London	LX03BXD	East London	LX03EEA	Go-Ahead London
LV52HEJ	East London	LV52HKN	East London	LX03BXE	East London	LX03EEB	Go-Ahead London
LV52HFA	East London	LV52HKO	East London	LX03BXF	East London	LX03EEF	Go-Ahead London
LV52HFB	East London	LV52HKP	East London	LX03BXG	East London	LX03EEG	Go-Ahead London
LV52HFC	East London	LV52HKT	East London	LX03BXH	East London	LX03EEH	Go-Ahead London
LV52HFD	East London	LV52HKU	East London	LX03BXJ	East London	LX03EEJ	Go-Ahead London
LV52HFE	East London	LV52USV	East London	LX03BXK	East London	LX03EEM	Go-Ahead London
LV52HFF	East London	LV52VFW	First London	LX03BXL	East London	LX03EXU	Go-Ahead London
LV52HFH	East London	LV52VFX	First London	LX03BXM	East London	LX03EXV	Go-Ahead London
LV52HFJ	East London	LV52VFY	First London	LX03BXN	East London	LX03EXW	Go-Ahead London
LV52HFK	East London	LV52VFZ	First London	LX03BXP	East London	LX03EXZ	Go-Ahead London
LV52HFL	East London	LV52VGA	First London	LX03BXR	East London	LX03HCE	East London
LV52HFM	East London	LW52AKK	Clarkes of London	LX03BXS	East London	LX03HCF	East London
LV52HFN	East London	LW52AKN	Clarkes of London	LX03BXU	East London	LX03HCG	East London
LV52HFO	East London	LX03BTE	East London	LX03BXV	East London	LX03HCH	East London
LV52HFP	East London	LX03BTF	East London	LX03BXW	East London	LX03HCJ	East London

Reg	Operator	Reg	Operator	Reg	Operator	Reg	Operator
LX03HCK	East London	LX03ORT	East London	LX04FYH	East London	LX05BWG	East London
LX03HCL	East London	LX03ORU	East London	LX04FYK	East London	LX05BWH	East London
LX03HCN	East London	LX03ORV	East London	LX04FYL	East London	LX05BWJ	East London
LX03HCP	East London	LX03ORW	East London	LX04FYM	East London	LX05BWK	East London
LX03HCU	East London	LX03ORY	East London	LX04FYN	East London	LX05EXZ	Go-Ahead London
LX03HCV	East London	LX03ORZ	East London	LX04FYP	East London	LX05EYA	Go-Ahead London
LX03HCY	East London	LX03OSA	East London	LX04FYR	East London	LX05EYM	Go-Ahead London
LX03HCZ	East London	LX03OSB	East London	LX04FYS	East London	LX05EYO	Go-Ahead London
LX03HDC	East London	LX03OSC	East London	LX04FYT	East London	LX05EYP	Go-Ahead London
LX03HDD	East London	LX03OSD	East London	LX04FYT	East London	LX05EYR	Go-Ahead London
LX03HDE	East London	LX03OSE	East London	LX04FYU	East London	LX05EYS	Go-Ahead London
LX03HDF	East London	LX03OSG	East London	LX04FYV	East London	LX05EYT	Go-Ahead London
LX03HDG	East London	LX03OSJ	East London	LX04FYW	East London	LX05EYU	Go-Ahead London
LX03HDH	East London	LX03OSK	East London	LX04FYY	East London	LX05EYU	Go-Ahead London
LX03HDJ	East London	LX03OSL	East London	LX04FYZ	East London	LX05EYV	Go-Ahead London
LX03HDK	East London	LX03OSM	East London	LX04FZA	East London	LX05EYV	Go-Ahead London
LX03HDL	East London	LX03OSN	East London	LX04FZB	East London	LX05EYW	Go-Ahead London
LX03HDN	East London	LX03OSP	East London	LX04FZC	East London	LX05EYW	Go-Ahead London
LX03HDU	East London	LX03OSR	East London	LX04FZD	East London	LX05EYY	Go-Ahead London
LX03HDV	East London	LX03OSU	East London	LX04FZE	East London	LX05EYZ	Go-Ahead London
LX03HDY	East London	LX03OSV	East London	LX04FZF	East London	LX05EZA	Go-Ahead London
LX03HDZ	East London	LX03OSW	East London	LX04FZG	East London	LX05EZB	Go-Ahead London
LX03HEJ	East London	LX03OSY	East London	LX04FZH	East London	LX05EZC	Go-Ahead London
LX03HEU	East London	LX03OSZ	East London	LX04FZJ	East London	LX05EZD	Go-Ahead London
LX03HEV	East London	LX03OTA	East London	LX04FZK	East London	LX05EZE	Go-Ahead London
LX03KRD	Redwing	LX03OTB	East London	LX04KZG	East London	LX05EZF	Go-Ahead London
LX03KRE	Redwing	LX03OTC	East London	LX04KZJ	East London	LX05EZG	Go-Ahead London
LX03NEU	East London	LX03OTD	East London	LX04KZK	East London	LX05EZH	Go-Ahead London
LX03NEY	East London	LX03OTE	East London	LX04KZL	East London	LX05EZJ	Go-Ahead London
LX03NFA	East London	LX03OTF	East London	LX04KZM	East London	LX05EZK	Go-Ahead London
LX03NFC	East London	LX03OTG	East London	LX04KZN	East London	LX05EZL	Go-Ahead London
LX03NFD	East London	LX03OTH	East London	LX04KZP	East London	LX05EZM	Go-Ahead London
LX03NFE	East London	LX03OTJ	East London	LX04KZR	East London	LX05EZN	Go-Ahead London
LX03NFF	East London	LX04FWL	East London	LX04KZS	East London	LX05EZO	Go-Ahead London
LX03NFG	East London	LX04FWM	East London	LX04KZT	East London	LX05EZP	Go-Ahead London
LX03NFH	East London	LX04FWN	East London	LX04KZU	East London	LX05EZR	Go-Ahead London
LX03NFJ	East London	LX04FWP	East London	LX04KZV	East London	LX05EZS	Go-Ahead London
LX03NFK	East London	LX04FWR	East London	LX04KZW	East London	LX05EZT	Go-Ahead London
LX03NFL	East London	LX04FWS	East London	LX04KZY	East London	LX05EZU	Go-Ahead London
LX03NFM	East London	LX04FWT	East London	LX04KZZ	East London	LX05EZV	Go-Ahead London
LX03NFN	East London	LX04FWU	East London	LX04LBA	East London	LX05EZW	Go-Ahead London
LX03NFP	East London	LX04FWV	East London	LX04LBE	East London	LX05EZZ	Go-Ahead London
LX03NFR	East London	LX04FWW	East London	LX04LBF	East London	LX05FAA	Go-Ahead London
LX03NFT	East London	LX04FWY	East London	LX04LBG	East London	LX05FAF	Go-Ahead London
LX03NFV	East London	LX04FWZ	East London	LX04LBJ	East London	LX05FAF	Go-Ahead London
LX03NFY	East London	LX04FXA	East London	LX04LBK	East London	LX05FAJ	Go-Ahead London
LX03NFZ	East London	LX04FXB	East London	LX04LBL	East London	LX05FAK	Go-Ahead London
LX03NGE	East London	LX04FXC	East London	LX04LBN	East London	LX05FAM	Go-Ahead London
LX03NGF	East London	LX04FXD	East London	LX04LBP	East London	LX05FAO	Go-Ahead London
LX03NGJ	East London	LX04FXE	East London	LX04LBU	East London	LX05FAU	Go-Ahead London
LX03NGU	East London	LX04FXF	East London	LX04LBV	East London	LX05FBA	Go-Ahead London
LX03NGV	East London	LX04FXG	East London	LX04LBY	East London	LX05FBB	Go-Ahead London
LX03NGY	East London	LX04FXH	East London	LX04LBZ	East London	LX05FBC	Go-Ahead London
LX03NGZ	East London	LX04FXJ	East London	LX04LCA	East London	LX05FBD	Go-Ahead London
LX03NHA	East London	LX04FXK	East London	LX04LCC	East London	LX05FBD	Go-Ahead London
LX03OJN	Metrobus	LX04FXL	East London	LX04LCE	East London	LX05FBE	Go-Ahead London
LX03OJP	Metrobus	LX04FXM	East London	LX04LCF	East London	LX05FBE	Go-Ahead London
LX03OPT	East London	LX04FXP	East London	LX04LCG	East London	LX05FBF	Go-Ahead London
LX03OPU	East London	LX04FXR	East London	LX04LCJ	East London	LX05FBJ	Go-Ahead London
LX03OPV	East London	LX04FXS	East London	LX04LCK	East London	LX05FBK	Go-Ahead London
LX03OPW	East London	LX04FXT	East London	LX04LCM	East London	LX05FBL	Go-Ahead London
LX03OPY	East London	LX04FXU	East London	LX04LCN	East London	LX05FBN	Go-Ahead London
LX03OPZ	East London	LX04FXV	East London	LX04LCP	East London	LX05FBO	Go-Ahead London
LX03ORA	East London	LX04FXW	East London	LX04LCT	East London	LX05FBU	Go-Ahead London
LX03ORC	East London	LX04FXY	East London	LX04LCU	East London	LX05FBV	Go-Ahead London
LX03ORF	East London	LX04FXZ	East London	LX05BVY	East London	LX05FBY	Go-Ahead London
LX03ORG	East London	LX04FYA	East London	LX05BVZ	East London	LX05FBZ	Go-Ahead London
LX03ORH	East London	LX04FYB	East London	LX05BWA	East London	LX05FCA	Go-Ahead London
LX03ORJ	East London	LX04FYC	East London	LX05BWC	East London	LX05FCC	Go-Ahead London
LX03ORK	East London	LX04FYD	East London	LX05BWC	East London	LX05FCD	Go-Ahead London
LX03ORN	East London	LX04FYE	East London	LX05BWD	East London	LX05FCE	Go-Ahead London
LX03ORP	East London	LX04FYF	East London	LX05BWE	East London	LX05FCF	Go-Ahead London
LX03ORS	East London	LX04FYG	East London	LX05BWF	East London	LX05FFA	Go-Ahead London

Reg	Operator	Reg	Operator	Reg	Operator	Reg	Operator
LX05GDV	Arriva Original Tour	LX06EBC	Go-Ahead London	LX51FGO	East London	LX51FME	East London
LX05GDY	Arriva Original Tour	LX06EBD	Go-Ahead London	LX51FGP	East London	LX51FMF	East London
LX05GDZ	Arriva Original Tour	LX06EBE	Go-Ahead London	LX51FGU	East London	LX51FMG	East London
LX05GEJ	Arriva Original Tour	LX06EBG	Go-Ahead London	LX51FGV	East London	LX51FMJ	East London
LX05HRO	Arriva Original Tour	LX06EBJ	Go-Ahead London	LX51FGZ	East London	LX51FMK	East London
LX05HSC	Arriva Original Tour	LX06EBK	Go-Ahead London	LX51FHA	East London	LX51FML	East London
LX05KNZ	Arriva Original Tour	LX06EBL	Go-Ahead London	LX51FHB	East London	LX51FMM	East London
LX05KOA	Arriva Original Tour	LX06EBM	Go-Ahead London	LX51FHC	East London	LX51FMO	East London
LX05LLM	East London	LX06EBN	Go-Ahead London	LX51FHD	East London	LX51FMP	East London
LX05LLN	East London	LX06EBO	Go-Ahead London	LX51FHE	East London	LX51FMU	East London
LX05LLO	East London	LX06EBP	Go-Ahead London	LX51FHF	East London	LX51FMV	East London
LX05LLP	East London	LX06EBU	Go-Ahead London	LX51FHG	East London	LX51FMY	East London
LX06AFF	East London	LX06EBW	Go-Ahead London	LX51FHH	East London	LX51FMZ	East London
LX06AFJ	East London	LX06EBZ	Go-Ahead London	LX51FHJ	East London	LX51FNA	East London
LX06AFK	East London	LX06ECA	Go-Ahead London	LX51FHK	East London	LX51FNC	East London
LX06AFN	East London	LX06ECC	Go-Ahead London	LX51FHL	East London	LX51FND	East London
LX06AFO	East London	LX06ECD	Go-Ahead London	LX51FHN	East London	LX51FNE	East London
LX06AFU	East London	LX06ECE	Go-Ahead London	LX51FHO	East London	LX51FNF	East London
LX06AFV	East London	LX06ECF	Go-Ahead London	LX51FHP	East London	LX51FNG	East London
LX06AFY	East London	LX06ECJ	Go-Ahead London	LX51FHS	East London	LX51FNH	East London
LX06AFZ	East London	LX06ECN	Go-Ahead London	LX51FHT	East London	LX51FNJ	East London
LX06AGO	East London	LX06ECT	Go-Ahead London	LX51FHU	East London	LX51FNK	East London
LX06AGU	East London	LX06ECV	Go-Ahead London	LX51FHV	East London	LX51FNL	East London
LX06AGV	East London	LX06EYT	Go-Ahead London	LX51FHW	East London	LX51FNM	East London
LX06AGY	East London	LX06EYY	Go-Ahead London	LX51FHY	East London	LX51FNN	East London
LX06AGZ	East London	LX06EYZ	Go-Ahead London	LX51FHZ	East London	LX51FNO	East London
LX06AHA	East London	LX06EZA	Go-Ahead London	LX51FJA	East London	LX51FNP	East London
LX06AHC	East London	LX06EZB	Go-Ahead London	LX51FJC	East London	LX51FNR	East London
LX06AHD	East London	LX06EZC	Go-Ahead London	LX51FJD	East London	LX51FNS	East London
LX06AHE	East London	LX06EZD	Go-Ahead London	LX51FJE	East London	LX51FNT	East London
LX06AHF	East London	LX06EZE	Go-Ahead London	LX51FJF	East London	LX51FNU	East London
LX06DXS	Go-Ahead London	LX06EZF	Go-Ahead London	LX51FJJ	East London	LX51FNV	East London
LX06DXT	Go-Ahead London	LX06EZG	Go-Ahead London	LX51FJK	East London	LX51FNW	East London
LX06DXU	Go-Ahead London	LX06EZH	Go-Ahead London	LX51FJN	East London	LX51FNY	East London
LX06DXV	Go-Ahead London	LX06EZJ	Go-Ahead London	LX51FJO1	East London	LX51FNZ	East London
LX06DXW	Go-Ahead London	LX06EZK	Go-Ahead London	LX51FJP	East London	LX51FOA	East London
LX06DXY	Go-Ahead London	LX06EZL	Go-Ahead London	LX51FJV	East London	LX51FOC	East London
LX06DZA	Go-Ahead London	LX06EZM	Go-Ahead London	LX51FJY	East London	LX51FOD	East London
LX06DZB	Go-Ahead London	LX06EZN	Go-Ahead London	LX51FJZ	East London	LX51FOF	East London
LX06DZC	Go-Ahead London	LX06EZO	Go-Ahead London	LX51FKA	East London	LX51FOH	East London
LX06DZD	Go-Ahead London	LX06EZP	Go-Ahead London	LX51FKB	East London	LX51FOJ	East London
LX06DZE	Go-Ahead London	LX06EZR	Go-Ahead London	LX51FKD	East London	LX51FOK	East London
LX06DZF	Go-Ahead London	LX06EZS	Go-Ahead London	LX51FKE	East London	LX51FOM	East London
LX06DZG	Go-Ahead London	LX06EZT	Go-Ahead London	LX51FKF	East London	LX51FON	East London
LX06DZH	Go-Ahead London	LX06EZU	Go-Ahead London	LX51FKG	East London	LX51FOP	East London
LX06DZJ	Go-Ahead London	LX06EZV	Go-Ahead London	LX51FKJ	East London	LX51FOT	East London
LX06DZK	Go-Ahead London	LX06EZW	Go-Ahead London	LX51FKL	East London	LX51FOU	East London
LX06DZL	Go-Ahead London	LX06EZZ	Go-Ahead London	LX51FKO	East London	LX51FOV	East London
LX06DZM	Go-Ahead London	LX06FAJ	Go-Ahead London	LX51FKR	East London	LX51FPA	East London
LX06DZN	Go-Ahead London	LX06FAK	Go-Ahead London	LX51FKT	East London	LX51FPC	East London
LX06DZO	Go-Ahead London	LX06FAM	Go-Ahead London	LX51FKU	East London	LX51FPD	East London
LX06DZP	Go-Ahead London	LX06FAO	Go-Ahead London	LX51FKW	East London	LX51FPE	East London
LX06DZR	Go-Ahead London	LX06FAU	Go-Ahead London	LX51FKZ	East London	LX51FPF	East London
LX06DZS	Go-Ahead London	LX06FBA	Go-Ahead London	LX51FLB	East London	LX51FPJ	East London
LX06DZT	Go-Ahead London	LX06FBB	Go-Ahead London	LX51FLC	East London	LX53AYM	Go-Ahead London
LX06DZU	Go-Ahead London	LX06FBC	Go-Ahead London	LX51FLD	East London	LX53AYN	Go-Ahead London
LX06DZV	Go-Ahead London	LX06FFA	Epsom Coaches	LX51FLE	East London	LX53AYO	Go-Ahead London
LX06DZW	Go-Ahead London	LX06FFB	Epsom Coaches	LX51FLF	East London	LX53AYP	Go-Ahead London
LX06DZY	Go-Ahead London	LX06FKL	Go-Ahead London	LX51FLG	East London	LX53AYT	Go-Ahead London
LX06DZZ	Go-Ahead London	LX06FKM	Go-Ahead London	LX51FLH	East London	LX53AYU	Go-Ahead London
LX06EAA	Go-Ahead London	LX06FKN	Go-Ahead London	LX51FLJ	East London	LX53AYV	Go-Ahead London
LX06EAC	Go-Ahead London	LX06FKO	Go-Ahead London	LX51FLK	East London	LX53AYW	Go-Ahead London
LX06EAF	Go-Ahead London	LX51FFO	East London	LX51FLL	East London	LX53AYY	Go-Ahead London
LX06EAG	Go-Ahead London	LX51FFW	East London	LX51FLM	East London	LX53AYZ	Go-Ahead London
LX06EAJ	Go-Ahead London	LX51FGA	East London	LX51FLN	East London	LX53AZA	Go-Ahead London
LX06EAK	Go-Ahead London	LX51FGD	East London	LX51FLP	East London	LX53AZB	Go-Ahead London
LX06EAL	Go-Ahead London	LX51FGE	East London	LX51FLR	East London	LX53AZC	Go-Ahead London
LX06EAM	Go-Ahead London	LX51FGF	East London	LX51FLV	East London	LX53AZD	Go-Ahead London
LX06EAO	Go-Ahead London	LX51FGG	East London	LX51FLW	East London	LX53AZF	Go-Ahead London
LX06EAP	Go-Ahead London	LX51FGJ	East London	LX51FLZ	East London	LX53AZG	Go-Ahead London
LX06EAW	Go-Ahead London	LX51FGK	East London	LX51FMA	East London	LX53AZJ	Go-Ahead London
LX06EAY	Go-Ahead London	LX51FGM	East London	LX51FMC	East London	LX53AZL	Go-Ahead London
LX06EBA	Go-Ahead London	LX51FGN	East London	LX51FMD	East London	LX53AZN	Go-Ahead London

LX53AZO	Go-Ahead London	LX53KBO	East London	LX55EPE	East London	LY52ZFD	East London
LX53AZP	Go-Ahead London	LX53KBP	East London	LX55EPF	East London	LY52ZFE	East London
LX53AZR	Go-Ahead London	LX53KBV	East London	LX55EPJ	East London	LY52ZFF	East London
LX53AZT	Go-Ahead London	LX53KBW	East London	LX55EPK	East London	LY52ZFG	East London
LX53AZU	Go-Ahead London	LX53KBZ	East London	LX55EPL	East London	LY52ZFH	East London
LX53AZV	Go-Ahead London	LX53KCA	East London	LX55EPN	East London	LYR854	Blue Triangle
LX53AZW	Go-Ahead London	LX53KCC	East London	LX55EPO	East London	M35CHS	Go-Ahead (Docklands)
LX53AZZ	Go-Ahead London	LX53KCE	East London	LX55EPP	East London	M290FAE	First London
LX53BAA	Go-Ahead London	LX53KCF	East London	LX55EPU	East London	M502VJO	Metrobus
LX53BAO	Go-Ahead London	LX53KCG	East London	LX55EPV	East London	M506VJO	Metrobus
LX53BBZ	Go-Ahead London	LX53KCJ	East London	LX55EPY	East London	M507VJO	Metrobus
LX53BDO	Go-Ahead London	LX53KCK	East London	LX55EPZ	East London	M508VJO	Metrobus
LX53BDY	Go-Ahead London	LX53LGF	East London	LX55ERJ	East London	M511VJO	Metrobus
LX53BEY	Go-Ahead London	LX53LGG	East London	LX55ERK	East London	M516VJO	Metrobus
LX53BFK	Go-Ahead London	LX53LGJ	East London	LX55ERO	East London	M518VJO	Metrobus
LX53BGE	Go-Ahead London	LX53LGK	East London	LX55ERU	East London	M520VJO	Metrobus
LX53BJK	Go-Ahead London	LX53LGL	East London	LX55ERV	East London	M721CGO	Metrobus
LX53BJO	Go-Ahead London	LX53LGN	East London	LX55ERY	East London	M777ASH	Ashford Luxury
LX53BJU	Go-Ahead London	LX53LGO	East London	LX55ERZ	East London	M796MPM	First London
LX53JXU	East London	LX53LGU	East London	LX55ESF	East London	MCH51	MCH
LX53JXV	East London	LX53LGV	East London	LX55ESG	East London	MCH85	MCH
LX53JXW	East London	LX53LGW	East London	LX55ESN	East London	MCH96	MCH
LX53JXY	East London	LX53NMV	Go-Ahead Docklands	LX55ESO	East London	MCH98	MCH
LX53JYA	East London	LX54GYV	Go-Ahead London	LX55HGC	East London	MCH252	MCH
LX53JYB	East London	LX54GYW	Go-Ahead London	LX56DZU	East London	MCH298	MCH
LX53JYC	East London	LX54GYY	Go-Ahead London	LX56DZV	East London	MCH384	MCH
LX53JYD	East London	LX54GYZ	Go-Ahead London	LX56DZW	East London	MCH456	MCH
LX53JYE	East London	LX54GZB	Go-Ahead London	LX56DZY	East London	MCH547	MCH
LX53JYF	East London	LX54GZC	Go-Ahead London	LX56DZZ	East London	MCH709	MCH
LX53JYG	East London	LX54GZD	Go-Ahead London	LX56EAA	East London	MCH815	MCH
LX53JYH	East London	LX54GZE	Go-Ahead London	LX56EAC	East London	MCH957	MCH
LX53JYJ	East London	LX54GZF	Go-Ahead London	LX56EAE	East London	MCH994	MCH
LX53JYK	East London	LX54GZG	Go-Ahead London	LX56EAF	East London	MCH999	MCH
LX53JYL	East London	LX54GZH	Go-Ahead London	LX56EAG	East London	MC02ALC	Ashford Luxury
LX53JYN	East London	LX54GZK	Go-Ahead London	LX56EAJ	East London	MC06ASH	Ashford Luxury
LX53JYO	East London	LX54GZL	Go-Ahead London	LX56EAK	East London	MLL963	First London
LX53JYP	East London	LX54GZM	Go-Ahead London	LX56EAM	East London	MM03TGM	Tellings-Golden Miller
LX53JYR	East London	LX54GZN	Go-Ahead London	LX56EAO	East London	MNT595W	Chalfont
LX53JYT	East London	LX54GZO	Go-Ahead London	LX56EAP	East London	MU51VZT	MCH
LX53JYU	East London	LX54GZP	Go-Ahead London	LX56EAW	East London	MX55VJU	MCH
LX53JYV	East London	LX54GZR	Go-Ahead London	LX56EAY	East London	N119DWE	First London
LX53JYW	East London	LX54GZT	Go-Ahead London	LX56EBA	East London	N136YRW	Transdev
LX53JYY	East London	LX54GZU	Go-Ahead London	LY02OAA	East London	N137YRW	Transdev
LX53JYZ	East London	LX54GZV	Go-Ahead London	LY02OAB	East London	N138YRW	Transdev
LX53JZA	East London	LX54GZW	Go-Ahead London	LY02OAC	East London	N139YRW	Transdev
LX53JZC	East London	LX54GZY	Go-Ahead London	LY02OAD	East London	N140YRW	Transdev
LX53JZD	East London	LX54GZZ	Go-Ahead London	LY02OAE	East London	N205YJM	Go-Ahead Docklands
LX53JZE	East London	LX54HAA	Go-Ahead London	LY02OAG	East London	N208YJM	Go-Ahead Docklands
LX53JZF	East London	LX54HAE	Go-Ahead London	LY02OAN	East London	N281DWY	Transdev
LX53JZG	East London	LX54HAO	Go-Ahead London	LY02OAO	East London	N282DWY	Transdev
LX53JZH	East London	LX54HAU	Go-Ahead London	LY02OAP	East London	N283DWY	Transdev
LX53JZJ	East London	LX54HBA	Go-Ahead London	LY02OAS	East London	N284DWY	Transdev
LX53JZK	East London	LX54HBB	Go-Ahead London	LY02OAU	East London	N285DWY	Transdev
LX53JZL	East London	LX55AAE	First London	LY02OAV	East London	N286DWY	Transdev
LX53JZM	East London	LX55AAF	First London	LY02OAW	East London	N287DWY	Transdev
LX53JZN	East London	LX55AAJ	First London	LY02OAX	East London	N288DWY	Transdev
LX53JZO	East London	LX55AAN	First London	LY02OAZ	East London	N305DHE	Travel London
LX53JZP	East London	LX55AAU	First London	LY02OBB	East London	N417MPN	Metrobus
LX53JZR	East London	LX55AAV	First London	LY02OBC	East London	N418MPN	Metrobus
LX53JZT	East London	LX55AAX	First London	LY02OBD	East London	N605XJM	First London
LX53JZU	East London	LX55AAY	First London	LY02OBE	East London	N726KGF	Metrobus
LX53JZV	East London	LX55AAZ	First London	LY02OBF	East London	N821KWS	First London
LX53JZW	East London	LX55ABF	First London	LY02OBG	East London	N822KWS	First London
LX53KAE	East London	LX55ACO	First London	LY02OBH	East London	N852CPU	First London
LX53KAJ	East London	LX55ACU	First London	LY02OBJ	East London	N853CPU	First London
LX53KAK	East London	LX55EAC	Go-Ahead London	LY02OBK	East London	N854CPU	First London
LX53KAO	East London	LX55EAE	Go-Ahead London	LY02OBL	East London	N950RBC	Excalibur
LX53KAU	East London	LX55EAF	Go-Ahead London	LY02OBM	East London	NML604E	Go-Ahead London
LX53KBE	East London	LX55EAG	Go-Ahead London	LY52ZDX	East London	NML604E	Go-Ahead London
LX53KBF	East London	LX55EAJ	Go-Ahead London	LY52ZDZ	East London	NML605E	Go-Ahead London
LX53KBJ	East London	LX55EPA	East London	LY52ZFA	East London	NML606E	Go-Ahead London
LX53KBK	East London	LX55EPC	East London	LY52ZFB	East London	NML612E	Go-Ahead London
LX53KBN	East London	LX55EPD	East London	LY52ZFC	East London	NML615E	Go-Ahead London

The London Bus Handbook

Reg	Operator	Reg	Operator	Reg	Operator	Reg	Operator
NML618E	Go-Ahead London	P740RYL	Go-Ahead London	PG04WHH	Transdev	PJ02RFO	Go-Ahead London
NML626E	Go-Ahead London	P741RYL	Go-Ahead London	PG04WHJ	Transdev	PJ02RFX	Go-Ahead London
NML631E	Go-Ahead London	P742RYL	Go-Ahead London	PG04WHK	Transdev	PJ02RFY	Go-Ahead London
NML637E	Go-Ahead London	P743RYL	Go-Ahead London	PG04WHL	Transdev	PJ02RFZ	Go-Ahead London
NML640E	Go-Ahead London	P744RYL	Go-Ahead London	PG04WHM	Transdev	PJ02RGO	Go-Ahead London
NML644E	Go-Ahead London	P746HND	Blue Triangle	PG04WHN	Transdev	PJ02RGU	Go-Ahead London
NML654E	Go-Ahead London	P801GMU	East London	PG04WHP	Transdev	PJ02RGV	Go-Ahead London
OJD809Y	Blue Triangle	P802GMU	East London	PG04WHR	Transdev	PJ02RHF	Go-Ahead London
OJD831Y	East Thames	P803GMU	East London	PG04WHS	Transdev	PJ02TVN	Go-Ahead London
OJD832Y	East Thames	P817SGP	Metrobus	PG04WHT	Transdev	PJ02TVO	Go-Ahead London
OJD840Y	Arriva Original Tour	P818SGP	Metrobus	PG04WHU	Transdev	PJ02TVP	Go-Ahead London
OJD859Y	First London	P819SGP	Metrobus	PG04WHV	Transdev	PJ02TVT	Go-Ahead London
OJD863Y	Arriva Original Tour	P821SGP	Metrobus	PG04WHW	Transdev	PJ02TVU	Go-Ahead London
P10TGM	Tellings-Golden Miller	P822SGP	Metrobus	PG04WHX	Transdev	PJ52LVP	Go-Ahead London
P27TTX	Westway	P823SGP	Metrobus	PG04WHY	Transdev	PJ52LVR	Go-Ahead London
P41MLE	Metroline	P824SGP	Metrobus	PG04WJA	Transdev	PJ52LVS	Go-Ahead London
P101OLX	Metroline	P825SGP	Metrobus	PJ02PYU	Go-Ahead London	PJ52LVT	Go-Ahead London
P102OLX	Metroline	P826SGP	Metrobus	PJ02PYV	Go-Ahead London	PJ52LVU	Go-Ahead London
P286MLD	Metroline	P828SGP	Metrobus	PJ02PYW	Go-Ahead London	PJ52LVV	Go-Ahead London
P288MLD	Metroline	P829SGP	Metrobus	PJ02PYX	Go-Ahead London	PJ52LVW	Go-Ahead London
P289MLD	Metroline	P895PWW	Metrobus	PJ02PYY	Go-Ahead London	PJ52LVX	Go-Ahead London
P301HDP	Metrobus	P904RYO	Go-Ahead London	PJ02PYZ	Go-Ahead London	PJ52LVY	Go-Ahead London
P302HDP	Metrobus	P907RYO	Go-Ahead London	PJ02PZA	Go-Ahead London	PJ52LVZ	Go-Ahead London
P303HDP	Metrobus	P909RYO	Go-Ahead London	PJ02PZB	Go-Ahead London	PJ52LWA	Go-Ahead London
P303MLD	Metroline	P910RYO	Go-Ahead London	PJ02PZC	Go-Ahead London	PJ52LWC	Go-Ahead London
P304HDP	Metrobus	P911RYO	Go-Ahead London	PJ02PZD	Go-Ahead London	PJ52LWD	Go-Ahead London
P305HDP	Metrobus	P912RYO	Go-Ahead London	PJ02PZE	Go-Ahead London	PJ52LWE	Go-Ahead London
P306HDP	Metrobus	P913RYO	Go-Ahead London	PJ02PZF	Go-Ahead London	PJ52LWF	Go-Ahead London
P307HDP	Metrobus	P914RYO	Go-Ahead London	PJ02PZG	Go-Ahead London	PJ52LWG	Go-Ahead London
P307MLD	Metroline	P916RYO	Go-Ahead London	PJ02PZH	Go-Ahead London	PJ52LWH	Go-Ahead London
P308HDP	Metrobus	P917RYO	Go-Ahead London	PJ02PZK	Go-Ahead London	PJ52LWK	Go-Ahead London
P308MLD	Metroline	P924RYO	Go-Ahead London	PJ02PZL	Go-Ahead London	PJ52LWL	Go-Ahead London
P309MLD	Metroline	P927RYO	Go-Ahead London	PJ02PZM	Go-Ahead London	PJ52LWM	Go-Ahead London
P310MLD	Metroline	P928RYO	Go-Ahead London	PJ02PZN	Go-Ahead London	PJ52LWN	Go-Ahead London
P311MLD	Metroline	PA04CYC	Transdev	PJ02PZO	Go-Ahead London	PJ52LWO	Go-Ahead London
P313MLD	Metroline	PA04CYE	Transdev	PJ02PZP	Go-Ahead London	PJ52LWP	Go-Ahead London
P314MLD	Metroline	PA04CYF	Transdev	PJ02PZR	Go-Ahead London	PJ52LWR	Go-Ahead London
P315MLD	Metroline	PA04CYG	Transdev	PJ02PZS	Go-Ahead London	PJ52LWS	Go-Ahead London
P316MLD	Metroline	PA04CYH	Transdev	PJ02PZT	Go-Ahead London	PJ52LWT	Go-Ahead London
P317MLD	Metroline	PA04CYJ	Transdev	PJ02PZU	Go-Ahead London	PJ52LWU	Go-Ahead London
P319MLD	Metroline	PA04CYK	Transdev	PJ02PZV	Go-Ahead London	PJ52LWV	Go-Ahead London
P320MLD	Metroline	PA04CYL	Transdev	PJ02PZW	Go-Ahead London	PJ52LWW	Go-Ahead London
P401MLA	First London	PA04CYP	Transdev	PJ02PZX	Go-Ahead London	PJ52LWX	Go-Ahead London
P402MLA	First London	PA04CYS	Transdev	PJ02PZY	Go-Ahead London	PJ53NJZ	Go-Ahead London
P403MLA	First London	PA04CYT	Transdev	PJ02PZZ	Go-Ahead London	PJ53NKA	Go-Ahead London
P404MLA	First London	PF52TFX	CT Plus	PJ02RAU	Go-Ahead London	PJ53NKC	Go-Ahead London
P405MLA	First London	PF52TGZ	CT Plus	PJ02RAX	Go-Ahead London	PJ53NKD	Go-Ahead London
P406MLA	First London	PF52WPT	Go-Ahead London	PJ02RBF	Go-Ahead London	PJ53NKE	Go-Ahead London
P481MBY	Metroline	PF52WPU	Go-Ahead London	PJ02RBO	Go-Ahead London	PJ53NKF	Go-Ahead London
P482MBY	Metroline	PF52WPV	Go-Ahead London	PJ02RBU	Go-Ahead London	PJ53NKG	Go-Ahead London
P483MBY	Metroline	PF52WPW	Go-Ahead London	PJ02RBV	Go-Ahead London	PJ53NKH	Go-Ahead London
P501PTM	Wings	PF52WPX	Go-Ahead London	PJ02RBX	Go-Ahead London	PJ53NKK	Go-Ahead London
P501RYM	Go-Ahead London	PF52WPY	Go-Ahead London	PJ02RBY	Go-Ahead London	PJ53NKL	Go-Ahead London
P502RYM	Go-Ahead London	PF52WPZ	Go-Ahead London	PJ02RBZ	Go-Ahead London	PJ53NKM	Go-Ahead London
P503RYM	Go-Ahead London	PF52WRA	Go-Ahead London	PJ02RCF	Go-Ahead London	PJ53NKN	Go-Ahead London
P504RYM	Go-Ahead London	PF52WRC	Go-Ahead London	PJ02RCO	Go-Ahead London	PJ53NKO	Go-Ahead London
P505RYM	Go-Ahead London	PF52WRD	Go-Ahead London	PJ02RCU	Go-Ahead London	PJ53NKP	Go-Ahead London
P506RYM	Go-Ahead London	PF52WRE	Go-Ahead London	PJ02RCV	Go-Ahead London	PJ53NKR	Go-Ahead London
P507RYM	Go-Ahead London	PF52WRG	Go-Ahead London	PJ02RCX	Go-Ahead London	PJ53NKS	Go-Ahead London
P508RYM	Go-Ahead London	PG04WGN	Transdev	PJ02RCY	Go-Ahead London	PJ53NKT	Go-Ahead London
P509RYM	Go-Ahead London	PG04WGP	Transdev	PJ02RCZ	Go-Ahead London	PJ53NKW	Go-Ahead London
P514RYM	Go-Ahead London	PG04WGU	Transdev	PJ02RDO	Go-Ahead London	PJ53NKX	Go-Ahead London
P515RYM	Go-Ahead London	PG04WGV	Transdev	PJ02RDU	Go-Ahead London	PJ53NKZ	Go-Ahead London
P516RYM	Go-Ahead London	PG04WGW	Transdev	PJ02RDV	Go-Ahead London	PJ53NLA	Go-Ahead London
P673MLE	Metroline	PG04WGX	Transdev	PJ02RDX	Go-Ahead London	PJ53NLC	Go-Ahead London
P673MLE	Metroline	PG04WGY	Transdev	PJ02RDY	Go-Ahead London	PJ53NLD	Go-Ahead London
P673MLE	Metroline	PG04WGZ	Transdev	PJ02RDZ	Go-Ahead London	PJ53NLE	Go-Ahead London
P674MLE	Metroline	PG04WHA	Transdev	PJ02REU	Go-Ahead London	PJ53NLF	Go-Ahead London
P724RYL	Metrobus	PG04WHB	Transdev	PJ02RFE	Go-Ahead London	PJ53OUN	Transdev
P725RYL	Metrobus	PG04WHC	Transdev	PJ02RFF	Go-Ahead London	PJ53OUO	Transdev
P726RYL	Metrobus	PG04WHD	Transdev	PJ02RFK	Go-Ahead London	PJ53OUP	Transdev
P727RYL	Metrobus	PG04WHE	Transdev	PJ02RFL	Go-Ahead London	PJ53OUU	Transdev
P737RYL	Go-Ahead London	PG04WHF	Transdev	PJ02RFN	Go-Ahead London	PJ53OUV	Transdev

Reg	Operator	Reg	Operator	Reg	Operator	Reg	Operator
PJ530UW	Transdev	PN02XCM	Go-Ahead London	PO56JFJ	Metrobus	R331LGH	Go-Ahead London
PJ530UX	Transdev	PN02XCO	Go-Ahead London	PO56JFK	Metrobus	R332LGH	Go-Ahead London
PJ530UY	Transdev	PN02XCP	Go-Ahead London	R58GNW	Metrobus	R334LGH	Go-Ahead London
PJ530VA	Transdev	PN02XCR	Go-Ahead London	R101GNW	Arriva	R337LGH	Go-Ahead London
PJ530VB	Transdev	PN02XCS	Go-Ahead London	R122EVX	East London	R338LGH	Go-Ahead London
PJ53SOF	Go-Ahead London	PN02XCT	Go-Ahead London	R122RLY	Metroline	R341LGH	Go-Ahead London
PJ53SOH	Go-Ahead London	PN03ULK	Go-Ahead London	R123EVX	East London	R342LGH	Go-Ahead London
PJ53SOU	Go-Ahead London	PN03ULL	Go-Ahead London	R123RLY	Metroline	R343LGH	Go-Ahead London
PJ53SPU	Go-Ahead London	PN03ULM	Go-Ahead London	R124RLY	Metroline	R344LGH	Go-Ahead London
PJ53SPV	Go-Ahead London	PN03ULP	Go-Ahead London	R125RLY	Metroline	R347LGH	Go-Ahead London
PJ53SPX	Go-Ahead London	PN03ULR	Go-Ahead London	R126RLY	Metroline	R361LGH	Go-Ahead London
PJ53SPZ	Go-Ahead London	PN03ULS	Go-Ahead London	R127RLY	Metroline	R362LGH	Go-Ahead London
PJ53SRO	Go-Ahead London	PN03ULT	Go-Ahead London	R128NFE	Clarkes of London	R363LGH	Go-Ahead London
PJ53SRU	Go-Ahead London	PN03ULU	Go-Ahead London	R128RLY	Metroline	R364LGH	Go-Ahead London
PL03AGZ	Go-Ahead London	PN03ULV	Go-Ahead London	R129RLY	Metroline	R365LGH	Go-Ahead London
PL05PLN	Epsom Coaches	PN03ULW	Go-Ahead London	R130RLY	Metroline	R366LGH	Go-Ahead London
PL05PLO	Epsom Coaches	PN03ULX	Go-Ahead London	R131RLY	Metroline	R367LGH	Go-Ahead London
PL05PLU	Epsom Coaches	PN03ULY	Go-Ahead London	R132RLY	Metroline	R368LGH	Go-Ahead London
PL05PLV	Epsom Coaches	PN03ULZ	Go-Ahead London	R133RLY	Metroline	R370LGH	Go-Ahead London
PL05PLX	Epsom Coaches	PN03UMA	Go-Ahead London	R134RLY	Metroline	R371LGH	Go-Ahead London
PL51LDJ	Go-Ahead London	PN03UMB	Go-Ahead London	R135RLY	Metroline	R373LGH	Go-Ahead London
PL51LDK	Go-Ahead London	PN03UMC	Go-Ahead London	R136RLY	Metroline	R374LGH	Go-Ahead London
PL51LDN	Go-Ahead London	PN03UMD	Go-Ahead London	R137RLY	Metroline	R375LGH	Go-Ahead London
PL51LDO	Go-Ahead London	PN03UME	Go-Ahead London	R138RLY	Metroline	R376LGH	Go-Ahead London
PL51LDU	Go-Ahead London	PN03UMF	Go-Ahead London	R139RLY	Metroline	R377LGH	Go-Ahead London
PL51LDV	Go-Ahead London	PN03UMG	Go-Ahead London	R140RLY	Metroline	R378LGH	Go-Ahead London
PL51LDX	Go-Ahead London	PN03UMH	Go-Ahead London	R141RLY	Metroline	R380LGH	Go-Ahead London
PL51LDY	Go-Ahead London	PN03UMJ	Go-Ahead London	R142RLY	Metroline	R381LGH	Go-Ahead London
PL51LDZ	Go-Ahead London	PN03UMK	Go-Ahead London	R143RLY	Metroline	R382LGH	Go-Ahead London
PL51LEF	Go-Ahead London	PN06UYL	Metrobus	R144RLY	Metroline	R383LGH	Go-Ahead London
PL51LFE	Go-Ahead London	PN06UYM	Metrobus	R145RLY	Metroline	R385LGH	Go-Ahead London
PL51LFG	Go-Ahead London	PN06UYO	Metrobus	R146RLY	Metroline	R386LGH	Go-Ahead London
PL51LFJ	Go-Ahead London	PN06UYP	Metrobus	R147RLY	Metroline	R387LGH	Go-Ahead London
PL51LGA	Go-Ahead London	PN06UYR	Metrobus	R148RLY	Metroline	R421COO	Arriva
PL51LGC	Go-Ahead London	PN06UYS	Metrobus	R149RLY	Metroline	R422COO	Arriva
PL51LGD	Go-Ahead London	PN06UYT	Metrobus	R150RLY	Metroline	R423COO	Arriva
PL51LGE	Go-Ahead London	PN06UYU	Metrobus	R151RLY	Metroline	R424COO	Arriva
PL51LGF	Go-Ahead London	PN06UYV	Metrobus	R152RLY	Metroline	R425COO	Arriva
PL51LGG	Go-Ahead London	PN06UYW	Metrobus	R153RLY	Metroline	R426COO	Arriva
PL51LGJ	Go-Ahead London	PN06UYX	Metrobus	R154VLA	Metroline	R427COO	Arriva
PL51LGK	Go-Ahead London	PN06UYY	Metrobus	R155VLA	Metroline	R428COO	Arriva
PL51LGN	Go-Ahead London	PO51UGF	Blue Triangle	R156VLA	Metroline	R429COO	Arriva
PL51LGO	Go-Ahead London	PO51UMF	Blue Triangle	R157VLA	Metroline	R430COO	Arriva
PL51LGU	Go-Ahead London	PO51UMG	Blue Triangle	R158VLA	Metroline	R431COO	Arriva
PL51LGW	Go-Ahead London	PO51UMH	Blue Triangle	R159VLA	Metroline	R433LGH	Go-Ahead London
PL51LGX	Go-Ahead London	PO51UMJ	Blue Triangle	R160VLA	Metroline	R445LGH	Go-Ahead London
PN02XBH	Go-Ahead London	PO51UMK	Blue Triangle	R161VLA	Metroline	R446LGH	Go-Ahead London
PN02XBJ	Go-Ahead London	PO51UML	Blue Triangle	R162VLA	Metroline	R447LGH	Go-Ahead London
PN02XBK	Go-Ahead London	PO51UMM	Blue Triangle	R163VLA	Metroline	R448LGH	Go-Ahead London
PN02XBL	Go-Ahead London	PO51UMR	Blue Triangle	R164VLA	Metroline	R449LGH	Go-Ahead London
PN02XBM	Go-Ahead London	PO51UMS	Blue Triangle	R165VLA	Metroline	R451LGH	Go-Ahead London
PN02XBO	Go-Ahead London	PO51UMT	Blue Triangle	R166VLA	Metroline	R452LGH	Go-Ahead London
PN02XBP	Go-Ahead London	PO51UMV	Blue Triangle	R167VLA	Metroline	R453LGH	Go-Ahead London
PN02XBR	Go-Ahead London	PO51UMW	Blue Triangle	R168VLA	Metroline	R454LGH	Go-Ahead London
PN02XBS	Go-Ahead London	PO51UMX	Blue Triangle	R169VLA	Metroline	R455LGH	Go-Ahead London
PN02XBT	Go-Ahead London	PO51UMY	Blue Triangle	R170VLA	Metroline	R456LGH	Go-Ahead London
PN02XBU	Go-Ahead London	PO54ABZ	Transdev	R171VLA	Metroline	R457LGH	Go-Ahead London
PN02XBV	Go-Ahead London	PO54ACF	Transdev	R172VLA	Metroline	R458LGH	Go-Ahead London
PN02XBW	Go-Ahead London	PO54ACJ	Transdev	R173SUT	Clarkes of London	R459LGH	Go-Ahead London
PN02XBX	Go-Ahead London	PO54ACU	Transdev	R173VLA	Metroline	R460LGH	Go-Ahead London
PN02XBY	Go-Ahead London	PO54ACV	Transdev	R174VBM	Tellings-Golden Miller	R461LGH	Go-Ahead London
PN02XBZ	Go-Ahead London	PO54ACX	Transdev	R174VLA	Metroline	R462LGH	Go-Ahead London
PN02XCA	Go-Ahead London	PO54ACY	Transdev	R177SUT	Clarkes of London	R463LGH	Go-Ahead London
PN02XCB	Go-Ahead London	PO54ACZ	Transdev	R177TKU	Tellings-Golden Miller	R464LGH	Go-Ahead London
PN02XCC	Go-Ahead London	PO54ADU	Transdev	R179SUT	Clarkes of London	R465LGH	Go-Ahead London
PN02XCD	Go-Ahead London	PO54ADV	Transdev	R183LBC	Clarkes of London	R466LGH	Go-Ahead London
PN02XCE	Go-Ahead London	PO54OOD	Transdev	R229TLM	First London	R467LGH	Go-Ahead London
PN02XCF	Go-Ahead London	PO54OOE	Transdev	R230TLM	First London	R468LGH	Go-Ahead London
PN02XCG	Go-Ahead London	PO54OOF	Transdev	R232TLM	First London	R469LGH	Go-Ahead London
PN02XCH	Go-Ahead London	PO54OOG	Transdev	R233TLM	First London	R470LGH	Go-Ahead London
PN02XCJ	Go-Ahead London	PO56JEU	Metrobus	R234TLM	First London	R471LGH	Go-Ahead London
PN02XCK	Go-Ahead London	PO56JFA	Metrobus	R246XDA	Travel London	R472LGH	Go-Ahead London
PN02XCL	Go-Ahead London	PO56JFE	Metrobus	R309NGM	Metroline	R473LGH	Go-Ahead London

The London Bus Handbook

Reg	Operator	Reg	Operator	Reg	Operator	Reg	Operator
R474LGH	Go-Ahead London	R832MFR	Metrobus	RDZ6129	East London	S103EGK	Go-Ahead London
R475LGH	Go-Ahead London	R833MFR	Metrobus	RDZ6130	East London	S104EGK	Go-Ahead London
R476LGH	Go-Ahead London	R834MFR	Metrobus	RE03JAK	Royale European	S105EGK	Go-Ahead London
R477LGH	Go-Ahead London	R835MFR	Metrobus	RE53JAK	Royale European	S106EGK	Go-Ahead London
R478LGH	Go-Ahead London	R836MFR	Metrobus	RE54JAK	Royale European	S107EGK	Go-Ahead London
R481LGH	Go-Ahead London	R837MFR	Metrobus	RE56JAK	Royale European	S107HGF	Travel London
R482LGH	Go-Ahead London	R838MFR	Metrobus	RL02FOT	Travel London	S108EGK	Go-Ahead London
R483LGH	Go-Ahead London	R839MFR	Metrobus	RL02FOU	Travel London	S109EGK	Go-Ahead London
R484LGH	Go-Ahead London	R841MFR	Metrobus	RL02FVM	Travel London	S110EGK	Go-Ahead London
R485LGH	Go-Ahead London	R842MFR	Metrobus	RL02FVN	Travel London	S112EGK	Go-Ahead London
R486LGH	Go-Ahead London	R843MFR	Metrobus	RL02ZTB	Travel London	S113EGK	Go-Ahead London
R487LGH	Go-Ahead London	R844MFR	Metrobus	RL02ZTC	Travel London	S114EGK	Go-Ahead London
R488LGH	Go-Ahead London	R845MFR	Metrobus	RL51DNU	Metroline	S115EGK	Go-Ahead London
R489LGH	Go-Ahead London	R863MCE	Metroline	RL51DNV	Metroline	S116EGK	Go-Ahead London
R501SJM	Travel London	R864MCE	Metroline	RL51DNX	Metroline	S117EGK	Go-Ahead London
R502SJM	Travel London	R865MCE	Metroline	RL51DNY	Metroline	S124RLE	Metroline
R503SJM	Travel London	R866MCE	Metroline	RL51DOA	Metroline	S125RLE	Metroline
R504SJM	Travel London	R867MCE	Metroline	RL51DOH	Metroline	S126RLE	Metroline
R505SJM	Travel London	R868MCE	Metroline	RL51DOJ	Metroline	S127RLE	Metroline
R506SJM	Travel London	R869MCE	Metroline	RL51DOU	Metroline	S128RLE	Metroline
R507SJM	Travel London	R870MCE	Metroline	RL51ZKR	Tellings-Golden Miller	S129RLE	Metroline
R508SJM	Travel London	R871MCE	Metroline	RL51ZKS	Tellings-Golden Miller	S130RLE	Metroline
R509SJM	Travel London	R872MCE	Metroline	RN52EOB	Travel London	S131NRB	Tellings-Golden Miller
R50TGM	Tellings-Golden Miller	R873MCE	Metroline	RN52EOC	Travel London	S131RLE	Metroline
R510SJM	Travel London	R874MCE	Metroline	RN52EOD	Travel London	S132RLE	Metroline
R546KSG	Go-Ahead Docklands	R875MCE	Metroline	RN52EOE	Travel London	S133RLE	Metroline
R547KSG	Go-Ahead Docklands	R876MCE	Metroline	RN52EOV	Travel London	S134KRM	East London
R548LGH	Go-Ahead London	R877MCE	Metroline	RN52EOW	Travel London	S134RLE	Metroline
R552LGH	Go-Ahead London	R892MTL	Clarkes of London	RN52EOX	Travel London	S135RLE	Metroline
R649TLM	First London	R945YOV	Transdev	RN52ERO	Travel London	S136RLE	Metroline
R681MEW	Metroline	R946YOV	Transdev	RN52ERU	Travel London	S137RLE	Metroline
R682MEW	Metroline	R948YOV	Transdev	RN52ERV	Travel London	S138RLE	Metroline
R683MEW	Metroline	R949YOV	Transdev	RN52EYH	Tellings-Golden Miller	S169JUA	Arriva
R684MEW	Metroline	R950YOV	Transdev	RN52EYJ	Tellings-Golden Miller	S170JUA	Arriva
R685MEW	Metroline	R951YOV	Transdev	RN52EYK	Travel London	S171JUA	Arriva
R686MEW	Metroline	R952YOV	Transdev	RN52EYL	Travel London	S172JUA	Arriva
R687MEW	Metroline	R953YOV	Transdev	RN52FPA	Travel London	S173JUA	Arriva
R688MEW	Metroline	R954YOV	Transdev	RN52FPC	Travel London	S174JUA	Arriva
R689MEW	Metroline	R957RCH	Tellings-Golden Miller	RN52FRD	Travel London	S175JUA	Arriva
R690MEW	Metroline	R958RCH	Tellings-Golden Miller	RN52FRF	Travel London	S176JUA	Arriva
R691MEW	Metroline	R959RCH	Tellings-Golden Miller	RN52FVR	Travel London	S177JUA	Arriva
R692MEW	Metroline	R985EWU	Travel London	RN52FVS	Travel London	S178JUA	Arriva
R693MEW	Metroline	R990EWU	Travel London	RN52FXD	Travel London	S179JUA	Arriva
R694MEW	Metroline	R991EWU	Travel London	RN52FXF	Travel London	S180JUA	Arriva
R695MEW	Metroline	R992EWU	Travel London	RN52FZA	Travel London	S181JUA	Arriva
R696MEW	Metroline	RA51KGE	Travel London	RO06TUU	Metrobus	S182JUA	Arriva
R697MEW	Metroline	RA51KKD	Travel London	RSL602	Duck Tours	S183JUA	Arriva
R698MEW	Metroline	RA51KKE	Travel London	RX51FGG	Travel London	S202JUA	Arriva
R699MEW	Metroline	RA51KKF	Travel London	RX51FGJ	Travel London	S203JUA	Arriva
R701MEW	Metroline	RA51KKG	Travel London	RX51FGK	Travel London	S204JUA	Arriva
R702MEW	Metroline	RA51KKH	Travel London	RX51FGM	Travel London	S205JUA	Arriva
R703MEW	Metroline	RA51KLE	Travel London	RX51FGN	Travel London	S206JUA	Arriva
R704MEW	Metroline	RA51KVS	Travel London	RX51FGO	Travel London	S207JUA	Arriva
R705MEW	Metroline	RD02BJK	Travel London	RX51FGP	Travel London	S208JUA	Arriva
R705MJH	Travel London	RD02BJO	Travel London	RX51FNP	Metroline	S209JUA	Arriva
R706MEW	Metroline	RD02BJU	Travel London	RX51FNS	Metroline	S210JUA	Arriva
R706MJH	Travel London	RD02BJV	Travel London	RX51FNT	Metroline	S211JUA	Arriva
R707MEW	Metroline	RD02BJX	Travel London	RX51FNU	Metroline	S212JUA	Arriva
R708MEW	Metroline	RD02BJZ	Travel London	RX51FNV	Metroline	S213JUA	Arriva
R709MEW	Metroline	RDZ6115	East London	RX51FNW	Metroline	S214JUA	Arriva
R710MEW	Metroline	RDZ6116	East London	RX51FNY	Metroline	S215JUA	Arriva
R711MEW	Metroline	RDZ6117	East London	RYK819Y	Blue Triangle	S215LLO	First London
R741BMY	Metrobus	RDZ6118	East London	RYK820Y	Blue Triangle	S216JUA	Arriva
R742BMY	Metrobus	RDZ6119	East London	S91EGK	Go-Ahead London	S216LLO	First London
R743BMY	Metrobus	RDZ6120	East London	S92EGK	Go-Ahead London	S217JUA	Arriva
R744BMY	Metrobus	RDZ6121	East London	S93EGK	Go-Ahead London	S218JUA	Arriva
R745BMY	Metrobus	RDZ6122	East London	S94EGK	Go-Ahead London	S218LLO	First London
R746FGX	Metrobus	RDZ6123	East London	S95EGK	Go-Ahead London	S219JUA	Arriva
R747FGX	Metrobus	RDZ6124	East London	S96EGK	Go-Ahead London	S220JUA	Arriva
R763DUB	Tellings-Golden Miller	RDZ6125	East London	S97EGK	Go-Ahead London	S221JUA	Arriva
R778WSB	Westway	RDZ6126	East London	S98EGK	Go-Ahead London	S223JUA	Arriva
R830MFR	Metrobus	RDZ6127	East London	S101EGK	Go-Ahead London	S224JUA	Arriva
R831MFR	Metrobus	RDZ6128	East London	S102EGK	Go-Ahead London	S225JUA	Arriva

Reg	Operator	Reg	Operator	Reg	Operator	Reg	Operator
S226JUA	Arriva	S286JUA	Arriva	S523KFL	Metroline	SK52MPY	Transdev
S227JUA	Arriva	S287JLP	Metroline	S524KFL	Metroline	SK52MRO	Go-Ahead London
S228JUA	Arriva	S287JUA	Arriva	S525KFL	Metroline	SK52MRU	Go-Ahead London
S229JUA	Arriva	S288JLP	Metroline	S526KFL	Metroline	SK52MRV	Go-Ahead London
S230JUA	Arriva	S288JUA	Arriva	S527KFL	Metroline	SK52MRX	Go-Ahead London
S231JUA	Arriva	S289JLP	Metroline	S528KFL	Metroline	SK52MRY	Go-Ahead London
S232JUA	Arriva	S289JUA	Arriva	S529JLM	Metroline	SK52MSO	Transdev
S233JUA	Arriva	S290JLP	Metroline	S529KFL	Metroline	SK52URV	Transdev
S233RLH	Metroline	S290JUA	Arriva	S530JLM	Metroline	SK52URW	Transdev
S234JUA	Arriva	S291JLP	Metroline	S531JLM	Metroline	SK52URX	Transdev
S235JUA	Arriva	S291JUA	Arriva	S532JLM	Metroline	SK52URY	Transdev
S235KLM	First London	S292JLP	Metroline	S533JLM	Metroline	SK52URZ	Transdev
S236JUA	Arriva	S292JUA	Arriva	S534JLM	Metroline	SK52USB	Transdev
S236KLM	First London	S293JLP	Metroline	S535JLM	Metroline	SK52USC	Transdev
S237JUA	Arriva	S294JLP	Metroline	S536JLM	Metroline	SK52USD	Transdev
S237KLM	First London	S295JLP	Metroline	S537JLM	Metroline	SK52USF	Transdev
S238JUA	Arriva	S296JLP	Metroline	S538JLM	Metroline	SK52USG	Transdev
S238KLM	First London	S297JLP	Metroline	S539JLM	Metroline	SK52USH	Transdev
S239JUA	Arriva	S298JLP	Metroline	S540JLM	Metroline	SK52USJ	Transdev
S239KLM	First London	S299JLP	Metroline	S549BNV	Travel London	SK52USL	Transdev
S240JUA	Arriva	S300ASH	Ashford Luxury	S580ACT	Wings	SMK665F	East London
S240KLM	First London	S301JLP	Metroline	S590ACT	Wings	SMK669F	Go-Ahead London
S241JUA	Arriva	S301JUA	Arriva	S638JGP	Go-Ahead London	SMK673F	Go-Ahead London
S241KLM	First London	S301MKH	Transdev	S707JJH	Travel London	SMK680F	Go-Ahead London
S242JUA	Arriva	S302JUA	Arriva	S708TCF	Travel London	SMK693F	Go-Ahead London
S242KLM	First London	S302MKH	Transdev	S801BWC	East London	SMK725F	Go-Ahead London
S243JUA	Arriva	S303JUA	Arriva	S905JHG	East London	SMK732F	Go-Ahead London
S243KLM	First London	S303MKH	Transdev	S906JHG	East London	SMK736F	Go-Ahead London
S244JUA	Arriva	S304JUA	Arriva	S954JGX	Go-Ahead London	SMK760F	East London
S244KLM	First London	S304MKH	Transdev	S955JGX	Go-Ahead London	SN03DZJ	Transdev
S245JUA	Arriva	S305JUA	Arriva	SK02XGT	Transdev	SN03DZK	Transdev
S245KLM	First London	S305MKH	Transdev	SK02XGU	Transdev	SN03DZM	Transdev
S246JUA	Arriva	S306JUA	Arriva	SK02XGV	Transdev	SN03DZP	Transdev
S246KLM	First London	S306MKH	Transdev	SK02XGW	Transdev	SN03DZR	Transdev
S247JUA	Arriva	S307JUA	Arriva	SK02XGX	Transdev	SN03DZS	Transdev
S247KLM	First London	S307MKH	Transdev	SK02XHD	Transdev	SN03DZT	Transdev
S248JUA	Arriva	S308JUA	Arriva	SK02XHE	Transdev	SN03DZV	Transdev
S248KLM	First London	S308MKH	Transdev	SK02XHF	Transdev	SN03DZW	Transdev
S249JUA	Arriva	S309JUA	Arriva	SK02XHG	Transdev	SN03DZX	Transdev
S250JUA	Arriva	S309MKH	Transdev	SK02XHH	Transdev	SN03EAA	Transdev
S251JUA	Arriva	S310JUA	Arriva	SK02XHJ	Transdev	SN03EAC	Transdev
S252JUA	Arriva	S310MKH	Transdev	SK02XHL	Transdev	SN03EAE	Transdev
S253JLP	First London	S311JUA	Arriva	SK02XHM	Transdev	SN03EAF	Transdev
S253JUA	Arriva	S311MKH	Transdev	SK02XHN	Transdev	SN03EAG	Transdev
S254JLP	First London	S312JUA	Arriva	SK02XHO	Transdev	SN03EAJ	Transdev
S254JUA	Arriva	S313JUA	Arriva	SK02XHP	Transdev	SN03EAM	Transdev
S255JLP	First London	S314JUA	Arriva	SK02XHR	Transdev	SN03EAP	Transdev
S255JUA	Arriva	S315JUA	Arriva	SK52MKV	Transdev	SN03EAW	Transdev
S256JLP	First London	S316JUA	Arriva	SK52MKX	Go-Ahead London	SN03EAX	Transdev
S256JUA	Arriva	S317JUA	Arriva	SK52MKZ	Go-Ahead London	SN03EBA	Transdev
S257JUA	Arriva	S318JUA	Arriva	SK52MLU	Go-Ahead London	SN03EBC	Transdev
S258JUA	Arriva	S322JUA	Arriva	SK52MLV	Go-Ahead London	SN03EBD	Transdev
S259JUA	Arriva	S399WTU	Go-Ahead Docklands	SK52MLX	Go-Ahead London	SN03EBF	Transdev
S260JUA	Arriva	S451WAT	Ashford Luxury	SK52MLY	Go-Ahead London	SN03EBG	Transdev
S261JUA	Arriva	S452LGN	Epsom Coaches	SK52MLZ	Go-Ahead London	SN03EBJ	Transdev
S262JUA	Arriva	S459LGN	Epsom Coaches	SK52MMA	Go-Ahead London	SN03EBK	Transdev
S263JUA	Arriva	S460LGN	Epsom Coaches	SK52MME	Go-Ahead London	SN03EBL	Transdev
S264JUA	Arriva	S464LGN	Epsom Coaches	SK52MMF	Go-Ahead London	SN03EBM	Transdev
S272JUA	Arriva	S513KFL	Metroline	SK52MMJ	Go-Ahead London	SN03LDY	Transdev
S273JUA	Arriva	S514KFL	Metroline	SK52MMO	Go-Ahead London	SN03LDZ	Transdev
S274JUA	Arriva	S515JJH	Travel London	SK52MMU	Go-Ahead London	SN03LEF	Transdev
S275JUA	Arriva	S515KFL	Metroline	SK52MMV	Go-Ahead London	SN03LEJ	Transdev
S276JUA	Arriva	S516JJH	Travel London	SK52MMX	Go-Ahead London	SN03LEV	Transdev
S277JUA	Arriva	S516KFL	Metroline	SK52MOA	Go-Ahead London	SN03LFA	Transdev
S278JUA	Arriva	S517JJH	Travel London	SK52MOF	Go-Ahead London	SN03LFB	Transdev
S279JUA	Arriva	S517KFL	Metroline	SK52MOU	Go-Ahead London	SN03LFD	Transdev
S280JUA	Arriva	S518KFL	Metroline	SK52MOV	Go-Ahead London	SN03LFE	Transdev
S281JUA	Arriva	S518TCF	Travel London	SK52MPE	Go-Ahead London	SN03LFF	Transdev
S282JUA	Arriva	S519KFL	Metroline	SK52MPF	Go-Ahead London	SN03LFG	Transdev
S283JUA	Arriva	S519TCF	Travel London	SK52MPO	Go-Ahead London	SN03LFH	Transdev
S284JUA	Arriva	S520KFL	Metroline	SK52MPU	Transdev	SN03LFJ	Transdev
S285JUA	Arriva	S521KFL	Metroline	SK52MPV	Transdev	SN03LFK	Transdev
S286JLP	Metroline	S522KFL	Metroline	SK52MPX	Transdev	SN03LFL	Transdev

Reg	Operator	Reg	Operator	Reg	Operator	Reg	Operator
SN03LFM	Transdev	SN51SXS	Transdev	SN51UAK	Go-Ahead London	SN53KKR	Go-Ahead London
SN03LFP	Transdev	SN51SXT	Transdev	SN51UAL	Go-Ahead London	SN53KKT	Go-Ahead London
SN03LFR	Transdev	SN51SXU	Transdev	SN51UAM	Go-Ahead London	SN53KKU	Go-Ahead London
SN03LFS	Transdev	SN51SXV	Transdev	SN51UAO	Go-Ahead London	SN53KKV	Go-Ahead London
SN03LFT	Transdev	SN51SXW	Transdev	SN51UAP	Go-Ahead London	SN53KKW	Go-Ahead London
SN03WKU	Metrobus	SN51SXX	Transdev	SN51UAR	Go-Ahead London	SN53KKX	Go-Ahead London
SN03WKY	Metrobus	SN51SXY	Transdev	SN51UAS	Go-Ahead London	SN54GPV	Metrobus
SN03WLA	Metrobus	SN51SXZ	Transdev	SN51UAT	Go-Ahead London	SN54GPX	Metrobus
SN03WLE	Metrobus	SN51SYA	Transdev	SN51UAU	Go-Ahead London	SN54GPY	Metrobus
SN03WLF	Metrobus	SN51SYC	Transdev	SN51UAV	Go-Ahead London	SN54GPZ	Metrobus
SN03WLH	Metrobus	SN51SYE	Transdev	SN51UAW	Go-Ahead London	SN54GRF	Metrobus
SN03WLL	Metrobus	SN51SYF	Transdev	SN51UAX	Go-Ahead London	SN54GRK	Metrobus
SN03WLP	Metrobus	SN51SYG	Transdev	SN51UAY	Go-Ahead London	SN56AYD	Blue Triangle
SN03WLU	Metrobus	SN51SYH	Transdev	SN51UAZ	Go-Ahead London	SSL609	First London
SN03WLX	Metrobus	SN51SYJ	Transdev	SN51UCH	Epsom Coaches	SVS615	Blue Triangle
SN03WLZ	Metrobus	SN51SYO	Transdev	SN51UCJ	Epsom Coaches	SX02TZN	Travel London
SN03WMC	Metrobus	SN51SYR	Transdev	SN51UCL	Epsom Coaches	SX02TZO	Travel London
SN03WMF	Metrobus	SN51SYS	Transdev	SN51UCM	Epsom Coaches	SX02TZP	Travel London
SN03WMG	Metrobus	SN51SYT	Transdev	SN51UCO	Epsom Coaches	SX02TZR	Travel London
SN03WMK	Metrobus	SN51SYU	Transdev	SN51UCP	Epsom Coaches	SX02TZS	Travel London
SN03WMP	Metrobus	SN51SYV	Transdev	SN51UCR	Epsom Coaches	SX02TZT	Travel London
SN03WMT	Metrobus	SN51SYW	Transdev	SN51UCS	Epsom Coaches	SX02TZU	Travel London
SN03WMV	Metrobus	SN51SYX	Transdev	SN53ETT	Go-Ahead London	SX02TZV	Travel London
SN03WMY	Metrobus	SN51SYY	Transdev	SN53ETU	Go-Ahead London	SX02TZW	Travel London
SN03YBA	Metrobus	SN51SYZ	Transdev	SN53ETV	Go-Ahead London	SX02TZX	Travel London
SN03YBB	Metrobus	SN51SZC	Transdev	SN53ETX	Go-Ahead London	SYC852	East London
SN03YBC	Metrobus	SN51SZD	Transdev	SN53ETY	Go-Ahead London	T3APT	Westbus
SN03YBG	Metrobus	SN51SZE	Transdev	SN53ETZ	Go-Ahead London	T4APT	Westbus
SN03YBH	Metrobus	SN51SZF	Transdev	SN53EUF	Transdev	T35KLD	Metroline
SN03YBK	Metrobus	SN51SZG	Transdev	SN53EUH	Transdev	T37KLD	Metroline
SN03YBR	Metrobus	SN51SZJ	Transdev	SN53EUJ	Transdev	T38KLD	Metroline
SN03YBS	Metrobus	SN51SZK	Transdev	SN53EUK	Transdev	T39KLD	Metroline
SN03YBT	Metrobus	SN51SZL	Transdev	SN53EUL	Transdev	T41KLD	Metroline
SN03YBX	Metrobus	SN51SZO	Transdev	SN53EUM	Transdev	T43KLD	Metroline
SN03YBY	Metrobus	SN51SZP	Transdev	SN53EUO	Transdev	T45RJL	Go-Ahead (Docklands)
SN03YBZ	Metrobus	SN51SZR	Transdev	SN53EUP	Transdev	T47KLD	Metroline
SN03YCD	Metrobus	SN51SZT	Transdev	SN53EUR	Transdev	T48KLD	Metroline
SN03YCE	Metrobus	SN51SZU	Transdev	SN53EUT	Transdev	T49KLD	Metroline
SN03YCF	Metrobus	SN51SZV	Transdev	SN53EUU	Transdev	T51KLD	Metroline
SN03YCK	Metrobus	SN51SZW	Transdev	SN53EUV	Transdev	T52KLD	Metroline
SN03YCL	Metrobus	SN51SZX	Transdev	SN53EUW	Transdev	T53KLD	Metroline
SN03YCM	Metrobus	SN51SZY	Transdev	SN53EUX	Transdev	T54KLD	Metroline
SN03YCT	Metrobus	SN51SZZ	Transdev	SN53EUY	Transdev	T54PDA	Allied
SN06BNA	Go-Ahead London	SN51TAU	Transdev	SN53EUZ	Transdev	T56KLD	Metroline
SN06BNB	Go-Ahead London	SN51TAV	Transdev	SN53EVA	Go-Ahead London	T61KLD	Metroline
SN06BND	Go-Ahead London	SN51TBO	Transdev	SN53EVB	Go-Ahead London	T63KLD	Metroline
SN06BNE	Go-Ahead London	SN51TBU	Transdev	SN53EVC	Go-Ahead London	T64KLD	Metroline
SN06BNF	Go-Ahead London	SN51TBV	Transdev	SN53EVD	Go-Ahead London	T65KLD	Metroline
SN06BNJ	Go-Ahead London	SN51TBX	Transdev	SN53EVE	Go-Ahead London	T67KLD	Metroline
SN06BNK	Go-Ahead London	SN51TBY	Transdev	SN53KHR	Transdev	T68KLD	Metroline
SN06BNL	Go-Ahead London	SN51TBZ	Transdev	SN53KHT	Transdev	T69KLD	Metroline
SN06BNO	Go-Ahead London	SN51TCJ	Transdev	SN53KHU	Transdev	T71KLD	Metroline
SN06BNU	Go-Ahead London	SN51TCK	Transdev	SN53KHV	Transdev	T72KLD	Metroline
SN06BNV	Go-Ahead London	SN51TCO	Transdev	SN53KHW	Transdev	T73KLD	Metroline
SN06BNX	Go-Ahead London	SN51TCU	Transdev	SN53KHX	Transdev	T74KLD	Metroline
SN06BNY	Go-Ahead London	SN51TCV	Transdev	SN53KHY	Transdev	T75KLD	Metroline
SN06BNZ	Go-Ahead London	SN51TCX	Transdev	SN53KHZ	Transdev	T76KLD	Metroline
SN06BOF	Go-Ahead London	SN51TCY	Transdev	SN53KJA	Transdev	T78KLD	Metroline
SN06JPV	Transdev	SN51TCZ	Transdev	SN53KJE	Transdev	T79KLD	Metroline
SN06JPX	Transdev	SN51TDO	Transdev	SN53KJF	Transdev	T81KLD	Metroline
SN51SXC	Transdev	SN51TDU	Transdev	SN53KJJ	Transdev	T87KLD	Metroline
SN51SXD	Transdev	SN51TDV	Transdev	SN53KJK	Transdev	T97KLD	Metroline
SN51SXE	Transdev	SN51TDX	Transdev	SN53KJO	Transdev	T98KLD	Metroline
SN51SXF	Transdev	SN51TDZ	Transdev	SN53KJU	Transdev	T101KLD	Metroline
SN51SXG	Transdev	SN51TEJ	Transdev	SN53KJV	Transdev	T103KLD	Metroline
SN51SXH	Transdev	SN51TEO	Transdev	SN53KKF	Go-Ahead London	T104KLD	Metroline
SN51SXJ	Transdev	SN51TEU	Transdev	SN53KKG	Go-Ahead London	T105KLD	Metroline
SN51SXK	Transdev	SN51UAD	Go-Ahead London	SN53KKH	Go-Ahead London	T106KGP	Go-Ahead London
SN51SXL	Transdev	SN51UAE	Go-Ahead London	SN53KKJ	Go-Ahead London	T106KLD	Metroline
SN51SXM	Transdev	SN51UAF	Go-Ahead London	SN53KKL	Go-Ahead London	T107KGP	Go-Ahead London
SN51SXO	Transdev	SN51UAG	Go-Ahead London	SN53KKM	Go-Ahead London	T107KLD	Metroline
SN51SXP	Transdev	SN51UAH	Go-Ahead London	SN53KKO	Go-Ahead London	T108KGP	Go-Ahead London
SN51SXR	Transdev	SN51UAJ	Go-Ahead London	SN53KKP	Go-Ahead London	T108KLD	Metroline

Reg	Operator	Reg	Operator	Reg	Operator	Reg	Operator
T109KGP	Go-Ahead London	T195CLO	Metroline	T294JLD	First London	T348PRH	Transdev
T109KLD	Metroline	T196CLO	Metroline	T295FGN	Arriva	T349PRH	Transdev
T10TGM	Tellings-Golden Miller	T197CLO	Metroline	T295JLD	First London	T350PRH	Transdev
T110GGO	Arriva	T198CLO	Metroline	T296FGN	Arriva	T351PRH	Transdev
T110KLD	Metroline	T199CLO	Metroline	T296JLD	First London	T352PRH	Transdev
T112KLD	Metroline	T200ALC	Ashford Luxury	T297FGN	Arriva	T353PRH	Transdev
T113KLD	Metroline	T2000CL	Clarkes of London	T297JLD	First London	T354PRH	Transdev
T114KLD	Metroline	T201CLO	Metroline	T298FGN	Arriva	T356PRH	Transdev
T115KLD	Metroline	T202CLO	Metroline	T298JLD	First London	T357PRH	Transdev
T116KLD	Metroline	T202XBV	Arriva Original Tour	T299FGN	Arriva	T358PRH	Transdev
T117KLD	Metroline	T203XBV	Arriva Original Tour	T299JLD	First London	T359PRH	Transdev
T118KGP	Go-Ahead London	T204CLO	Metroline	T2APT	Westbus	T360PRH	Transdev
T118KLD	Metroline	T204XBV	Arriva Original Tour	T301FGN	Arriva	T361PRH	Transdev
T119KGP	Go-Ahead London	T205CLO	Metroline	T301JLD	First London	T362PRH	Transdev
T119KLD	Metroline	T205XBV	Arriva Original Tour	T302FGN	Arriva	T363PRH	Transdev
T120KGP	Go-Ahead London	T206CLO	Metroline	T302JLD	First London	T364PRH	Transdev
T120KLD	Metroline	T206XBV	Arriva Original Tour	T303FGN	Arriva	T365PRH	Transdev
T122KGP	Go-Ahead London	T207CLO	Metroline	T303JLD	First London	T366PRH	Transdev
T122KLD	Metroline	T207XBV	Arriva Original Tour	T304FGN	Arriva	T367PRH	Transdev
T124KGP	Go-Ahead London	T208XBV	Arriva Original Tour	T304JLD	First London	T368PRH	Transdev
T124KLD	Metroline	T208XBV	Arriva Original Tour	T305FGN	Arriva	T369PRH	Transdev
T125KGP	Go-Ahead London	T20TGM	Tellings-Golden Miller	T305JLD	First London	T370PRH	Transdev
T125KLD	Metroline	T210XBV	Arriva Original Tour	T306FGN	Arriva	T371PRH	Transdev
T126KGP	Go-Ahead London	T211XBV	Arriva Original Tour	T306JLD	First London	T372PRH	Transdev
T126KLD	Metroline	T212XBV	Arriva Original Tour	T307FGN	Arriva	T373PRH	Transdev
T127KGP	Go-Ahead London	T213XBV	Arriva Original Tour	T308FGN	Arriva	T374PRH	Transdev
T127KLD	Metroline	T214XBV	Arriva Original Tour	T309FGN	Arriva	T375PRH	Transdev
T128KGP	Go-Ahead London	T215XBV	Arriva	T309SMV	Metrobus	T392AGP	Go-Ahead London
T128KLD	Metroline	T216XBV	Arriva	T310FGN	Arriva	T401AGP	Go-Ahead London
T129KLD	Metroline	T217XBV	Arriva	T310SMV	Metrobus	T402AGP	Go-Ahead London
T132CLO	Metroline	T218CLO	Metroline	T311FGN	Arriva	T4020WA	Go-Ahead Docklands
T133CLO	Metroline	T218XBV	Arriva	T311SMV	Metrobus	T403AGP	Go-Ahead London
T134CLO	Metroline	T219XBV	Arriva	T312FGN	Arriva	T404AGP	Go-Ahead London
T135AUA	Travel London	T220XBV	Arriva	T312SMV	Metrobus	T406AGP	Go-Ahead London
T135CLO	Metroline	T257JLD	First London	T313FGN	Arriva	T408AGP	Go-Ahead London
T136CLO	Metroline	T258JLD	First London	T313SMV	Metrobus	T410AGP	Go-Ahead London
T137CLO	Metroline	T259JLD	First London	T314FGN	Arriva	T411AGP	Go-Ahead London
T138CLO	Metroline	T260JLD	First London	T314SMV	Metrobus	T412AGP	Go-Ahead London
T139CLO	Metroline	T261JLD	First London	T315FGN	Arriva	T412KAG	Transdev
T140AUA	Metroline	T262JLD	First London	T315SMV	Metrobus	T413KAG	Transdev
T140CLO	Metroline	T263JLD	First London	T316FGN	Arriva	T414AGP	Go-Ahead London
T141AUA	Metroline	T264JLD	First London	T316SMV	Metrobus	T414KAG	Transdev
T141CLO	Metroline	T265JLD	First London	T317FGN	Arriva	T415AGP	Go-Ahead London
T142AUA	Metroline	T266JLD	First London	T318FGN	Arriva	T415KAG	Transdev
T142CLO	Metroline	T267JLD	First London	T319FGN	Arriva	T416KAG	Transdev
T143AUA	Metroline	T268JLD	First London	T320FGN	Arriva	T417AGP	Go-Ahead London
T143CLO	Metroline	T269JLD	First London	T322FGN	Arriva	T417KAG	Transdev
T144AUA	Metroline	T270JLD	First London	T323FGN	Arriva	T418AGP	Go-Ahead London
T144CLO	Metroline	T271JLD	First London	T324FGN	Arriva	T418KAG	Transdev
T145AUA	Metroline	T272JLD	First London	T325FGN	Arriva	T419AGP	Go-Ahead London
T145CLO	Metroline	T273JLD	First London	T334PRH	Transdev	T419KAG	Transdev
T146AUA	Metroline	T274JLD	First London	T335PRH	Transdev	T420KAG	Transdev
T146CLO	Metroline	T275JLD	First London	T336ALR	First London	T421GGO	Arriva
T147AUA	Metroline	T276JLD	First London	T336PRH	Transdev	T421KAG	Transdev
T148AUA	Metroline	T277JLD	First London	T337ALR	First London	T422KAG	Transdev
T148CLO	Metroline	T278JLD	First London	T337PRH	Transdev	T423KAG	Transdev
T149AUA	Metroline	T279JLD	First London	T338ALR	First London	T424KAG	Transdev
T150AUA	Metroline	T280JLD	First London	T338PRH	Transdev	T425KAG	Transdev
T151AUA	Metroline	T281JLD	First London	T339ALR	First London	T426KAG	Transdev
T152AUA	Metroline	T282JLD	First London	T339PRH	Transdev	T427KAG	Transdev
T182CLO	Metroline	T283JLD	First London	T340ALR	First London	T428KAG	Transdev
T183CLO	Metroline	T284JLD	First London	T340PRH	Transdev	T429KAG	Transdev
T184CLO	Metroline	T285JLD	First London	T341ALR	First London	T430KAG	First London
T185CLO	Metroline	T286JLD	First London	T341PRH	Transdev	T430KAG	Transdev
T186CLO	Metroline	T287JLD	First London	T342ALR	First London	T431KAG	Transdev
T187CLO	Metroline	T288JLD	First London	T342PRH	Transdev	T431LGP	CT Plus
T188CLO	Metroline	T289JLD	First London	T343ALR	First London	T432KAG	Transdev
T189CLO	Metroline	T290JLD	First London	T343PRH	Transdev	T432LGP	CT Plus
T190CLO	Metroline	T291JLD	First London	T344ALR	First London	T433KAG	Transdev
T191CLO	Metroline	T292JLD	First London	T344PRH	Transdev	T433LGP	CT Plus
T192CLO	Metroline	T293FGN	Arriva	T345PRH	Transdev	T455AGP	Go-Ahead London
T193CLO	Metroline	T293JLD	First London	T346PRH	Transdev	T455PRH	Transdev
T194CLO	Metroline	T294FGN	Arriva	T347PRH	Transdev	T503JPP	Transdev

T504JPP	Transdev	T885KLF	First London	V120MEV	East London	V155MEV	East London
T521AGP	Go-Ahead London	T89KLD	Metroline	V122GBY	Metroline	V156MEV	East London
T523AGP	Go-Ahead London	T976SRH	Transdev	V122LGC	Go-Ahead London	V156MVX	East London
T553HNH	East Thames	T977SRH	Transdev	V122MEV	East London	V157MEV	East London
T571FFC	Tellings-Golden Miller	T978SRH	Transdev	V124GBY	Metroline	V157MVX	East London
T574KGB	Go-Ahead Docklands	T979SRH	Transdev	V124LGC	Go-Ahead London	V158MEV	East London
T576FFC	Tellings-Golden Miller	T980SRH	Transdev	V124MEV	East London	V158MVX	East London
T648KPU	East London	T999ASH	Ashford Luxury	V125GBY	Metroline	V159MEV	East London
T649KPU	East London	THX101S	Metroline	V125LGC	Go-Ahead London	V159MVX	East London
T664KPU	East London	THX401S	East London	V125MEV	East London	V160MEV	East London
T665KPU	East London	THX402S	Blue Triangle	V126GBY	Metroline	V161MEV	East London
T680KPU	East London	TIL8795	Westway	V126LGC	Go-Ahead London	V161MVX	East London
T682KPU	East London	TSL931	Duck Tours	V126MEV	East London	V162MEV	East London
T683KPU	East London	UK03LLC	Tellings-Golden Miller	V127GBY	Metroline	V162MVX	East London
T684KPU	East London	UK03TGM	Tellings-Golden Miller	V127LGC	Go-Ahead London	V163MEV	East London
T685KPU	East London	UK04TGM	Tellings-Golden Miller	V127MEV	East London	V163MVX	East London
T686KPU	East London	V1GMT	Go-Ahead London	V128GBY	Metroline	V164MEV	East London
T687KPU	East London	V2GMT	Go-Ahead London	V128LGC	Go-Ahead London	V164MVX	East London
T688KPU	East London	V3GMT	Go-Ahead London	V128MEV	East London	V165MEV	East London
T689KPU	East London	V4GMT	Go-Ahead London	V129GBY	Metroline	V165MVX	East London
T690KPU	East London	V5GMT	Go-Ahead London	V129LGC	Go-Ahead London	V166MEV	East London
T691KPU	East London	V6GMT	Go-Ahead London	V129MEV	East London	V166MVX	East London
T692KPU	East London	V7GMT	Go-Ahead London	V130GBY	Metroline	V167MEV	East London
T693KPU	East London	V8AEC	Blue Triangle	V130LGC	Go-Ahead London	V167MVX	East London
T694KPU	East London	V8GMT	Go-Ahead London	V130MEV	East London	V168MEV	East London
T695KPU	East London	V9GMT	Go-Ahead London	V131GBY	Metroline	V168MVX	East London
T696KPU	East London	V10GMT	Go-Ahead London	V131LGC	Go-Ahead London	V169MEV	East London
T697KPU	East London	V12GMT	Go-Ahead London	V131MEV	East London	V169MVX	East London
T698KPU	East London	V13GMT	Go-Ahead London	V132GBY	Metroline	V170MEV	East London
T705SUT	Go-Ahead (Docklands)	V14GMT	Go-Ahead London	V132LGC	Go-Ahead London	V170MVX	East London
T801LLC	First London	V15GMT	Go-Ahead London	V132MEV	East London	V171MEV	East London
T804LLC	First London	V16GMT	Go-Ahead London	V133GBY	Metroline	V171MVX	East London
T806LLC	First London	V17GMT	Go-Ahead London	V133LGC	Go-Ahead London	V172MEV	East London
T807LLC	First London	V101LGC	Go-Ahead London	V133MEV	East London	V172MVX	East London
T808TGP	Epsom Coaches	V102LGC	Go-Ahead London	V134GBY	Metroline	V173MEV	East London
T809LLC	First London	V102MEV	East London	V134LGC	Go-Ahead London	V174MEV	East London
T810LLC	First London	V103LGC	Go-Ahead London	V134MEV	East London	V175MEV	East London
T813LLC	First London	V103MEV	East London	V135LGC	Go-Ahead London	V176MEV	East London
T814LLC	First London	V104LGC	Go-Ahead London	V135MEV	East London	V176OOE	Transdev
T815LLC	First London	V104MEV	East London	V136LGC	Go-Ahead London	V177MEV	East London
T816LLC	First London	V105LGC	Go-Ahead London	V136MEV	East London	V177OOE	Transdev
T818LLC	First London	V105MEV	East London	V137LGC	Go-Ahead London	V178MEV	East London
T822LLC	First London	V106LGC	Go-Ahead London	V137MEV	East London	V178OOE	Transdev
T838LLC	First London	V106MEV	East London	V138LGC	Go-Ahead London	V179MEV	East London
T839LLC	First London	V107LGC	Go-Ahead London	V138MEV	East London	V179OOE	Transdev
T840LLC	First London	V107MEV	East London	V139LGC	Go-Ahead London	V180OOE	Transdev
T841LLC	First London	V108LGC	Go-Ahead London	V139MEV	East London	V181MEV	East London
T842LLC	First London	V108MEV	East London	V140LGC	Go-Ahead London	V181OOE	Transdev
T843LLC	First London	V109LGC	Go-Ahead London	V140MEV	East London	V182MEV	East London
T844LLC	First London	V109MEV	East London	V141LGC	Go-Ahead London	V182OOE	Transdev
T845LLC	First London	V110LGC	Go-Ahead London	V141MEV	East London	V183MEV	East London
T847LLC	First London	V112LGC	Go-Ahead London	V142LGC	Go-Ahead London	V183OOE	Transdev
T849LLC	First London	V112MEV	East London	V142MEV	East London	V184MEV	East London
T850LLC	First London	V113LGC	Go-Ahead London	V143LGC	Go-Ahead London	V184OOE	Transdev
T851LLC	First London	V113MEV	East London	V143MEV	East London	V185MEV	East London
T852LLC	First London	V114LGC	Go-Ahead London	V144LGC	Go-Ahead London	V185OOE	Transdev
T853LLC	First London	V114MEV	East London	V144MEV	East London	V186MEV	East London
T854KLF	First London	V115LGC	Go-Ahead London	V145LGC	Go-Ahead London	V186OOE	Transdev
T864KLF	First London	V115MEV	East London	V145MEV	East London	V187OOE	Transdev
T865KLF	First London	V116LGC	Go-Ahead London	V146LGC	Go-Ahead London	V188MEV	East London
T866KLF	First London	V116MEV	East London	V147MEV	East London	V188OOE	Transdev
T868KLF	First London	V117LGC	Go-Ahead London	V147MVX	East London	V189MEV	East London
T870KLF	First London	V117MEV	East London	V148MEV	East London	V189OOE	Transdev
T871KLF	First London	V117MVX	East London	V148MVX	East London	V190MEV	East London
T873KLF	First London	V118GBY	Metroline	V149MEV	East London	V190OOE	Transdev
T875KLF	First London	V118LGC	Go-Ahead London	V149MVX	East London	V191MEV	East London
T876KLF	First London	V118MEV	East London	V150MEV	East London	V191OOE	Transdev
T878KLF	First London	V119GBY	Metroline	V150MVX	East London	V192MEV	East London
T879KLF	First London	V119LGC	Go-Ahead London	V151MEV	East London	V192OOE	Transdev
T880KLF	First London	V119MEV	East London	V152MEV	East London	V193MEV	East London
T881KLF	First London	V11GMT	Go-Ahead London	V152MVX	East London	V193OOE	Transdev
T883KLF	First London	V120GBY	Metroline	V153MEV	East London	V194MEV	East London
T884KLF	First London	V120LGC	Go-Ahead London	V154MEV	East London	V194OOE	Transdev

Reg	Operator	Reg	Operator	Reg	Operator	Reg	Operator
V195MEV	East London	V309GLB	Metroline	V330DGT	Arriva	V426DGT	Arriva
V196MEV	East London	V309KGW	Travel London	V330KGW	Travel London	V427DGT	Arriva
V197MEV	East London	V309MDP	Travel London	V330KMY	Metrobus	V428DGT	Arriva
V198MEV	East London	V310GBY	First London	V330LGC	Go-Ahead London	V429DGT	Arriva
V199MEV	East London	V310GLB	Metroline	V331DGT	Arriva	V430DGT	Arriva
V201MEV	East London	V310KGW	Travel London	V331KMY	Metrobus	V431DGT	Arriva
V202MEV	East London	V310LGC	Go-Ahead London	V331LGC	Go-Ahead London	V432DGT	Arriva
V202OOE	Transdev	V311GBY	First London	V332DGT	Arriva	V433DGT	Arriva
V203MEV	East London	V311GLB	Metroline	V332LGC	Go-Ahead London	V434DGT	Arriva
V203OOE	Transdev	V311KGW	Travel London	V334DGT	Arriva	V435DGT	Arriva
V204MEV	East London	V311LGC	Go-Ahead London	V334LGC	Go-Ahead London	V470RDN	Chalfont
V204OOE	Transdev	V312GBY	First London	V335DGT	Arriva	V476KJN	East London
V205MEV	East London	V312GLB	Metroline	V335LGC	Go-Ahead London	V477KJN	East London
V205OOE	Transdev	V312KGW	Travel London	V336DGT	Arriva	V478KJN	East London
V206MEV	East London	V312LGC	Go-Ahead London	V336LGC	Go-Ahead London	V479KJN	East London
V206OOE	Transdev	V313GBY	First London	V336MBV	Travel London	V506JBH	Transdev
V207MEV	East London	V313GLB	Metroline	V337DGT	Arriva	V507JBH	Transdev
V207OOE	Transdev	V313KGW	Travel London	V337LGC	Go-Ahead London	V508JBH	Transdev
V208MEV	East London	V313LGC	Go-Ahead London	V337MBV	Travel London	V509JBH	Transdev
V208OOE	Transdev	V314GBY	First London	V338DGT	Arriva	V510JBH	Transdev
V209LGC	Go-Ahead London	V314GLB	Metroline	V338LGC	Go-Ahead London	V511JBH	Transdev
V209MEV	East London	V314KGW	Travel London	V338MBV	Travel London	V512JBH	Transdev
V210MEV	East London	V314LGC	Go-Ahead London	V339DGT	Arriva	V513JBH	Transdev
V211LGC	Go-Ahead London	V315GBY	First London	V341DGT	Arriva	V514JBH	Transdev
V211MEV	East London	V315GLB	Metroline	V342DGT	Arriva	V515JBH	Transdev
V212MEV	East London	V315KGW	Travel London	V343DGT	Arriva	V516JBH	Transdev
V213MEV	East London	V315LGC	Go-Ahead London	V344DGT	Arriva	V517JBH	Transdev
V214MEV	East London	V316GBY	First London	V345DGT	Arriva	V518JBH	Transdev
V215MEV	East London	V316GLB	Metroline	V345DLH	First London	V519JBH	Transdev
V216MEV	East London	V316KGW	Travel London	V346DGT	Arriva	V520JBH	Transdev
V217MEV	East London	V317GBY	First London	V346DLH	First London	V521JBH	Transdev
V218LGC	Go-Ahead London	V317GLB	Metroline	V347DGT	Arriva	V522JBH	Transdev
V218MEV	East London	V317KGW	Travel London	V347DLH	First London	V523JBH	Transdev
V219MEV	East London	V317LGC	Go-Ahead London	V348DGT	Arriva	V524JBH	Transdev
V220LGC	Go-Ahead London	V318GBY	First London	V348DLH	First London	V525JBH	Transdev
V220MEV	East London	V318KGW	Travel London	V349DGT	Arriva	V526JBH	Transdev
V221LGC	Go-Ahead London	V319GBY	First London	V349DLH	First London	V527JBH	Transdev
V221MEV	East London	V319KGW	Travel London	V350DLH	First London	V528JBH	Transdev
V223LGC	Go-Ahead London	V319LGC	Go-Ahead London	V351DGT	Arriva	V529JBH	Transdev
V226LGC	Go-Ahead London	V320GBY	First London	V351DLH	First London	V530JBH	Transdev
V228LGC	Go-Ahead London	V320KGW	Travel London	V352DGT	Arriva	V531JBH	Transdev
V233LGC	Go-Ahead London	V322GBY	First London	V352DLH	First London	V532JBH	Transdev
V278NAD	Go-Ahead (Docklands)	V322KGW	Travel London	V353DGT	Arriva	V533JBH	Transdev
V301KGW	Travel London	V322KMY	Metrobus	V353DLH	First London	V534JBH	Transdev
V301LGC	Travel London	V322LGC	Go-Ahead London	V354DGT	Arriva	V535JBH	Transdev
V301MDP	Travel London	V323GBY	First London	V354DLH	First London	V536JBH	Transdev
V302KGW	Travel London	V323KGW	Travel London	V355DGT	Arriva	V537JBH	Transdev
V302LGC	Go-Ahead London	V323KMY	Metrobus	V355DLH	First London	V538JBH	Transdev
V302MDP	Travel London	V324GBY	First London	V356DGT	Arriva	V539JBH	Transdev
V303GLB	Metroline	V324KGW	Travel London	V356DLH	First London	V551JBH	Transdev
V303KGW	Travel London	V324KMY	Metrobus	V357DGT	Arriva	V552JBH	Transdev
V303LGC	Go-Ahead London	V324LGC	Go-Ahead London	V357DLH	First London	V553JBH	Transdev
V303MDP	Travel London	V325GBY	First London	V358DGT	Arriva	V556JBH	Transdev
V304KGW	Travel London	V325KGW	Travel London	V358DLH	First London	V557JBH	Transdev
V304LGC	Go-Ahead London	V325KMY	Metrobus	V359DGT	Arriva	V558JBH	Transdev
V304MDP	Travel London	V325LGC	Go-Ahead London	V359DLH	First London	V559JBH	Transdev
V305KGW	Travel London	V326DGT	Arriva	V360DLH	First London	V560JBH	Transdev
V305LGC	Go-Ahead London	V326GBY	First London	V361DGT	Arriva	V561JBH	Transdev
V305MDP	Travel London	V326KGW	Travel London	V361DLH	First London	V562JBH	Transdev
V306KGW	Travel London	V326KMY	Metrobus	V362DGT	Arriva	V601LGC	Arriva Original Tour
V306LGC	Go-Ahead London	V327DGT	Arriva	V362OWC	East London	V609LGC	Arriva
V306MDP	Travel London	V327GBY	First London	V363DGT	Arriva	V610LGC	Arriva
V307GBY	First London	V327KGW	Travel London	V363OWC	East London	V611LGC	Arriva
V307GLB	Metroline	V327KMY	Metrobus	V364DGT	Arriva	V612LGC	Arriva
V307KGW	Travel London	V327LGC	Go-Ahead London	V364OWC	East London	V613LGC	Arriva
V307LGC	Go-Ahead London	V328GBY	First London	V365DGT	Arriva	V614LGC	Arriva
V307MDP	Travel London	V328KGW	Travel London	V392KGF	Go-Ahead London	V615LGC	Arriva
V308GBY	First London	V328KMY	Metrobus	V421DGT	Arriva	V616LGC	Arriva
V308GLB	Metroline	V329DGT	Arriva	V421HBY	First London	V617LGC	Arriva
V308KGW	Travel London	V329GBY	First London	V422DGT	Arriva	V618LGC	Arriva
V308LGC	Go-Ahead London	V329KGW	Travel London	V423DGT	Arriva	V619LGC	Arriva
V308MDP	Travel London	V329KMY	Metrobus	V424DGT	Arriva	V620LGC	Arriva
V309GBY	First London	V329LGC	Go-Ahead London	V425DGT	Arriva		

The London Bus Handbook

Reg	Operator	Reg	Operator	Reg	Operator	Reg	Operator
V621LGC	Arriva	V877HBY	First London	W128EON	Transdev	W224DNO	East London
V622LGC	Arriva	V882HBY	First London	W129EON	Transdev	W226DNO	East London
V623LGC	Arriva	V886FKH	Transdev	W131EON	Transdev	W227CDN	Westbus
V628LGC	Arriva	V886HBY	First London	W132EON	Transdev	W227DNO	East London
V633LGC	Arriva	V887HBY	First London	W132VLO	First London	W228CDN	Westbus
V640LGC	Arriva	V889HLH	First London	W132WGT	Metroline	W228DNO	East London
V650LGC	Arriva	V890HLH	First London	W133EON	Transdev	W229CDN	Westbus
V660LGC	Arriva	V891HLH	First London	W133ULR	Metroline	W229DNO	East London
V701LWT	Arriva	V892HLH	First London	W133VLO	First London	W231DNO	East London
V749HBY	Metroline	V893HLH	First London	W133WGT	Metroline	W232DNO	East London
V750HBY	Metroline	V894HLH	First London	W134EON	Transdev	W233DNO	East London
V751HBY	Metroline	V895HLH	First London	W134ULR	Metroline	W236DNO	East London
V752HBY	Metroline	V896HLH	First London	W134WGT	Metroline	W236PBR	Anderson
V753HBY	Metroline	V897HLH	First London	W136EON	Transdev	W317VGX	Metrobus
V754HBY	Metroline	V898HLH	First London	W136ULR	Metroline	W319VGX	Metrobus
V755HBY	Metroline	V899HLH	First London	W136VGJ	Arriva	W332VGX	Metrobus
V756HBY	Metroline	V901FEC	Blue Triangle	W137EON	Transdev	W334VGX	Metrobus
V757HBY	Metroline	V902FEC	Blue Triangle	W137ULR	Metroline	W335VGX	Metrobus
V758HBY	Metroline	V903FEC	Blue Triangle	W137VGJ	Arriva	W336VGX	Metrobus
V759HBY	Metroline	V904FEC	Blue Triangle	W138EON	Transdev	W337VGX	Metrobus
V760HBY	Metroline	V904KAG	Transdev	W138ULR	Metroline	W338VGX	Metrobus
V761HBY	Metroline	V905FEC	Blue Triangle	W138VGJ	Arriva	W339VGX	Metrobus
V762HBY	Metroline	V906FEC	Blue Triangle	W139EON	Transdev	W341VGX	Metrobus
V763HBY	Metroline	V907FEC	Blue Triangle	W139ULR	Metroline	W342VGX	Metrobus
V764HBY	Metroline	V908FEC	Blue Triangle	W141EON	Transdev	W343VGX	Metrobus
V765HBY	Metroline	V909FEC	Blue Triangle	W141ULR	Metroline	W358VLN	First London
V781FKH	Transdev	V921KGF	Go-Ahead London	W142ULR	Metroline	W359VLN	First London
V782FKH	Transdev	V943DNB	Epsom Coaches	W143ULR	Metroline	W361VLN	First London
V783FKH	Transdev	V988HLH	First London	W143WGT	Metroline	W362VLN	First London
V784FKH	Transdev	V990HLH	First London	W144ULR	Metroline	W363VLN	First London
V785FKH	Transdev	VLT5	Arriva	W146ULR	Metroline	W364VLN	First London
V787FKH	Transdev	VLT6	Arriva	W147ULR	Metroline	W365VLN	First London
V788FKH	Transdev	VLT9	Go-Ahead London	W148ULR	Metroline	W366VGJ	Arriva
V789FKH	Transdev	VLT12	Arriva	W149ULR	Metroline	W366VLN	First London
V790FKH	Transdev	VLT14	East London	W151ULR	Metroline	W367VGJ	Arriva
V791FKH	Transdev	VLT27	Arriva	W152ULR	Metroline	W367VLN	First London
V792FKH	Transdev	VLT32	Arriva	W153ULR	Metroline	W368VGJ	Arriva
V793FKH	Transdev	VLT47	Arriva	W173DNO	East London	W368VLN	First London
V794FKH	Transdev	VLT85	Blue Triangle	W174DNO	East London	W369VGJ	Arriva
V795FKH	Transdev	VLT110	Blue Triangle	W176DNO	East London	W369VLN	First London
V796FKH	Transdev	VLT173	Arriva	W177DNO	East London	W371VGJ	Arriva
V797FKH	Transdev	VLT179	Go-Ahead London	W178DNO	East London	W371VLN	First London
V798FKH	Transdev	VLT240	East London	W181DNO	East London	W372VGJ	Arriva
V799FKH	Transdev	VLT244	Arriva	W182DNO	East London	W372VLN	First London
V801KAG	Transdev	VLT284	Go-Ahead London	W183DNO	East London	W373VGJ	Arriva
V802KAG	Transdev	VLT295	Arriva	W184DNO	East London	W373VLN	First London
V803KAG	Transdev	VLT298	Blue Triangle	W185DNO	East London	W374VGJ	Arriva
V805KAG	Transdev	VSC16	Westway	W186DNO	East London	W374VLN	First London
V806KAG	Transdev	W1NGS	Wings	W187CNO	East London	W376VGJ	Arriva
V807KAG	Transdev	W11NGS	Wings	W187DNO	East London	W376VLN	First London
V808KAG	Transdev	W18APT	Westbus	W188DNO	East London	W377VGJ	Arriva
V809KAG	Transdev	W30BCL	Tellings-Golden Miller	W189DNO	East London	W377VLN	First London
V810KAG	Transdev	W50BCL	Tellings-Golden Miller	W191DNO	East London	W378VGJ	Arriva
V811KAG	Transdev	W50TGM	Tellings-Golden Miller	W192DNO	East London	W378VLN	First London
V812KAG	Transdev	W80TGM	Tellings-Golden Miller	W193DNO	East London	W379VGJ	Arriva
V813KAG	Transdev	W112WGT	Metroline	W194DNO	East London	W379VLN	First London
V814KAG	Transdev	W114WGT	Metroline	W196DNO	East London	W381VGJ	Arriva
V815KAG	Transdev	W116EON	Transdev	W198DNO	East London	W382VGJ	Arriva
V816KAG	Transdev	W116WGT	Metroline	W199DNO	East London	W383VGJ	Arriva
V816KGF	Go-Ahead London	W117DNO	Transdev	W201DNO	East London	W384VGJ	Arriva
V855HBY	First London	W117WGT	Metroline	W202DNO	East London	W385VGJ	Arriva
V856HBY	First London	W118EON	Transdev	W203DNO	East London	W386VGJ	Arriva
V857HBY	First London	W118WGT	Metroline	W204DNO	East London	W387VGJ	Arriva
V858HBY	First London	W119EON	Transdev	W207DNO	East London	W388VGJ	Arriva
V859HBY	First London	W119WGT	Metroline	W208DNO	East London	W389VGJ	Arriva
V860HBY	First London	W122EON	Transdev	W209DNO	East London	W391VGJ	Arriva
V861HBY	First London	W122WGT	Metroline	W211DNO	East London	W392VGJ	Arriva
V862HBY	First London	W124EON	Transdev	W215DNO	East London	W3930UF	Tellings-Golden Miller
V863HBY	First London	W124WGT	Metroline	W216DNO	East London	W393VGJ	Arriva
V867HBY	First London	W126EON	Transdev	W218CDN	Arriva	W394VGJ	Arriva
V869HBY	First London	W126WGT	Metroline	W218DNO	East London	W395VGJ	Arriva
V872HBY	First London	W127EON	Transdev	W219DNO	East London	W396VGJ	Arriva
V874HBY	First London	W127WGT	Metroline	W223DNO	East London	W397VGJ	Arriva

Reg	Operator	Reg	Operator	Reg	Operator	Reg	Operator
W398VGJ	Arriva	W458WGH	Go-Ahead London	W498WGH	Go-Ahead London	W723ULL	First London
W399VGJ	Arriva	W459BCW	Transdev	W499WGH	Go-Ahead London	W724ULL	First London
W399WGH	Go-Ahead London	W459WGH	Go-Ahead London	W501WGH	Go-Ahead London	W726ULL	First London
W400ALC	Ashford Luxury	W461BCW	Transdev	W502WGH	Go-Ahead London	W727ULL	First London
W401UGM	Travel London	W461WGH	Go-Ahead London	W503WGH	Go-Ahead London	W728VLO	First London
W401VGJ	Arriva	W461XKX	Arriva	W504WGH	Go-Ahead London	W791VMV	Metrobus
W401WGH	Go-Ahead London	W462BCW	Transdev	W506WGH	Go-Ahead London	W792VMV	Metrobus
W402UGM	Travel London	W462WGH	Go-Ahead London	W507WGH	Go-Ahead London	W793VMV	Metrobus
W402VGJ	Arriva	W462XKX	Arriva	W508WGH	Go-Ahead London	W794VMV	Metrobus
W402WGH	Go-Ahead London	W463BCW	Transdev	W509WGH	Go-Ahead London	W795VMV	Metrobus
W403UGM	Travel London	W463WGH	Go-Ahead London	W511WGH	Go-Ahead London	W796VMV	Metrobus
W403VGJ	Arriva	W463XKX	Arriva	W512WGH	Go-Ahead London	W797VMV	Metrobus
W403WGH	Go-Ahead London	W464BCW	Transdev	W513WGH	Go-Ahead London	W798VMV	Metrobus
W404UGM	Travel London	W464WGH	Go-Ahead London	W514WGH	Go-Ahead London	**W799VMV**	**Metrobus**
W404VGJ	Arriva	W464XKX	Arriva	W516WGH	Go-Ahead London	W840VLO	First London
W404WGH	Go-Ahead London	W465BCW	Transdev	W517WGH	Go-Ahead London	W840WGH	Go-Ahead London
W407UGM	Travel London	W465WGH	Go-Ahead London	W518WGH	Go-Ahead London	W871VGT	Epsom Coaches
W407VGJ	Arriva	W465XKX	Arriva	W519WGH	Go-Ahead London	W872VGT	Epsom Coaches
W408UGM	Travel London	W466BCW	Transdev	W521WGH	Go-Ahead London	W873GBX	Go-Ahead Docklands
W408VGJ	Arriva	W466WGH	Go-Ahead London	W522WGH	Go-Ahead London	W873VGT	Epsom Coaches
W408WGH	Go-Ahead London	W466XKX	Arriva	W523WGH	Go-Ahead London	W874GBX	Go-Ahead Docklands
W409UGM	Travel London	W467BCW	Transdev	W524WGH	Go-Ahead London	W874VGT	Epsom Coaches
W409VGJ	Arriva	W467WGH	Go-Ahead London	W526WGH	Go-Ahead London	W875VGT	Epsom Coaches
W409WGH	Go-Ahead London	W467XKX	Arriva	W527WGH	Go-Ahead London	W876VGT	Epsom Coaches
W40TGM	Tellings-Golden Miller	W468BCW	Transdev	W529WGH	Go-Ahead London	W889UJB	MCH
W411UGM	Travel London	W468WGH	Go-Ahead London	W531WGH	Go-Ahead London	W895VLN	First London
W411VGJ	Arriva	W468XKX	Arriva	W532WGH	Go-Ahead London	W896VLN	First London
W412UGM	Travel London	W469BCW	Transdev	W533WGH	Go-Ahead London	W897VLN	First London
W412VGJ	Arriva	W469WGH	Go-Ahead London	W534WGH	Go-Ahead London	W898VLN	First London
W413UGM	Travel London	W469XKX	Arriva	W536WGH	Go-Ahead London	W899VLN	First London
W413VGJ	Arriva	W471BCW	Transdev	W537WGH	Go-Ahead London	W901VLN	First London
W414VGJ	Arriva	W471WGH	Go-Ahead London	W538WGH	Go-Ahead London	W902VLN	First London
W415WGH	Go-Ahead London	W471XKX	Arriva	W539WGH	Go-Ahead London	W903VLN	First London
W425VLO	First London	W472BCW	Transdev	W541WGH	Go-Ahead London	W904VLN	First London
W425WGH	Go-Ahead London	W472WGH	Go-Ahead London	W542WGH	Go-Ahead London	W905WGH	Go-Ahead London
W428WGH	Go-Ahead London	W472XKX	Arriva	W543WGH	Go-Ahead London	W906VLN	First London
W431WGJ	Arriva	W473BCW	Transdev	W544WGH	Go-Ahead London	W907VLN	First London
W432WGJ	Arriva	W473WGH	Go-Ahead London	W555ASH	Ashford Luxury	W908VLN	First London
W433UMX	Tellings-Golden Miller	W473XKX	Arriva	W578DGU	Go-Ahead London	W909VLN	First London
W433WGJ	Arriva	W474BCW	Transdev	W582WCA	Go-Ahead Docklands	W912VLN	First London
W434WGJ	Arriva	W474WGH	Go-Ahead London	W583WCA	Go-Ahead Docklands	W913VLN	First London
W435CRN	Travel London	W474XKX	Arriva	W601UGM	Travel London	W914VLN	First London
W435WGH	Go-Ahead London	W475BCW	Transdev	W602UGM	Travel London	W915VLN	First London
W435WGJ	Arriva	W475WGH	Go-Ahead London	W602VGJ	Arriva	W916VLN	First London
W436CRN	Travel London	W475XKX	Arriva	W603UGM	Travel London	W917VLN	First London
W436WGJ	Arriva	W476BCW	Transdev	W603VGJ	Arriva	W918VLN	First London
W437CRN	Travel London	W476WGH	Go-Ahead London	W604UGM	Travel London	W919VLN	First London
W437WGJ	Arriva	W476XKX	Arriva	W604VGJ	Arriva	W921VLN	First London
W438CRN	Travel London	W477BCW	Transdev	W605UGM	Travel London	W922VLN	First London
W438WGJ	Arriva	W477WGH	Go-Ahead London	W605VGJ	Arriva	W923VLN	First London
W439WGH	Go-Ahead London	W477XKX	Arriva	W606UGM	Travel London	W924VLN	First London
W441WGH	Go-Ahead London	W478BCW	Transdev	W606VGJ	Arriva	W926VLN	First London
W442CWX	Tellings-Golden Miller	W478WGH	Go-Ahead London	W607UGM	Travel London	W927VLN	First London
W442WGH	Go-Ahead London	W478XKX	Arriva	W607VGJ	Arriva	W928VLN	First London
W443WGH	Go-Ahead London	W479WGH	Go-Ahead London	W608UGM	Travel London	W929VLN	First London
W445WGH	Go-Ahead London	W479XKX	Arriva	W608VGJ	Arriva	W931ULL	First London
W446WGH	Go-Ahead London	W481WGH	Go-Ahead London	W609UGM	Travel London	W934ULL	First London
W447WGH	Go-Ahead London	W481XKX	Arriva	W611UGM	Travel London	W935ULL	First London
W448BCW	Transdev	W482WGH	Go-Ahead London	W612UGM	Travel London	W936ULL	First London
W448WGH	Go-Ahead London	W483WGH	Go-Ahead London	W627UMV	Tellings-Golden Miller	W937ULL	First London
W449BCW	Transdev	W484WGH	Go-Ahead London	W629WMA	Westway	W939ULL	First London
W449WGH	Go-Ahead London	W485WGH	Go-Ahead London	W667SJF	Isleworth	W941ULL	First London
W451BCW	Transdev	W486WGH	Go-Ahead London	W681ULL	First London	W942ULL	First London
W451WGH	Go-Ahead London	W487WGH	Go-Ahead London	W682ULL	First London	W946ULL	First London
W452BCW	Transdev	W488WGH	Go-Ahead London	W683ULL	First London	W947ULL	First London
W452WGH	Go-Ahead London	W489WGH	Go-Ahead London	W684ULL	First London	W948ULL	First London
W453BCW	Transdev	W491WGH	Go-Ahead London	W685ULL	First London	W949ULL	First London
W453WGH	Go-Ahead London	W492WGH	Go-Ahead London	W686ULL	First London	W951ULL	First London
W454BCW	Transdev	W493WGH	Go-Ahead London	W687ULL	First London	W952ULL	First London
W454WGH	Go-Ahead London	W494WGH	Go-Ahead London	W718ULL	First London	W956WGH	Go-Ahead London
W457BCW	Transdev	W495WGH	Go-Ahead London	W719ULL	First London	W963TRP	Metroline
W457WGH	Go-Ahead London	W496WGH	Go-Ahead London	W721ULL	First London	W964TRP	Metroline
W458BCW	Transdev	W497WGH	Go-Ahead London	W722ULL	First London	W965TRP	Metroline

The London Bus Handbook

Reg	Operator	Reg	Operator	Reg	Operator	Reg	Operator
W966TRP	Metroline	WLT751	Arriva	X229NNO	East London	X295NNO	East London
W967TRP	Metroline	WLT807	Arriva	X229WNO	East London	X296NNO	East London
W968TRP	Metroline	WLT826	Metroline	X231NNO	East London	X297NNO	East London
W969TRP	Metroline	WLT852	Wings	X231WNO	East London	X298NNO	East London
W971TRP	Metroline	WLT871	East London	X232NNO	East London	X299NNO	East London
W972TRP	Metroline	WLT880	Transdev	X232WNO	East London	X301NNO	East London
W973TRP	Metroline	WLT886	East London	X233NNO	East London	X302NNO	East London
W974TRP	Metroline	WLT888	Arriva	X233WNO	East London	X303NNO	East London
W975TRP	Metroline	WLT891	Wings	X234NNO	East London	X304NNO	East London
W976TRP	Metroline	WLT892	Arriva	X234WNO	East London	X307NNO	East London
W977TRP	Metroline	WLT895	Arriva	X235NNO	East London	X308NNO	East London
W996WGH	Go-Ahead London	WLT897	Arriva	X235WNO	East London	X309NNO	East London
W997WGH	Go-Ahead London	WLT900	Blue Triangle	X236NNO	East London	X311KRX	Travel London
W998WGH	Go-Ahead London	WLT901	Arriva	X236WNO	East London	X311NNO	East London
WA03HRG	Westbus	WLT903	Metroline	X237NNO	East London	X312KRX	Travel London
WA03HRK	Westbus	WLT931	Wings	X237WNO	East London	X312NNO	East London
WA03UEE	Westway	WLT970	Arriva	X238NNO	East London	X313KRX	Travel London
WA04EWS	Westbus	WLT982	Wings	X238WNO	East London	X313NNO	East London
WA04MHJ	Chalfont	WLT987	Wings	X239NNO	East London	X314KRX	Travel London
WA04MHK	Chalfont	WLT997	Arriva	X239PGT	Arriva	X314NNO	East London
WA04MHL	Chalfont	WN03ASH	Ashford Luxury	X241NNO	East London	X315KRX	Travel London
WA05JWJ	Anderson	WN05ASH	Ashford Luxury	X241PGT	Arriva	X315NNO	East London
WA05JWK	Anderson	WN52ASH	Ashford Luxury	X242NNO	East London	X317KRX	Travel London
WA05JWL	Anderson	WYV4T	Blue Triangle	X242PGT	Arriva	X317NNO	East London
WA06CDX	Chalfont	WYV8T	Blue Triangle	X243NNO	East London	X319HLL	Metroline
WA06CDY	Chalfont	WYV9T	Blue Triangle	X243PGT	Arriva	X319KRX	Travel London
WA06CDZ	Chalfont	WYV11T	Blue Triangle	X244PGT	Arriva	X319NNO	East London
WA06GRU	Anderson	WYV22T	Blue Triangle	X246NNO	East London	X322HLL	Metroline
WA06GRX	Anderson	WYV23T	Blue Triangle	X246PGT	Arriva	X322KRX	Travel London
WA06GRZ	Anderson	WYV33T	Blue Triangle	X247NNO	East London	X322NNO	East London
WA06GSO	Westway	WYW28T	Blue Triangle	X247PGT	Arriva	X324HLL	Metroline
WA06JGU	Westway	WYW46T	Transdev	X248NNO	East London	X324NNO	East London
WA06NCC	Westbus	X93FOR	Travel London	X248PGT	Arriva	X326HLL	Metroline
WA54EDC	Isleworth	X149FBB	East Thames	X249NNO	East London	X326NNO	East London
WA54HXU	Chalfont	X151FBB	East Thames	X249PGT	Arriva	X327HLL	Metroline
WA54HXV	Chalfont	X152ENJ	Tellings-Golden Miller	X251NNO	East London	X327NNO	East London
WA54HXW	Chalfont	X152FBB	East Thames	X252NNO	East London	X329HLL	Metroline
WA54HXX	Chalfont	X153ENJ	Tellings-Golden Miller	X253NNO	East London	X329NNO	East London
WA56ENK	Chalfont	X153FBB	East Thames	X254NNO	East London	X331HLL	Metroline
WA56ENL	Chalfont	X154ENJ	Tellings-Golden Miller	X256NNO	East London	X331NNO	East London
WA56ENM	Chalfont	X154FBB	East Thames	X257NNO	East London	X332HLL	Metroline
WE51WAY	Westway	X157ENJ	Tellings-Golden Miller	X258NNO	East London	X332NNO	East London
WE52BUS	Westbus	X157FBB	East Thames	X259NNO	East London	X334HLL	Metroline
WE53BUS	Westbus	X158ENJ	Tellings-Golden Miller	X261NNO	East London	X334NNO	East London
WET342	Wings	X158FBB	East Thames	X262NNO	East London	X335HLL	Metroline
WET476	Westway	X159ENJ	Tellings-Golden Miller	X263NNO	East London	X335NNO	East London
WET590	Wings	X159FBB	East Thames	X264NNO	East London	X336HLL	Metroline
WET725	Wings	X161FBB	East Thames	X265NNO	East London	X336NNO	East London
WIB117	Westbus	X162FBB	East Thames	X266NNO	East London	X337HLL	Metroline
WIB255	Westbus	X163FBB	East Thames	X267NNO	East London	X337NNO	East London
WIB300	Westbus	X164FBB	East Thames	X268NNO	East London	X338HLL	Metroline
WJ02VRL	Westbus	X165FBB	East Thames	X269NNO	East London	X338NNO	East London
WJ02VRM	Westbus	X166FBB	East Thames	X271NNO	East London	X339HLL	Metroline
WJ02VRN	Westbus	X167FBB	East Thames	X272NNO	East London	X339NNO	East London
WJ55EWF	Westway	X168FBB	East Thames	X273NNO	East London	X341HLL	Metroline
WLT324	East London	X169FBB	East Thames	X274NNO	East London	X341NNO	East London
WLT348	Arriva	X171FBB	East Thames	X276NNO	East London	X342HLL	Metroline
WLT372	Arriva	X172FBB	East Thames	X277NNO	East London	X342NNO	East London
WLT385	Arriva	X173FBB	East Thames	X278NNO	East London	X343HLL	Metroline
WLT461	East London	X179BNH	Metroline	X279NNO	East London	X343NNO	East London
WLT491	East London	X201UMS	Transdev	X281NNO	East London	X344NNO	East London
WLT516	Go-Ahead London	X202UMS	Transdev	X282NNO	East London	X344YGU	Metrobus
WLT531	Arriva	X203UMS	Transdev	X283NNO	East London	X346NNO	East London
WLT554	Arriva	X216HCD	Tellings-Golden Miller	X284NNO	East London	X347NNO	East London
WLT560	Wings	X217HCD	Tellings-Golden Miller	X285NNO	East London	X348NNO	East London
WLT575	East London	X218HCD	Tellings-Golden Miller	X286NNO	East London	X349NNO	East London
WLT644	Metroline	X219HCD	Tellings-Golden Miller	X287NNO	East London	X351NNO	East London
WLT652	East London	X221HCD	Tellings-Golden Miller	X288NNO	East London	X352NNO	East London
WLT659	First London	X223HCD	Tellings-Golden Miller	X289NNO	East London	X353NNO	East London
WLT664	Arriva	X224WNO	East London	X291NNO	East London	X354NNO	East London
WLT676	Arriva	X226WNO	East London	X292NNO	East London	X356NNO	East London
WLT719	Arriva	X227WNO	East London	X293NNO	East London	X357NNO	East London
WLT746	Wings	X228WNO	East London	X294NNO	East London	X358NNO	East London

X361NNO	East London	X436FGP	Arriva	X529UAT	Transdev	X599EGK	Go-Ahead London
X362NNO	East London	X437FGP	Arriva	X531GGO	Arriva	X601EGK	Go-Ahead London
X363NNO	East London	X438FGP	Arriva	X531UAT	Transdev	X601OKH	Transdev
X364NNO	East London	X439FGP	Arriva	X532GGO	Arriva	X602EGK	Go-Ahead London
X365NNO	East London	X441FGP	Arriva	X532UAT	Transdev	X602OKH	Transdev
X366NNO	East London	X442FGP	Arriva	X533GGO	Arriva	X603EGK	Go-Ahead London
X367NNO	East London	X443FGP	Arriva	X533UAT	Transdev	X603OKH	Transdev
X368NNO	East London	X444ASH	Ashford Luxury	X534GGO	Arriva	X604EGK	Go-Ahead London
X369NNO	East London	X445FGP	Arriva	X536GGO	Arriva	X604OKH	Transdev
X371CUY	Travel London	X446FGP	Arriva	X537GGO	Arriva	X605EGK	Go-Ahead London
X371NNO	East London	X447FGP	Arriva	X538GGO	Arriva	X605OKH	Transdev
X372NNO	East London	X448FGP	Arriva	X541GGO	Arriva	X606EGK	Go-Ahead London
X373NNO	East London	X449FGP	Arriva	X544EGK	Go-Ahead London	X606OKH	Transdev
X376NNO	East London	X451FGP	Arriva	X546EGK	Go-Ahead London	X607EGK	Go-Ahead London
X377NNO	East London	X452FGP	Arriva	X546GGO	Arriva	X607OKH	Transdev
X378NNO	East London	X453FGP	Arriva	X547EGK	Go-Ahead London	X608EGK	Go-Ahead London
X379NNO	East London	X454FGP	Arriva	X548EGK	Go-Ahead London	X608OKH	Transdev
X381HLR	First London	X471GGO	Arriva	X549EGK	Go-Ahead London	X609EGK	Go-Ahead London
X381NNO	East London	X474ROA	Clarkes of London	X551EGK	Go-Ahead London	X609OKH	Transdev
X382HLR	First London	X475GGO	Arriva	X552EGK	Go-Ahead London	X611EGK	Go-Ahead London
X382NNO	East London	X477ROA	Clarkes of London	X553EGK	Go-Ahead London	X611HLT	First London
X383HLR	First London	X478GGO	Arriva	X554EGK	Go-Ahead London	X611OKH	Transdev
X383NNO	East London	X481GGO	Arriva	X556EGK	Go-Ahead London	X612EGK	Go-Ahead London
X384HLR	First London	X485GGO	Arriva	X557EGK	Go-Ahead London	X612HLT	First London
X384NNO	East London	X501EGK	Go-Ahead London	X558EGK	Go-Ahead London	X613EGK	Go-Ahead London
X385HLR	First London	X501GGO	Arriva	X559EGK	Go-Ahead London	X613HLT	First London
X385NNO	East London	X501JLO	First London	X561EGK	Go-Ahead London	X614HLT	First London
X386HLR	First London	X502EGK	Go-Ahead London	X562EGK	Go-Ahead London	X615EGK	Go-Ahead London
X386NNO	East London	X502GGO	Arriva	X563EGK	Go-Ahead London	X616EGK	Go-Ahead London
X387HLR	First London	X502JLO	First London	X564EGK	Go-Ahead London	X635LLX	Metroline
X387NNO	East London	X503EGK	Go-Ahead London	X566EGK	Go-Ahead London	X636LLX	Metroline
X388HLR	First London	X503GGO	Arriva	X567EGK	Go-Ahead London	X637LLX	Metroline
X388NNO	East London	X503JLO	First London	X568EGK	Go-Ahead London	X638LLX	Metroline
X389HLR	First London	X504EGK	Go-Ahead London	X569EGK	Go-Ahead London	X639LLX	Metroline
X389NNO	East London	X504GGO	Arriva	X571EGK	Go-Ahead London	X641LLX	Metroline
X391HLR	First London	X504JLO	First London	X572EGK	Go-Ahead London	X642LLX	Metroline
X391NNO	East London	X506EGK	Go-Ahead London	X573EGK	Go-Ahead London	X643LLX	Metroline
X392HLR	First London	X506GGO	Arriva	X574EGK	Go-Ahead London	X644LLX	Metroline
X392NNO	East London	X506HLR	First London	X575EGK	Go-Ahead London	X645LLX	Metroline
X393HLR	First London	X507EGK	Go-Ahead London	X576EGK	Go-Ahead London	X646LLX	Metroline
X393NNO	East London	X507GGO	Arriva	X577EGK	Go-Ahead London	X647LLX	Metroline
X394HLR	First London	X507HLR	First London	X578EGK	Go-Ahead London	X648LLX	Metroline
X394NNO	East London	X508EGK	Go-Ahead London	X578RJW	First London	X649LLX	Metroline
X395HLR	First London	X508GGO	Arriva	X579BYD	Chalfont	X651LLX	Metroline
X395NNO	East London	X508HLR	First London	X579EGK	Go-Ahead London	X652LLX	Metroline
X396HLR	First London	X509EGK	Go-Ahead London	X581EGK	Go-Ahead London	X653LLX	Metroline
X396NNO	East London	X509HLR	First London	X582EGK	Go-Ahead London	X654LLX	Metroline
X397HLR	First London	X511HLR	First London	X583EGK	Go-Ahead London	X656EGK	Go-Ahead London
X397NNO	East London	X511UAT	Transdev	X584EGK	Go-Ahead London	X656LLX	Metroline
X398HLR	First London	X512HLR	First London	X5840RV	CT Plus	X657LLX	Metroline
X398NNO	East London	X512UAT	Transdev	X585EGK	Go-Ahead London	X658LLX	Metroline
X399HLR	First London	X513HLR	First London	X5850RV	CT Plus	X659LLX	Metroline
X401HLR	First London	X513UAT	Transdev	X586EGK	Go-Ahead London	X661LLX	Metroline
X402HLR	First London	X514HLR	First London	X5860RV	CT Plus	X662LLX	Metroline
X415FGP	Arriva	X514UAT	Transdev	X587EGK	Go-Ahead London	X663LLX	Metroline
X416FGP	Arriva	X516UAT	Transdev	X5870RV	CT Plus	X664LLX	Metroline
X417FGP	Arriva	X517UAT	Transdev	X588EGK	Go-Ahead London	X665LLX	Metroline
X418FGP	Arriva	X518UAT	Transdev	X5880RV	CT Plus	X667LLX	Metroline
X419FGP	Arriva	X519GGO	Arriva	X589EGK	Go-Ahead London	X668LLX	Metroline
X421FGP	Arriva	X519UAT	Transdev	X5890RV	CT Plus	X688HLF	First London
X422FGP	Arriva	X521GGO	Arriva	X591EGK	Go-Ahead London	X689HLF	First London
X423FGP	Arriva	X521UAT	Transdev	X5910RV	CT Plus	X697HLF	First London
X424FGP	Arriva	X522GGO	Arriva	X592EGK	Go-Ahead London	X698HLF	First London
X425FGP	Arriva	X522UAT	Transdev	X5920RV	CT Plus	X699EGK	Go-Ahead London
X426FGP	Arriva	X523GGO	Arriva	X593EGK	Go-Ahead London	X699HLF	First London
X427FGP	Arriva	X523UAT	Transdev	X5930RV	CT Plus	X701EGK	Go-Ahead London
X428FGP	Arriva	X524GGO	Arriva	X594EGK	Go-Ahead London	X702EGK	Go-Ahead London
X429FGP	Arriva	X524UAT	Transdev	X5940RV	CT Plus	X705EGK	Go-Ahead London
X431FGP	Arriva	X526GGO	Arriva	X595EGK	Go-Ahead London	X707EGK	Go-Ahead London
X432FGP	Arriva	X526UAT	Transdev	X5950RV	CT Plus	X729HLF	First London
X433FGP	Arriva	X527GGO	Arriva	X596EGK	Go-Ahead London	X731HLF	First London
X434FGP	Arriva	X527UAT	Transdev	X597EGK	Go-Ahead London	X732HLF	First London
X435FGP	Arriva	X529GGO	Arriva	X598EGK	Go-Ahead London	X733HLF	First London

Reg	Operator	Reg	Operator	Reg	Operator	Reg	Operator
X734HLF	First London	Y20TGM	Tellings-Golden Miller	Y202NLK	Metroline	Y285FJN	East London
X735HLF	First London	Y22APT	Westbus	Y203NLK	Metroline	Y286FJN	East London
X736HLF	First London	Y30TGM	Tellings-Golden Miller	Y204NLK	Metroline	Y287FJN	East London
X737HLF	First London	Y36HWB	Travel London	Y207NLK	Metroline	Y289FJN	East London
X738HLF	First London	Y38HWB	Travel London	Y208NLK	Metroline	Y291FJN	East London
X741HLF	First London	Y38YVV	Travel London	Y209NLK	Metroline	Y292FJN	East London
X742HLF	First London	Y102TGH	Arriva	Y215HWF	Travel London	Y292PDN	Tellings-Golden Miller
X743HLF	First London	Y111ASH	Ashford Luxury	Y223NLF	First London	Y293FJN	East London
X744HLF	First London	Y116HWB	Travel London	Y224NLF	First London	Y294FJN	East London
X745EGK	Go-Ahead London	Y117HWB	Travel London	Y232NLK	Metroline	Y295FJN	East London
X745HLF	First London	Y118HWB	Travel London	Y233NLK	Metroline	Y296FJN	East London
X746JLO	First London	Y131HWB	Travel London	Y234NLK	Metroline	Y297FJN	East London
X747JLO	First London	Y133HWB	Travel London	Y235HWB	Travel London	Y298FJN	East London
X748JLO	First London	Y134HWB	Travel London	Y235NLK	Metroline	Y299FJN	East London
X751HLR	First London	Y143NLK	Metroline	Y236NLK	Metroline	Y301FJN	East London
X752HLR	First London	Y144NLK	Metroline	Y237FJN	East London	Y302FJN	East London
X753HLR	First London	Y146NLK	Metroline	Y237NLK	Metroline	Y329FJN	East London
X754HLR	First London	Y147NLK	Metroline	Y238FJN	East London	Y32HWB	Travel London
X756HLR	First London	Y148NLK	Metroline	Y238NLK	Metroline	Y331FJN	East London
X757HLR	First London	Y149NLK	Metroline	Y239FJN	East London	Y332FJN	East London
X758HLR	First London	Y151NLK	Metroline	Y239NLK	Metroline	Y334FJN	East London
X759HLR	First London	Y152NLK	Metroline	Y241FJN	East London	Y335FJN	East London
X761HLR	First London	Y153NLK	Metroline	Y242FJN	East London	Y336FJN	East London
X762HLR	First London	Y154NLK	Metroline	Y243FJN	East London	Y337FJN	East London
X763HLR	First London	Y157NLK	Metroline	Y244FJN	East London	Y338FJN	East London
X764HLR	First London	Y158NLK	Metroline	Y246FJN	East London	Y339FJN	East London
X766HLR	First London	Y159NLK	Metroline	Y246NLK	Metroline	Y342FJN	East London
X767HLR	First London	Y15TGM	Tellings-Golden Miller	Y247FJN	East London	Y343FJN	East London
X768HLR	First London	Y161NLK	Metroline	Y248FJN	East London	Y344FJN	East London
X769HLR	First London	Y162NLK	Metroline	Y248NLK	Metroline	Y344NLF	First London
X771HLR	First London	Y163NLK	Metroline	Y249FJN	East London	Y346FJN	East London
X772HLR	First London	Y164NLK	Metroline	Y249NLK	Metroline	Y346NLF	First London
X773HLR	First London	Y165NLK	Metroline	Y251FJN	East London	Y347FJN	East London
X774HLR	First London	Y166NLK	Metroline	Y251NLK	Metroline	Y348FJN	East London
X776HLR	First London	Y167NLK	Metroline	Y252FJN	East London	Y348HMY	Metrobus
X778HLR	First London	Y168NLK	Metroline	Y252NLK	Metroline	Y349FJN	East London
X779HLR	First London	Y169NLK	Metroline	Y253FJN	East London	Y349HMY	Metrobus
X781HLR	First London	Y171NLK	Metroline	Y253NLK	Metroline	Y351FJN	East London
X782HLR	First London	Y172NLK	Metroline	Y254FJN	East London	Y351HMY	Metrobus
X783HLR	First London	Y173NLK	Metroline	Y254NLK	Metroline	Y352FJN	East London
X784HLR	First London	Y174NLK	Metroline	Y256FJN	East London	Y352HMY	Metrobus
X785HLR	First London	Y176NLK	Metroline	Y256NLK	Metroline	Y353FJN	East London
X787HLR	First London	Y177JSH	Excalibur	Y257FJN	East London	Y353HMY	Metrobus
X788HLR	First London	Y177NLK	Metroline	Y257NLK	Metroline	Y354FJN	East London
X78HLR	First London	Y178NLK	Metroline	Y258FJN	East London	Y354HMY	Metrobus
X79HLR	First London	Y179NLK	Metroline	Y258NLK	Metroline	Y356FJN	East London
X806NJB	Isleworth	Y181NLK	Metroline	Y259FJN	East London	Y356HMY	Metrobus
X954HLT	First London	Y181RCR	Blue Triangle	Y259NLK	Metroline	Y357HMY	Metrobus
X956HLT	First London	Y182NLK	Metroline	Y261FJN	East London	Y358HMY	Metrobus
X957HLT	First London	Y182RCR	Blue Triangle	Y261NLK	Metroline	Y359HMY	Metrobus
X958HLT	First London	Y183NLK	Metroline	Y262FJN	East London	Y359NHK	East London
X959HLT	First London	Y183RCR	Blue Triangle	Y262NLK	Metroline	Y361HMY	Metrobus
X961HLT	First London	Y184NLK	Metroline	Y263FJN	East London	Y361NHK	East London
X962HLT	First London	Y184RCR	Blue Triangle	Y263NLK	Metroline	Y362HMY	Metrobus
X963HLT	First London	Y185NLK	Metroline	Y264FJN	East London	Y362NHK	East London
X964HLT	First London	Y185RCR	Blue Triangle	Y264NLK	Metroline	Y363HMY	Metrobus
X965HLT	First London	Y186NLK	Metroline	Y265FJN	East London	Y363NHK	East London
X966HLT	First London	Y186RCR	Blue Triangle	Y265NLK	Metroline	Y364HMY	Metrobus
X967HLT	First London	Y187NLK	Metroline	Y266FJN	East London	Y364NHK	East London
X968HLT	First London	Y187RCR	Blue Triangle	Y267FJN	East London	Y365HMY	Metrobus
X969HLT	First London	Y188NLK	Metroline	Y268FJN	East London	Y365NHK	East London
X971HLT	First London	Y188RCR	Blue Triangle	Y269FJN	East London	Y366HMY	Metrobus
X972HLT	First London	Y189NLK	Metroline	Y271FJN	East London	Y366NHK	East London
X973HLT	First London	Y191NLK	Metroline	Y272FJN	East London	Y367HMY	Metrobus
X974HLT	First London	Y192NLK	Metroline	Y273FJN	East London	Y367NHK	East London
X975HLT	First London	Y193NLK	Metroline	Y274FJN	East London	Y368HMY	Metrobus
X977HLT	First London	Y194NLK	Metroline	Y276FJN	East London	Y368NHK	East London
X978HLT	First London	Y195NLK	Metroline	Y277FJN	East London	Y368NHK	East London
X981HLT	First London	Y196NLK	Metroline	Y279FJN	East London	Y369HMY	Metrobus
XAZ774	Westbus	Y197NLK	Metroline	Y281FJN	East London	Y371FJN	East London
XAZ807	Westbus	Y198NLK	Metroline	Y282FJN	East London	Y371HMY	Metrobus
XDZ5917	Transdev	Y199NLK	Metroline	Y283FJN	East London	Y371NHK	East London
Y10TGM	Tellings-Golden Miller	Y201NLK	Metroline	Y284FJN	East London		

Reg	Operator	Reg	Operator	Reg	Operator	Reg	Operator	Reg	Operator
Y371UOM	Clarkes of London	Y463HUA	Westbus	Y536XAG	Transdev	Y748TGH	Go-Ahead London		
Y372FJN	East London	Y464HUA	Westbus	Y537XAG	Transdev	Y749TGH	Go-Ahead London		
Y372HMY	Metrobus	Y464NHK	East London	Y538XAG	Transdev	Y801DGT	Arriva		
Y372NHK	East London	Y471UGC	Arriva	Y539XAG	Transdev	Y801TGH	Go-Ahead London		
Y372UOM	Clarkes of London	Y472UGC	Arriva	Y541UGC	Arriva	Y802DGT	Arriva		
Y373FJN	East London	Y473UGC	Arriva	Y541XAG	Transdev	Y802TGH	Go-Ahead London		
Y373HMY	Metrobus	Y474UGC	Arriva	Y542UGC	Arriva	Y803DGT	Arriva		
Y373NHK	East London	Y475UGC	Arriva	Y542XAG	Transdev	Y803TGH	Go-Ahead London		
Y374FJN	East London	Y476UGC	Arriva	Y543UGC	Arriva	Y804DGT	Arriva		
Y374HMY	Metrobus	Y477UGC	Arriva	Y543XAG	Transdev	Y805DGT	Arriva		
Y374NHK	East London	Y478UGC	Arriva	Y544UGC	Arriva	Y805TGH	Go-Ahead London		
Y376FJN	East London	Y479UGC	Arriva	Y544XAG	Transdev	Y806DGT	Arriva		
Y376HMY	Metrobus	Y481UGC	Arriva	Y546UGC	Arriva	Y806TGH	Go-Ahead London		
Y376NHK	East London	Y482UGC	Arriva	Y546XAG	Transdev	Y808TGH	Go-Ahead London		
Y376UOM	Clarkes of London	Y483UGC	Arriva	Y547UGC	Arriva	Y809TGH	Go-Ahead London		
Y377HMY	Metrobus	Y484UGC	Arriva	Y547XAG	Transdev	Y811TGH	Go-Ahead London		
Y377NHK	East London	Y485UGC	Arriva	Y548UGC	Arriva	Y812TGH	Go-Ahead London		
Y377UOM	Clarkes of London	Y486UGC	Arriva	Y548XAG	Transdev	Y813TGH	Go-Ahead London		
Y378HMY	Metrobus	Y487UGC	Arriva	Y549UGC	Arriva	Y814TGH	Go-Ahead London		
Y378NHK	East London	Y488UGC	Arriva	Y549XAG	Transdev	Y815TGH	Go-Ahead London		
Y378UOM	Clarkes of London	Y489UGC	Arriva	Y551XAG	Transdev	Y816HHE	Westbus		
Y379HMY	Metrobus	Y491UGC	Arriva	Y552XAG	Transdev	Y816TGH	Go-Ahead London		
Y379NHK	East London	Y492UGC	Arriva	Y553XAG	Transdev	Y817TGH	Go-Ahead London		
Y37HWB	Travel London	Y493UGC	Arriva	Y554XAG	Transdev	Y818TGH	Go-Ahead London		
Y381HKE	Metrobus	Y494UGC	Arriva	Y556XAG	Transdev	Y819TGH	Go-Ahead London		
Y381NHK	East London	Y495UGC	Arriva	Y557XAG	Transdev	Y821TGH	Go-Ahead London		
Y382HKE	Metrobus	Y496UGC	Arriva	Y581UGC	Arriva	Y822TGH	Go-Ahead London		
Y382NHK	East London	Y497UGC	Arriva	Y585TOV	Clarkes of London	Y823TGH	Go-Ahead London		
Y383HKE	Metrobus	Y498UGC	Arriva	Y586TOV	Clarkes of London	Y824TGH	Go-Ahead London		
Y384HKE	Metrobus	Y499UGC	Arriva	Y587TOV	Clarkes of London	Y825TGH	Go-Ahead London		
Y384NHK	East London	Y501TGJ	Tellings-Golden Miller	Y63LTF	Metroline	Y826TGH	Go-Ahead London		
Y385HKE	Metrobus	Y501UGC	Arriva	Y641AVV	Metroline	Y827TGH	Go-Ahead London		
Y385NHK	East London	Y502UGC	Arriva	Y652NLO	Metroline	Y828TGH	Go-Ahead London		
Y386HKE	Metrobus	Y503UGC	Arriva	Y653NLO	Metroline	Y829TGH	Go-Ahead London		
Y386NHK	East London	Y504TGJ	Tellings-Golden Miller	Y654NLO	Metroline	Y831TGH	Go-Ahead London		
Y387HKE	Metrobus	Y504UGC	Arriva	Y656NLO	Metroline	Y832TGH	Go-Ahead London		
Y388HKE	Metrobus	Y506TGJ	Tellings-Golden Miller	Y657NLO	Metroline	Y833TGH	Go-Ahead London		
Y388NHK	East London	Y506UGC	Arriva	Y658NLO	Metroline	Y834TGH	Go-Ahead London		
Y389HKE	Metrobus	Y507TGJ	Tellings-Golden Miller	Y659NLO	Metroline	Y835TGH	Go-Ahead London		
Y389NHK	East London	Y507UGC	Arriva	Y661NLO	Metroline	Y836TGH	Go-Ahead London		
Y391HKE	Metrobus	Y508NHK	East London	Y662NLO	Metroline	Y837TGH	Go-Ahead London		
Y391NHK	East London	Y508UGC	Arriva	Y663NLO	Metroline	Y838TGH	Go-Ahead London		
Y392HKE	Metrobus	Y509NHK	East London	Y664NLO	Metroline	Y839TGH	Go-Ahead London		
Y392NHK	East London	Y509UGC	Arriva	Y665NLO	Metroline	Y840TGH	Go-Ahead London		
Y393HKE	Metrobus	Y511NHK	East London	Y667NLO	Metroline	Y841TGH	Go-Ahead London		
Y393NHK	East London	Y511UGC	Arriva	Y668NLO	Metroline	Y842TGH	Go-Ahead London		
Y395KCB	Chalfont	Y512NHK	East London	Y669NLO	Metroline	Y843TGH	Go-Ahead London		
Y395NHK	East London	Y512UGC	Arriva	Y671JSG	East London	Y844TGH	Go-Ahead London		
Y401NHK	East London	Y513HWE	Go-Ahead Docklands	Y671NLO	Metroline	Y845TGH	Go-Ahead London		
Y404NHK	East London	Y513UGC	Arriva	Y672NLO	Metroline	Y846TGH	Go-Ahead London		
Y407NHK	East London	Y514NHK	East London	Y673NLO	Metroline	Y847TGH	Go-Ahead London		
Y409NHK	East London	Y514UGC	Arriva	Y674NLO	Metroline	Y848TGH	Go-Ahead London		
Y429NHK	East London	Y516UGC	Arriva	Y675NLO	Metroline	Y849TGH	Go-Ahead London		
Y434NHK	East London	Y517NHK	East London	Y703TGH	Go-Ahead London	Y851TGH	Go-Ahead London		
Y436NHK	East London	Y517UGC	Arriva	Y704TGH	Go-Ahead London	Y852TGH	Go-Ahead London		
Y437NHK	East London	Y518UGC	Arriva	Y705TGH	Go-Ahead London	Y853TGH	Go-Ahead London		
Y438NHK	East London	Y519UGC	Arriva	Y729TGH	Go-Ahead London	Y854TGH	Go-Ahead London		
Y441NHK	East London	Y522NHK	East London	Y731TGH	Go-Ahead London	Y856TGH	Go-Ahead London		
Y442NHK	East London	Y522UGC	Arriva	Y732TGH	Go-Ahead London	Y857TGH	Go-Ahead London		
Y443NHK	East London	Y523UGC	Arriva	Y733TGH	Go-Ahead London	Y858TGH	Go-Ahead London		
Y445NHK	East London	Y524NHK	East London	Y734TGH	Go-Ahead London	Y859TGH	Go-Ahead London		
Y446NHK	East London	Y524UGC	Arriva	Y735TGH	Go-Ahead London	Y861TGH	Go-Ahead London		
Y447NHK	East London	Y526NHK	East London	Y736TGH	Go-Ahead London	Y862TGH	Go-Ahead London		
Y448NHK	East London	Y526UGC	Arriva	Y737TGH	Go-Ahead London	Y863TGH	Go-Ahead London		
Y449NHK	East London	Y527NHK	East London	Y738TGH	Go-Ahead London	Y864TGH	Go-Ahead London		
Y452NHK	East London	Y527UGC	Arriva	Y739TGH	Go-Ahead London	Y865TGH	Go-Ahead London		
Y452UGC	Arriva	Y529NHK	East London	Y741TGH	Go-Ahead London	Y866TGH	Go-Ahead London		
Y453NHK	East London	Y529UGC	Arriva	Y742TGH	Go-Ahead London	Y907TGH	Go-Ahead London		
Y454NHK	East London	Y531NHK	East London	Y743TGH	Go-Ahead London	Y908TGH	Go-Ahead London		
Y458NHK	East London	Y531UGC	Arriva	Y744TGH	Go-Ahead London	Y909TGH	Go-Ahead London		
Y461HUA	Westbus	Y532UGC	Arriva	Y745TGH	Go-Ahead London	Y932NLP	First London		
Y462HUA	Westbus	Y533UGC	Arriva	Y746TGH	Go-Ahead London	Y933NLP	First London		
Y462NHK	East London	Y534XAG	Transdev	Y747TGH	Go-Ahead London	Y934NLP	First London		

The London Bus Handbook

Reg	Operator	Reg	Operator	Reg	Operator	Reg	Operator
Y962KRX	Metroline	YJ53VHA	Westbus	YN04UKC	Excalibur	YN51KUU	Travel London
Y967TGH	Go-Ahead London	YJ53VHB	Westbus	YN04UKD	Excalibur	YN51KUV	Travel London
Y968TGH	Go-Ahead London	YK05CCD	Metroline	YN05ATO	Redwing	YN51KUW	Travel London
Y969TGH	Go-Ahead London	YK05CCE	Metroline	YN05ATU	Redwing	YN51KUX	Travel London
Y971TGH	Go-Ahead London	YK05CCJ	Metroline	YN05ATX	Redwing	YN51KUY	Travel London
Y972TGH	Go-Ahead London	YK05CCN	Metroline	YN05ATY	Redwing	YN51KVA	Travel London
Y973TGH	Go-Ahead London	YK05CCO	Metroline	YN05ATZ	Redwing	YN51KVC	Travel London
Y974TGH	Go-Ahead London	YM52TSV	Go-Ahead (Docklands)	YN05AUA	Redwing	YN51KVD	Travel London
Y975TGH	Go-Ahead London	YM52TSX	Go-Ahead (Docklands)	YN05AUC	Redwing	YN51KVE	Travel London
Y976TGH	Go-Ahead London	YM55SWU	Metrobus	YN05AUE	Redwing	YN51KVF	Travel London
Y978TGH	Go-Ahead London	YM55SWV	Metrobus	YN05AUF	Redwing	YN51KVG	Travel London
Y979TGH	Go-Ahead London	YM55SWX	Metrobus	YN05AUH	Redwing	YN51KVH	Travel London
Y981TGH	Go-Ahead London	YM55SWY	Metrobus	YN05AUJ	Redwing	YN51KVJ	Travel London
Y982TGH	Go-Ahead London	YM55SXA	Metrobus	YN05AUK	Redwing	YN51KVK	Travel London
Y983TGH	Go-Ahead London	YM55SXB	Metrobus	YN05AUL	Redwing	YN51KVL	Travel London
Y984NLP	First London	YM55SXC	Metrobus	YN05AUP	Isleworth	YN51KVM	Travel London
Y984TGH	Go-Ahead London	YM55SXD	Metrobus	YN05AYV	Redwing	YN51KVO	Travel London
Y985NLP	First London	YM55SXE	Metrobus	YN05BVC	Cavalier	YN51KVP	Travel London
Y985TGH	Go-Ahead London	YM55SXF	Metrobus	YN05BVD	Cavalier	YN51KVR	Travel London
Y986NLP	First London	YM55SXH	Metrobus	YN05HCA	Metrobus	YN51KVS	Travel London
Y986TGH	Go-Ahead London	YM55SXO	Metrobus	YN05HCC	Metrobus	YN51KVT	Travel London
Y987NLP	First London	YM55SXP	Metrobus	YN05HCD	Metrobus	YN51KVU	Travel London
Y987TGH	Go-Ahead London	YM55SXR	Metrobus	YN05HCE	Metrobus	YN51KVV	Travel London
Y988NLP	First London	YN03AXF	City Circle	YN05HCF	Metrobus	YN51KVW	Travel London
Y988TGH	Go-Ahead London	YN03AXG	City Circle	YN05HCG	Metrobus	YN51KVX	Travel London
Y989NLP	First London	YN03AXH	City Circle	YN05HFE	Metrobus	YN51KVZ	Travel London
Y989TGH	Go-Ahead London	YN03AXJ	City Circle	YN05HFF	Metrobus	YN51KWA	Travel London
Y991NLP	First London	YN03AXK	City Circle	YN05HFG	Metrobus	YN51KWB	Travel London
Y992NLP	First London	YN03AXP	MCH	YN05HFH	Metrobus	YN51KWC	Travel London
Y992OCT	MCH	YN03DFA	Metrobus	YN05HFJ	Metrobus	YN51KWD	Travel London
Y993NLP	First London	YN03DFC	Metrobus	YN05RXT	MCH	YN51KWE	Travel London
Y994NLP	First London	YN03DFD	Metrobus	YN05RXX	Royale European	YN51KWF	Travel London
Y995NLP	First London	YN03DFE	Metrobus	YN05UVG	MCH	YN51KWG	Travel London
Y996NLP	First London	YN03DFG	Metrobus	YN06CFF	MCH	YN51WGY	Tellings-Golden Miller
Y997NLP	First London	YN03DFJ	Metrobus	YN06CHJ	Excalibur	YN51WGZ	Tellings-Golden Miller
Y998NLP	First London	YN03DFK	Metrobus	YN06CHK	Excalibur	YN53RXF	Metrobus
YD02PXA	Anderson	YN03DFL	Metrobus	YN06CHL	Excalibur	YN53RXG	Metrobus
YD02PXB	Anderson	YN03DFP	Metrobus	YN06CJV	Tellings-Golden Miller	YN53RXH	Metrobus
YD02PXC	Anderson	YN03DFU	Metrobus	YN06CJX	Tellings-Golden Miller	YN53RXJ	Metrobus
YE52FGU	Epsom Coaches	YN03DFV	Metrobus	YN06CJY	Tellings-Golden Miller	YN53RXK	Metrobus
YE52FHH	Epsom Coaches	YN03DFX	Metrobus	YN06CJZ	Tellings-Golden Miller	YN53RXL	Metrobus
YE52FHJ	Epsom Coaches	YN03DFY	Metrobus	YN06CKG	Excalibur	YN53RXM	Metrobus
YE52FHK	Epsom Coaches	YN03UPM	Metrobus	YN06JFO	MCH	YN53RXO	Metrobus
YE52FHL	Epsom Coaches	YN03UWU	Metrobus	YN06JXR	Metrobus	YN53RXP	Metrobus
YE52FHM	Epsom Coaches	YN03UWY	Metrobus	YN06JXS	Excalibur	YN53RXR	Metrobus
YE52FHN	Epsom Coaches	YN03WPP	Metrobus	YN06JXS	Metrobus	YN53RXT	Metrobus
YE52FHO	Epsom Coaches	YN03WPR	Metrobus	YN06JXT	Metrobus	YN53RXU	Metrobus
YE52FHP	Epsom Coaches	YN03WPV	Excalibur	YN06JXU	Metrobus	YN53RXV	Metrobus
YE52FHR	Epsom Coaches	YN03WPX	Excalibur	YN06JXV	Metrobus	YN53RXW	Metrobus
YE52FHS	Epsom Coaches	YN03WPY	Excalibur	YN06JXW	Metrobus	YN53RXX	Metrobus
YJ03GXM	Anderson	YN03WPZ	Excalibur	YN06JXX	Metrobus	YN53RXY	Metrobus
YJ03GXN	Anderson	YN03WRF	Metrobus	YN06JXY	Metrobus	YN53RXZ	Metrobus
YJ03GXP	Anderson	YN03WRG	Metrobus	YN06JXZ	Metrobus	YN53RYA	Metrobus
YJ03GXR	Anderson	YN03WRJ	Metrobus	YN06JYB	Metrobus	YN53RYB	Metrobus
YJ04BNL	Anderson	YN03WRL	Metrobus	YN06JYC	Metrobus	YN53RYC	Metrobus
YJ04BNN	Anderson	YN03WRP	Metrobus	YN06JYD	Metrobus	YN53RYF	Metrobus
YJ04HHS	P & J Ellis	YN03WXW	Westbus	YN06JYE	Metrobus	YN53RYH	Metrobus
YJ04HVS	Westbus	YN03ZXF	Epsom Coaches	YN06JYF	Metrobus	YN53RYK	Metrobus
YJ04HVU	Westbus	YN04AYD	Cavalier	YN06JYG	Metrobus	YN53RYM	Metrobus
YJ05FXC	Anderson	YN04GHA	Clarkes of London	YN06JYH	Metrobus	YN53RYP	Metrobus
YJ05FXD	Anderson	YN04GHB	Clarkes of London	YN06JYJ	Metrobus	YN53RYR	Metrobus
YJ05FXE	Anderson	YN04GHD	Clarkes of London	YN06JYK	Metrobus	YN53RYT	Metrobus
YJ05FXF	Anderson	YN04GHF	Clarkes of London	YN06JYL	Metrobus	YN53RYV	Metrobus
YJ05FXG	Anderson	YN04GHG	Clarkes of London	YN06JYO	Metrobus	YN53RYW	Metrobus
YJ06GKY	Anderson	YN04GHH	Clarkes of London	YN06NYO	Clarkes of London	YN53RYX	Metrobus
YJ06GKZ	Anderson	YN04GHJ	Clarkes of London	YN06NYV	Clarkes of London	YN53RYY	Metrobus
YJ06LCX	City Circle	YN04GHK	Clarkes of London	YN06NYW	Clarkes of London	YN53RYZ	Metrobus
YJ06LDD	Westbus	YN04GHU	Clarkes of London	YN06PEO	Isleworth	YN53RZA	Metrobus
YJ06LDE	Westbus	YN04GHV	Clarkes of London	YN06PFD	Tellings-Golden Miller	YN53RZB	Metrobus
YJ06LDL	City Circle	YN04GHX	Clarkes of London	YN06PFE	Tellings-Golden Miller	YN53RZC	Metrobus
YJ06LFV	City Circle	YN04GHY	Clarkes of London	YN06PFF	Tellings-Golden Miller	YN53RZD	Metrobus
YJ51JWY	Metroline	YN04GHZ	Clarkes of London	YN06PFG	Tellings-Golden Miller	YN53RZE	Metrobus
YJ51JWZ	Metroline	YN04UKB	Excalibur	YN51KKP	Go-Ahead (Docklands)		

YN53RZF	Metrobus	YN55NHY	Transdev	YN55PZM	Metrobus	YT51EAW	Travel London
YN53SUF	Epsom Coaches	YN55NHZ	Transdev	YN55PZO	Metrobus	YT51EAX	Travel London
YN53SVK	Epsom Coaches	YN55NJE	Transdev	YN55PZP	Metrobus	YT51EAY	Travel London
YN53SVL	Epsom Coaches	YN55NJF	Transdev	YN55PZR	Metrobus	YT51EBA	Travel London
YN53SVO	Epsom Coaches	YN55NJJ	Transdev	YN55PZU	Metrobus	YT51EBF	Travel London
YN53SVP	Epsom Coaches	YN55NJK	Transdev	YN55PZV	Metrobus	YT51EBG	Travel London
YN53SVR	Epsom Coaches	YN55NJU	Transdev	YN55PZW	Metrobus	YU02GHA	East Thames
YN53SWF	Epsom Coaches	YN55NJV	Transdev	YN55PZX	Metrobus	YU02GHD	East Thames
YN53ZXA	Epsom Coaches	YN55NKA	Transdev	YN55WPD	Cavalier	YU02GHG	East Thames
YN53ZXB	Epsom Coaches	YN55NKC	Transdev	YN55WPJ	MCH	YU02GHH	East Thames
YN54AAE	Redwing	YN55NKD	Transdev	YN55WSU	Tellings-Golden Miller	YU02GHJ	East Thames
YN54AAF	Redwing	YN55NKE	Transdev	YN55WSV	Tellings-Golden Miller	YU02GHK	East Thames
YN54AAJ	Redwing	YN55NKF	Transdev	YN55WSW	Tellings-Golden Miller	YU02GHN	East Thames
YN54AAK	Redwing	YN55NKG	Transdev	YN56FCA	Transdev	YU02GHO	East Thames
YN54AAO	Redwing	YN55NKH	Transdev	YN56FCC	Transdev	YU04XJH	Redwing
YN54AAU	Redwing	YN55NKJ	Transdev	YN56FCD	Transdev	YU04XJJ	Redwing
YN54AAV	Redwing	YN55NKK	Transdev	YN56FCE	Transdev	YU52XVK	Metrobus
YN54AJU	Metrobus	YN55NKL	Transdev	YN56FCF	Transdev	YU52XVL	Metrobus
YN54AJV	Metrobus	YN55NKM	Transdev	YN56FCG	Transdev	YU52XVM	Metrobus
YN54AJX	Metrobus	YN55NKO	Transdev	YN56FCJ	Transdev	YU52XVN	Metrobus
YN54AJY	Metrobus	YN55NKP	Transdev	YN56FDA	Metrobus	YU52XVR	Metrobus
YN54OAA	Transdev	YN55NKR	Transdev	YN56FDC	Metrobus	YV03PZE	Metrobus
YN54OAB	Transdev	YN55NKS	Transdev	YN56FDD	Metrobus	YV03PZF	Metrobus
YN54OAC	Transdev	YN55NKT	Transdev	YN56FDE	Metrobus	YV03PZG	Metrobus
YN54OAE	Transdev	YN55NKU	Transdev	YN56FDF	Metrobus	YV03PZH	Metrobus
YN54OAG	Transdev	YN55NKW	Transdev	YN56FDG	Metrobus	YV03PZJ	Metrobus
YN54OAH	Transdev	YN55NKX	Transdev	YN56FDJ	Metrobus	YV03PZK	Metrobus
YN54WFD	MCH	YN55NKZ	Transdev	YN56FDK	Metrobus	YV03PZL	Metrobus
YN54WWF	Tellings-Golden Miller	YN55NLA	Transdev	YN56FDL	Metrobus	YV03PZM	Metrobus
YN54WWG	Tellings-Golden Miller	YN55NLC	Transdev	YN56FDM	Metrobus	YV03PZW	Metrobus
YN55KWH	Anderson	YN55NLD	Transdev	YN56FDO	Metrobus	YV03PZX	Metrobus
YN55KWO	Redwing	YN55NLE	Transdev	YN56FDP	Metrobus	YV03PZY	Metrobus
YN55KWP	Redwing	YN55NLG	Transdev	YN56FDU	Metrobus	YV03PZZ	Metrobus
YN55KWR	Redwing	YN55NLJ	Transdev	YN56FDV	Metrobus	YV03RAU	Metrobus
YN55KWS	Redwing	YN55NLK	Transdev	YN56FDX	Metrobus	YV03RAX	Metrobus
YN55KWT	Redwing	YN55NLL	Transdev	YN56FDY	Metrobus	YV03RBF	Metrobus
YN55KWU	Redwing	YN55NLM	Transdev	YN56FDX	Metrobus	YV03RBU	Metrobus
YN55NHA	Transdev	YN55NLO	Transdev	YN56FEF	Metrobus	YV03RBX	Metrobus
YN55NHB	Transdev	YN55NLP	Transdev	YN56FEG	Metrobus	YV03RBY	Metrobus
YN55NHC	Transdev	YN55NLR	Transdev	YO530AD	Cavalier	YV03RCY	Metrobus
YN55NHD	Transdev	YN55PWJ	Metrobus	YP02LCA	Travel London	YV03RCZ	Metrobus
YN55NHE	Transdev	YN55PWK	Metrobus	YP02LCC	Travel London	YX04DLZ	MCH
YN55NHF	Transdev	YN55PWL	Metrobus	YP02LCE	Travel London	YX05DHN	Wings
YN55NHG	Transdev	YN55PWO	Metrobus	YP02LCF	Travel London	YX05DHO	Wings
YN55NHH	Transdev	YN55PWU	Metrobus	YP52CTO	Metrobus	YX05DHY	Anderson
YN55NHJ	Transdev	YN55PWV	Metrobus	YP52CTY	Excalibur	YX05DHZ	Anderson
YN55NHK	Transdev	YN55PWX	Metrobus	YP52CUJ	Cavalier	YX05DJY	MCH
YN55NHL	Transdev	YN55PZC	Metrobus	YR02UNW	MCH	YX06AWN	MCH
YN55NHM	Transdev	YN55PZD	Metrobus	YR52VFH	East Thames	YX06DOJ	MCH
YN55NHO	Transdev	YN55PZE	Metrobus	YR52VFJ	East Thames	YX06DOU	MCH
YN55NHP	Transdev	YN55PZF	Metrobus	YR52VFK	East Thames	YX54BHU	MCH
YN55NHT	Transdev	YN55PZG	Metrobus	YR52VFL	East Thames	YX55ADO	MCH
YN55NHU	Transdev	YN55PZH	Metrobus	YR52VFM	East Thames	YX55ADV	MCH
YN55NHV	Transdev	YN55PZJ	Metrobus	YR52VFN	East Thames		
YN55NHX	Transdev	YN55PZL	Metrobus	YSK270	Blue Triangle		

ISBN 1 904875 45 9   © Published by *British Bus Publishing Ltd*, October 2006

British Bus Publishing Ltd, 16 St Margaret's Drive, Wellington, Telford, TF1 3PH
Telephone: 01952 255669 - Facsimile: 01952 222397

www.britishbuspublishing.co.uk - E-mail sales@britishbuspublishing.co.uk